Principles of
Soil-Plant
Interrelationships

Principles of
Soil-Plant
Interrelationships

Victor V. Rendig
Professor Emeritus, University of California,
Davis, California

Howard M. Taylor
Rockwell Professor, Texas Tech University,
Lubbock, Texas

McGraw-Hill Publishing Company
New York St. Louis San Francisco Auckland Bogotá
Caracas Hamburg Lisbon London Madrid Mexico
Milan Montreal New Delhi Oklahoma City
Paris San Juan São Paulo Singapore
Sydney Tokyo Toronto

Library of Congress Cataloging-in-Publication Data

Principles of soil-plant interrelationships/Victor V. Rendig, Howard
M. Taylor.
    p.   cm.
   Bibliography: p.
   Includes index.
   ISBN 0-07-051879-3
   1. Crops and soils. 2. Plant-soil relationships. I. Rendig, V. V.
(Victor V.) II. Taylor, H. M. (Howard M.)
   S596.7.P75   1989
582'.013--dc20   89-2579

1234567890 DOC/DOC 89432109

ISBN 0-07-051879-3

*The editors for this book were Jennifer Mitchell and Martha Glea-
son, the designer was Naomi Auerbach, and the production super-
visor was Suzanne W. Babeuf. This book was set in Century
Schoolbook. It was composed by the McGraw-Hill Publishing Company Professional and Reference Division composition unit.*

Printed and bound by R. R. Donnelley & Sons Company.

*For more information about other McGraw-Hill materials,
call 1-800-2-MCGRAW in the United States. In other
countries, call your nearest McGraw-Hill office.*

Contents

Preface

The subject of this book, soil-plant interrelationships, is about an association not yet found elsewhere in the universe. Certainly this association of inorganic and living matter is not the only feature unique to planet Earth, but the vital role of soil in the production of sustenance for a myriad of organisms, including human beings, receives relatively little public attention. That plants grow in soil is taken for granted. The complexity of the soil-plant relationships as a component of food chain ecosystems is beginning to receive due recognition as researchers now face challenges such as defining and managing the medium needed in order to grow foods for humans in the confines of space vehicles during long journeys into our solar system.

Much has been learned about soil-plant relationships, but much is yet unknown. An excuse for the lack of a better understanding can be that the subject has not been studied for very long. The span of time beginning less than about three centuries ago that soil and plant scientists have been investigating soil-plant relationships is, in the words of Viets (1977), "only a minute in the time span through which man and animals have been eating food and forages." Through research many fundamental concepts relating soil properties to plant establishment, growth, and survival have been developed. These endeavors have been motivated in part by a search for new knowledge per se, but more often they have been directed toward ways of producing larger amounts of foods, feeds, and fibers. Applications of the findings from this research have been a major contributor toward making it possible for plants, both directly and through their being consumed by other species, to amply provide the food and fiber needs for 5 billion human beings. Very serious world hunger problems certainly do persist, but mostly for reasons other than a lack of knowledge as to ways of producing adequate quantities of food from plants, or to a lack of soil resources.

Historically, most studies of soil-plant relationships in an agricultural context have focused on specific reactions or processes, or on evaluating responses to one or a few treatment variables, typically using empirical approaches. Research with a broader perspective is now needed in order to include other dimensions of soil resource use. Among the concerns now needing to be addressed are the possible impact, on the environment and on consumer health, of much more extensive agricultural uses, and some misuses, of chemicals to achieve higher yields of food and fiber. The improper use of these additives can seriously degrade the environment. These concerns emphasize the need for greater attention to a more efficient use of water and chemicals, and thus a greater focus toward defining soil-plant relationships in more quantitative terms. One approach to deal more effectively with the greater number of variables and interactions involved is to design appropriate predictive models to help identify and test the parameters required to quantitatively define the characteristics of soil-plant systems.

Two aspects regarding the acquisition of water and nutrients by plants are now receiving increased attention: (1) the nature and dynamic features of the soil-plant root interface, and (2) the feasibility of using breeding techniques, tissue culture, and genetic manipulation to develop new cultivars that are more efficient in obtaining water and nutrients, and in resisting toxins, in different soil environments. Progress in these two areas should certainly help to develop management practices that are more effective and environmentally sound in using soil resources. New tools such as NMR and electron probes are providing a clearer picture of the soil-plant root interface and processes occurring there, and great strides are being made in biotechnology. Nevertheless, we should be aware of the possible risk of overestimating the prospects for ready answers from these new approaches and better techniques. To realize their potential, many years of research will be required, and basic knowledge about soils and plants, and new concepts about their interrelationships, still need to be generated by creative minds. To meet the challenge of new frontiers will require bringing together expertise in both mineral nutrition and soil-plant-water relationships, and thus greater collaboration and communication between soil scientists, geneticists, and plant physiologists.

This book is intended primarily as a text for more advanced undergraduate and graduate courses in soil-plant interrelationships. Students enrolled in such courses should have a good background in the soil and water sciences, including the physical, chemical, and microbiological aspects, and in plant physiology. Many references to published literature are included in the text, but it is not intended to provide a comprehensive review of the topics discussed. It is expected that in courses in which this book is used, the subject matter would be supplemented by material from other sources, particularly from current literature. We believe that the book will also be a valuable reference source for researchers and professionals working in the field.

We are grateful to those who reviewed the complete original text, including D. E. Kissel, Betty Klepper, and J. F. Power, and to E. Epstein, M. B. Jones, and D. N. Munns, who reviewed portions of the text. Other colleagues contributed comments and suggestions and raised questions. Parts of early drafts were used for the instruction of graduate courses in soil-plant relationships, and feedback from students was helpful.

Victor V. Rendig

Howard M. Taylor

Table of Botanical and Common Plant Names

Common name	Botanical name	Common name	Botanical name
Alder	*Alnus* spp.	Cauliflower	*Brassica oleracea* var. *botrytis* L.
Alfalfa	*Medicago sativa* L.	Celery	*Apium graveolens* L.
Allium	*Allium porrum* L.	Chickpea	*Cicer arietinum* L.
Apple	*Malus sylvestrios* Mill.	Clover, white or Dutch	*Trifolium repens* L.
Barley	*Hordeum vulgare* L.	Clover, red	*Trifolium pratense* L.
Bean, bush and french	*Phaseolus vulgaris* L.	Clover, subterranean	*Trifolium subterraneum* L.
Bermudagrass	*Cynodon dactylon* L.	Coffee	*Coffea arabica* L.
Bird's-foot trefoil	*Lotus corniculatus* L.	Collards	*Brassica oleracea* L. var. *acephala*, DC
Blueberry, low-bush	*Vaccinium pennsylvanicum* Ait	Corn (maize)	*Zea mays* L.
Blueberry, high-bush	*Vaccinium corymbosum* L.	Cotton	*Gossypium hirsutum* L.
Broadbeans	*Vicia faba* L.	Cowpea	*Vigna unguiculata* L. Walp.
Bromegrass	*Bromus inermis* L.	Cranberry	*Vaccinium macrocarpon* Ait
Cacti	*Opuntia* spp.	Douglas fir	*Pseudosuga menziessi* Mirb.
Canarygrass, reed	*Phalaris arundinacea* L.		
Carrots	*Daucus carota* L.		
Cassava	*Manihot* spp.		

Common name	Botanical name	Common name	Botanical name
Eucalyptus	*Eucalyptus* spp.	Peas, garden or green	*Pisum sativum* L.
Fescue, tall	*Festuca arundinacea* Shreb.	Pine	*Pinus* spp.
		Poplar	*Liriodendron* spp.
Fir	*Abies* spp.	Potatoes	*Solanum tuberosum* L.
Flax	*Linum usitatissimum* L.	Purple nutsedge	*Cyperus rotundus*
Ginger	*Zingiber officinale* Roscoe	Quackgrass	*Agropyron repens* L.
Grape	*Vitis vinifera* L.	Radish	*Raphanus sativa* L.
Guayule	*Parthenium argentatum* Gray	Rape	*Brassica napus* L.
		Raspberry	*Rubus idaeus* L.
Hemlock, western	*Tsuga heterophylla* (Raf.) Sarag.	Rhododendron	*Rhododendrun loderi*
Kale	*Brassica oleracea* L. var. *acephala* DC	Rice	*Oryza sativa* L.
		Rubber	*Hevea brasiliensis*
Lamb's quarter	*Chonopodum album*	Russian thistle	*Salsola kali*
		Rye	*Secale cereale* L.
Lettuce	*Lactuca sativa* L.	Ryegrass, Italian	*Lolium multiflorum* L.
Lupin, white	*Lupinus albus* L.		
Mesquite	*Prosopis juliflora*	Ryegrass, perennial	*Lolium perenne* L.
Milk thistle	*Silybum marianum*	Saltbush	*Atriplex spongiosa*
Millet	*Panicum miliacum* L.	Snapbeans	*Phaseolus vulgaris* L.
Oak	*Quercus* spp.	Sorghum	*Sorghum vulgare* L.
Oats	*Avena sativa* L.		
Onion	*Allium cepa* L.	Southern beech	*Nothofagus* spp.
Orchardgrass	*Dactylis glomerata* L.	Soybean	*Glycine max* (L.) Max.
Papaya	*Carica papaya* L.	Spinach	*Spinacia oleracea* L.
Peach	*Prunus persica* L. Batsch	Spring (sweet vernal) grass	*Anthoxanthum odoratum* L.
Peanut	*Arachis hypogaea* L.	Spruce	*Picea* spp.

Common name	Botanical name	Common name	Botanical name
Squash, summer	*Curcurbita pepo* L.	Tea	*Thea sinensis* L.
Strawberry	*Fragaria chiloensis* × Duchesne	Timothy	*Phleum pratense* L.
		Tomato	*Lycopersicum esculentum* L.
Subclover	*Trifolium subterraneum* L.	Trefoil, yellow (black medic)	*Medicago lupulina* L.
Sudangrass	*Sorghum sudanense* Staph.	Turnip	*Brassica rapa* L.
		Velvetleaf	*Abutilon theophrasti*
Sugar beets	*Beta vulgaris* L.		
Sugarcane	*Saccharum officinarum* L.	Wheat	*Triticum aestivum* L.
Sunflower	*Helianthus annuus* L.	Willow	*Salix viminalis* L.

Principles of
Soil-Plant
Interrelationships

Water and Mineral Nutrient Needs of Plants

Introduction

All plants grow and reproduce in response to an interaction of dynamic and ever-changing components in their environment. Maximum growth rate and yield result when these components are in adequate supply and the plants can compete successfully for their requirements.

Liebig's law of the minimum indicates that, if any one growth factor is in short supply, plant growth often will be reduced in proportion to the reduced supply rate. Conversely, if the supply of a limiting factor is increased, plant growth rate is increased (Russell, 1973). If two factors limit or nearly limit growth, adding only one of them will have little effect, while adding both together will cause a considerable response.

Plants require favorable soil and air temperatures, adequate available water and soil air, adequate light and carbon dioxide for photosynthesis, and essential elements sufficient for satisfactory and balanced nutrition. Plants also require support, provided either by the anchorage of roots in a satisfactory growth medium or by artificial means. Inorganic chemicals or biochemicals that are toxic to plants, if present, must be below levels that impair growth.

Supplies of water and essential mineral nutrients are controlled largely by below-ground characteristics of the soil and plant. The plant's demand for water is controlled largely by aboveground plant and environmental characteristics. The plant's demand for nutrients is controlled largely by the requirement during growth. Each strain or cultivar of each species differs in its combination of supply and demand relationships. We intend to limit our discussion to general principles because it will be impossible to discuss all specific soil-cultivar-management interactions for widely different environments.

Water Needs

Life as we know it cannot exist without water, which constitutes more than 70 percent of the fresh weight of actively growing herbaceous plants and usually more than 50 percent of the weight of woody plants. In fact, plants can transpire daily an amount of water nearly equal to their total water content.

We study water in a course on principles of soil-plant interrelationships because water

- Acts as a solvent in most physiological processes.
- Participates in many chemical reactions, such as the processes involved in photosynthesis.
- As it evaporates, helps keep the plant cool.
- Is necessary to maintain turgor (hydrostatic) pressure in the plant.
- Exerts control over many soil conditions, such as aeration, temperature, strength, and microbiological activity.
- Flows across the soil surface causing erosion.
- Moves through the soil profile, carrying dissolved mineral nutrients, organic compounds, and toxic chemicals.

For centuries people have been concerned with using water more efficiently in the production of crops. During the three decades from 1890 to 1920, agronomists conducted many experiments to evaluate the quantity of water necessary to produce a unit quantity of yield, defined as the *water use requirement*. Many of these experiments were reviewed by Briggs and Shantz (1913), who concluded that both plant species and crop environment affect the water use requirement, but that water loss rates from an evaporation pan can be used to normalize the transpiration component of water use across major distances. For example, Briggs and Shantz (1917) reported water use by Grimm alfalfa grown in containers at four widely scattered locations during 1912. Although the water requirement varied from 518 to 1005 kg of water transpired per kilogram of dry matter produced and "free water evaporation" varied from 4.04 to 7.77 mm day^{-1}, the ratio of water required divided by free water evaporation varied only from 1.28 to 1.49 days mm^{-1}.

DeWit (1958) analyzed transpiration-biomass data from many different sources and formulated a postulate that, for dry, high-radiation climates,

$$\frac{Y}{T} = \frac{m}{T_{\max}} \tag{1.1}$$

where Y = total dry matter mass per area, kg m^{-2}
  T = total transpiration per area during growth to harvest, mm mm^{-2}
  $T_{\max}$ = mean daily free water evaporation for the same period, mm day^{-1}
  m = a constant that depends largely on plant species

DeWit (1958) and Hanks (1983) present values for the crop coefficient m calculated from the data of Shantz and Piemiesel (1927), and Hanks (1983) presents data for the crop coefficient using some modern genotypes (Table 1.1). The crop coefficient is greater for C-4 carbon pathway plants such as corn than for C-3 carbon pathway plants such as alfalfa. In addition, modern genotypes of corn have a greater crop coefficient than the genotype used by Shantz and Piemiesel (1927). Biomass production increases with the total amount of water transpired (Fig. 1.1a), but the data scatter is reduced when biomass production is correlated with the ratio of transpiration to free water evaporation (Fig. 1.1b).

When someone uses the deWit (1958) equation, the $T_{\max}$ term is estimated either from pan evaporation or from the Penman (1948) combination formula. The constant m is approximately related to the water requirement WR used by Briggs and Shantz (1913), by the relationship $(1/m \sim \text{WR/Pan})$ (Tanner and Sinclair, 1983), where Pan is evaporation from a class A Weather Bureau pan.

Tanner and Sinclair (1983) discussed other simple models of water

TABLE 1.1 **Values for the Crop Coefficient m of Various Species Calculated Using Eq. 1.1**

Crop	Coefficient m_1, kg ha^{-1} day^{-1}	References
Sorghum	207	deWit (1958)
Wheat	115	deWit (1958)
	108	Fischer and Turner (1978)
	112	Hanks (1983)
Alfalfa	55	deWit (1958)
	63	Hanks (1983)*
Corn	151	Hanks (1983)*
	238–324	Hanks (1983)
Barley	106	Hanks (1983)*
Oats	90	Hanks (1983)*

*Calculated from the data of Shantz and Piemeisel (1927).

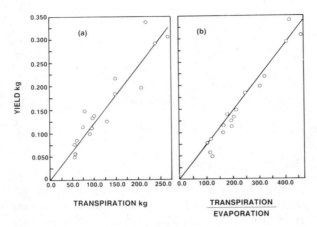

Figure 1.1 (a) Relationship of yield to transpiration, and (b) of yield to the ratio of transpiration to free water evaporation for alfalfa. (*From Hanks, 1983. Reproduced from Limitations to Efficient Water Use in Crop Production, by permission of the American Society of Agronomy, Inc.*)

use efficiency (Stewart, 1972; Hanks, 1974; Arkley, 1963; Bierhuizen and Slatyer, 1965). Tanner and Sinclair (1983) concluded that the proper geographical correction factor was the vapor pressure deficit ($e^* - e$), where e^* is the saturation vapor pressure of the air at mean temperature and e is the vapor pressure. Tanner and Sinclair (1983) argued that the vapor pressure deficit technique was the appropriate one because it separated the climatic terms that influence growth from those that express differences in transpirational demand.

The close relationship between water transpired and biomass produced occurs because the stomates simultaneously control the inward flux of carbon dioxide and the outward flux of water vapor. In addition, the same radiation that drives the photosynthetic reaction also supplies energy to evaporate the water during transpiration. However, some energy is supplied for transpiration by warm winds flowing across somewhat cooler leaf surfaces and the photosynthetic apparatus can become energy-saturated.

No unique relationship exists between the total quantity of water transpired and the grain, protein, latex, nut, or sugar yield. In some rain-fed conditions, for example, considerable biomass, but almost no grain, will be produced if water has not been available during the grain filling period, resulting in a low harvest index (the fraction of total biomass that is grain). A limited water supply later in the life cycle may reduce the total biomass of crops grown for sugar and latex but may increase the concentration of these components in that biomass.

Many other studies have been conducted to understand the dynamics of water demand by plants. Reports from these studies have used several different terms to describe the efficiency of water use, including (1) the units of production per unit of water available to the farm from rainfall and from water delivered to the farm boundary, (2) the units of production per unit of evapotranspiration, (3) the units of production per unit of water transpired, (4) the yield of seed or other marketable fraction of biomass per unit of evapotranspiration, (5) the yield of seed or other marketable fraction of biomass per unit of transpiration, and (6) the amount of CO_2 fixed per unit of leaf area, sunlit leaf area, or land area per unit of water transpired. This wide variety of definitions for the efficient use of water has led inevitably to considerable confusion. Whenever we report the results of a specific experiment, we will define the terms of reference in order to keep from compounding these ambiguities.

Soil-plant-atmosphere continuum

Water exists as a liquid from the soil through the soil-root interface, through the roots and stem to the substomatal cavities, and then as vapor across the leaf epidermis and through the air boundary layer to the atmosphere above the plant's canopy. During the night, water is absorbed by well-watered plants only in small quantities that provide enough water for cell enlargement and for replacement of water lost through cuticular flows of vapor or through pressure-induced flows, called *guttation*.

When the sun's radiant energy strikes the leaves in early morning, the stomates open to facilitate CO_2 assimilation. Loss of water by transpiration is an inevitable consequence. As water loss accelerates, leaf water content is reduced. The reduced leaf water content causes a reduced or lowered leaf water potential. The lowered leaf water potential then causes the withdrawal of water from other plant tissues and from soil.

In humid areas, most of the energy required to vaporize the liquid water comes directly from solar radiation. In desert areas, however, hot, dry winds can increase the transpiration rates above those predicted from direct solar radiation measurements. Transpiration rate, thus, is controlled by the rate at which energy is supplied to the leaf.

In late afternoon, the plants rehydrate because the uptake of water from the soil is at a greater rate than the water loss through transpiration. If the plants are growing under conditions of a moderate water stress, the stomates may close during midday, reducing the transpiration rate to the available supply rate and increasing the leaf temperature. As the soil water supply is further reduced and plant water stress is increased, stomatal closure occurs earlier in the day and tissue rehydration occurs more slowly in the evening. At severe plant water stresses, plants may fail to rehydrate overnight, causing the volume of the plant to decrease from one day to the next.

When the plant grows, more leaf area is exposed to sunlight and total transpiration of the plant is increased because leaves and other transpiring surfaces increase in extent. The increase in transpiration per plant usually levels off when the leaf area per unit land area (the leaf area index) reaches about 3.0 to 3.5, or when a continuous canopy has developed. Root mass and root length increase as plant tops grow, causing plant supply rates to increase as demand for water increases.

Absorption and transport of water are downhill in terms of the energy status of water. Leaves and shoots must be at a lower energy status than roots, and some portions of the roots must be at a lower status than the soil surrounding them. Other things being equal, water flows through the system increase with the steepness of the energy gradient. The other major factor involved is that of conductance, the inverse of resistance. Any increase in uptake and transpiration or decrease in conductance results in a lower leaf water status, even if the roots are located in moist soil.

Ideas concerning the soil-plant-atmosphere continuum were clarified and put on a sounder scientific basis by three classic papers published in the late 1950s and early 1960s. The first of these papers (Philip, 1957) described the physical principles of soil water movement during an irrigation cycle. The second paper (Slatyer and Taylor, 1960) provided the unified terminology of water potential to describe the energy status of liquid water, whether located in the soil or the plant. The third paper (Gardner, 1960) described the dynamic aspects of water availability to plants. We will now review some of the ideas expressed in these three papers as a prelude to other sections of the textbook.

Water potential

All discussion of water potential must be based on a standard reference system because water moves from points of higher to lower potential. The standard often used is a pool of *pure, free* water at temperature T_o, height h_o, and atmospheric pressure P_o (International Society of Soil Science, 1975). The term *pure* means that the water is not influenced by dissolved salts, and the term *free* means that the water is not influenced by the soil's solid phase. Because the various physical mechanisms that affect water potential have different consequences, it is necessary to identify specific components of water potential.

Water in the soil and plant is in equilibrium when it is at the same chemical potential μ. A general statement of the components of the chemical potential is as follows:

$$d\mu = \overline{V}_{T,0,n}\, dP - \overline{S}_{P,0,n}\, dT + \left(\frac{\partial \mu}{\partial \theta}\right)_{T,P,n} d\theta + \left(\frac{\partial \mu}{\partial n}\right)_{T,P,0} dn + Mgh \qquad (1.2)$$

where μ = chemical potential
  $\overline{V}$ = molar volume
  P = external pressure
  $\overline{S}$ = molar entropy
  T = temperature
  n = mole fraction of solute
  θ = volumetric water content
  M = molar mass of water
  g = acceleration due to gravity
  h = height above a reference level

The first term in Eq. 1.2, $\overline{V}\, dP$, is the pressure component, which may be the hydrostatic pressure of a column of water, an increase above atmospheric pressure within plant cells, or the overburden pressure where part of the load is carried by soil water. The entropy term, $\overline{S}\, dT$, in Eq. 1.2 is not precise because it usually is derived at constant pressure [see Nye and Tinker (1977) for a discussion]. The third term, $(\partial\mu/\partial\theta)_{T,P,n}\, d\theta$, is the matric component which includes all the interactions of water with the solid matrix, either surface tension or surface adsorption effects. The fourth term, $(\partial\mu/\partial n)_{T,P,\theta}\, dn$, is the osmotic or solute component. This term requires considerable care in its use because liquid flow carries the dissolved ions, but a phase change from liquid to vapor leaves the ions behind. The last component, Mgh, allows for the effects of gravity, which are particularly significant when the soil has a high water content.

Considerable confusion has arisen in agricultural literature from the three different definitions that have been used for "water potential" (ψ_w). In addition, several different names have been used for the same energy state.

The first definition is that of *weight water potential*, which is the potential energy required to move a unit weight of water from the system under consideration to the reference position. The units of weight water potential in the International System of Units (SI, meter-kilogram-second) are meters of head.

The second definition is that of *specific water potential*, which is the potential energy required to move a unit mass of water from the system under consideration to the reference position. The units of specific water potential are joules per kilogram. Weight water potential is multiplied by the acceleration of gravity, which varies with position over the earth's surface, to obtain a value for specific water potential.

The third water potential is that of *volumetric water potential,* which is the potential energy required to move a unit volume of water from the system under consideration to the reference position. The units of volumetric water potential are pascals. Weight water potential is multiplied by the acceleration of gravity and the specific density of water, which varies with temperature, to obtain volumetric water potential.

Much of the literature published in the United States before about 1980 contained either the English, or centimeter-gram-second, system of measurement or other terms to describe the energy status of water. Some of the literature expressed pressure in terms of bars or atmospheres. One bar (bar) is 10^5 pascals (Pa) and one atmosphere (atm) is 101,325 Pa. In the English system, stress is expressed as pounds-force per square inch (lbf/in^2). One pound-force per square inch is approximately equal to 6895 Pa. Some of the literature also contained such terms as suction, tension, diffusion pressure deficit (DPD), and pF. The suction tension and DPD terms are devices to allow positive, rather than negative, values of water potential. The pF term is the negative logarithm of water potential, in terms of weight water potential, measured in centimeters of head.

Richards (1965) developed an illustration that often helps in understanding the components of total soil water weight potential. He considers the membrane system shown in Fig. 1.2. A chamber of wet soil at atmospheric pressure is in contact with the bulk phases of water and soil solution through appropriate membranes. Matric weight potential is indicated by the middle manometer. In this case, the permeable membrane, the soil, and the closed water system are connected to a pressure indicator, the equivalent of a soil tensiometer useful in irrigation scheduling. This matric weight potential reading is relatively unaffected if ion concentration in the soil solution differs from that in the manometer.

In Fig. 1.2, the left (differential) manometer reads osmotic weight potential, which is the equilibrium pressure difference across a membrane freely permeable to water, but impermeable to solutes. The right manometer indicates the combined effects of matric and osmotic weight potential. The combined potentials are the result of an equilibrium pressure difference across a membrane permeable only to water separating the solution in the soil from pure water.

Soil water characteristic curves

The relationship between soil volumetric water content and soil water matric potential (the soil water characteristic) is affected by soil tex-

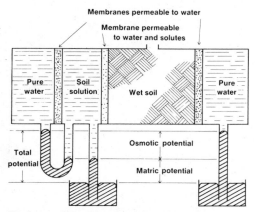

Figure 1.2 In an isothermal equilibrium system, matric potential is the potential difference across a membrane separating soil solution (equilibrium dialyzate) in bulk from soil containing the solution, the membrane being permeable to solution but not to matrix or bulk flow of gas; osmotic potential is the potential difference across a semipermeable membrane separating bulk phases of pure water and the soil solution; total potential is the sum of matric and osmotic potentials and is the pressure potential across a semipermeable membrane separating pure water and soil that contains solution. An ideal membrane is permeable to water alone. (*Richards, 1965.*)

ture. There are more surface area and more points of contact, per unit volume of soil, in clay than in a loam or a sandy soil. As a result, water content at a particular matric water potential is greater in clay than in loam or sand (Fig. 1.3). The surface area available for water adsorption is greater in a thoroughly puddled soil than in an undisturbed soil, so a puddled soil will hold more water at a specific matric potential than a nonpuddled soil (Fig. 1.4). If a clay soil is compacted, it will hold less water at high matric potentials than a noncompacted soil, but soil compaction causes little or no difference in water retention in a sandy soil within the available water range (Fig. 1.5).

Hysteresis in the characteristic curve.   There are two ways to obtain the relationship between soil matric potential and soil water content. The first is by saturating a soil sample with water and then applying increasing amounts of air pressure (pneumatic pressure is equal to the negative of the matric potential at equilibrium) to gradually dry the soil in a pressure plate apparatus. These curves are illustrated in Fig. 1.3 by the descending arrows. The second way is to start with an initially dry soil and allow the samples to absorb water under an increas-

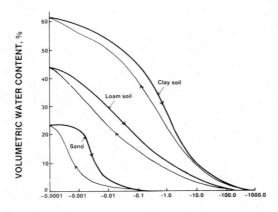

SOIL VOLUMETRIC WATER POTENTIAL MPa

Figure 1.3 Representative relationships between soil volumetric water potential and volumetric water content. Direction of the arrows shows whether the sample was losing or gaining water.

ingly lower pneumatic pressure. The curves obtained by this technique are shown with ascending arrows in Fig. 1.3. The two different relationships for a particular soil are the result of a phenomenon called *hysteresis*. The hysteresis effect can be attributed to several causes (Hillel, 1980):

1. The individual pores are nonuniform in geometry.
2. The contact angle is greater and the radius of curvature is greater in advancing than in receding menisci.
3. Entrapped air decreases the water content of newly wetted soil.
4. Differential changes occur in soil structure, associated with swelling, shrinking, and aging effects.

Because of the complexity and difficulty in handling hysteresis mathematically, it often is ignored by using only the desorption curve. However, hysteresis is a real phenomenon in the soil rhizosphere. By day, the plant root has a lower water potential than its surrounding soil, and, consequently, soil in the rhizosphere tends to dry. By night, the plant roots in the upper soil layers sometimes will have a greater water potential than that of the surrounding soil, and the soil in the rhizosphere will tend to rewet. This hysteresis in the water potential–water content relations of the rhizosphere soil usually is disgarded, but may be of vital importance in the uptake of ions from

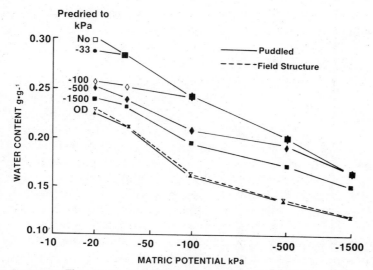

Figure 1.4 The effects of puddling and then predrying to specified water potentials on the relationship between matric potential and gravimetric soil water content. (*After Taylor, 1972.*)

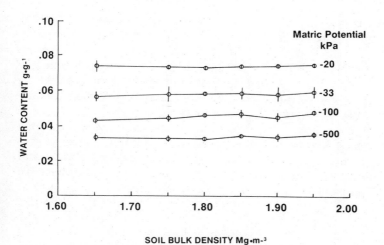

Figure 1.5 Effect of soil bulk density on the gravimetric water content at four matric potentials. (*From unpublished data of J. J. Parker, Jr., U.S. Department of Agriculture. Used with permission.*)

dry soil and also of importance in maintaining vesicular-arbuscular (VA) mycorrhizae in the rhizosphere.

Other useful soil water criteria

Observations that the rate of water content change decreases with time (Veihmeyer and Hendrickson, 1931) led to the conclusion that drainage virtually ceases within a short time after a thorough wetting. We now know that drainage rates decrease with time, but some drainage continues indefinitely. Despite this fact, certain soil water constants often are useful in irrigation practice. These constants are saturation, field capacity, wilting point, and available water.

The soil is *saturated* when all the space between the soil particles is filled with water. If a saturated soil volume is allowed to drain freely into unsaturated soil for 24 to 48 h, the downward velocity of the water becomes slow enough to be negligible in many situations and the soil is at *field capacity* water content. At the *wilting point* (sometimes called the *permanent wilting percentage*), the plants wilt and will not recover their turgidity when placed overnight in a dark, humid atmosphere. The difference between field capacity and wilting point is considered to be the soil's *available water capacity*. However, water between soil saturation and field capacity can be used by the plant during the initial drainage period, and some water can be absorbed by plants even if the soil is below the wilting point. Field capacity, wilting point, and available water are useful concepts but should not be considered as arbitrary constants for a specific soil.

Relative water content. Although we now use volumetric and weight water potentials for defining plant water deficiency, many of the early researchers used water content on a dry weight basis. Because the dry weight of a plant part changes with age, this procedure usually is unsatisfactory. An alternative procedure used water content changes on a wet weight basis. This method is even less satisfactory than the dry weight method to assess plant water stress changes.

The difficulties of using water content either on a dry weight or a wet weight basis led to the development of a plant water stress method based on water content of a turgid plant. Barrs and Weatherley (1962) used a 4-h period with a leaf part in contact with free water for a relative water content calculation:

$$\text{Relative water content} = \frac{\text{field weight} - \text{oven dry weight}}{\text{turgid weight} - \text{oven dry weight}} \times 100 \quad (1.3)$$

This calculation shows the relative saturation of the leaf tissue. A specific value for relative water content does not represent the same level of water potential in the same plant part in different species or ages or in plants grown in different environments. This fact has led to considerable controversy about the relative utility of water potential and relative water content in specifying levels of plant water deficiency (Sinclair and Ludlow, 1985).

Expansive growth of plants

Expansion of the root system increases the root surface area available for uptake of minerals and water. Similarly, expansion of the canopy increases the leaf area available to absorb CO_2 and sunlight for photosynthesis and to lose water by transpiration. Rates of increase in root surface and leaf area are reduced by plant water stress.

Let us first consider the expansion of an individual root cell in a nutrient solution when initially the volumetric water potential ψ^w internally is in equilibrium with that of the external solution. Under these conditions,

$$\text{External } \psi_w = \text{internal } \psi_w = \psi_p + \psi_o + \psi_m \qquad (1.4)$$

and the total water potential components of pressure potential ψ_p, osmotic potential ψ_o, and matric potential ψ_m must be considered. The pressure potential inside the cell is balanced by constraint of the cell walls on the cellular contents. The cell walls will be strained elastically and will return to their original area when matric potential (turgor pressure) is relieved.

If some cellular process then causes the cell wall to relax, ψ_p will fall and external ψ_w will be greater than internal ψ_w so water will be absorbed by the cell. The water absorption increases ψ_p, causing expansion of the cell walls and dilution of the solutes, thus increasing osmotic potential until internal $\psi_w = \text{external } \psi_w = \psi_p + \psi_o + \psi_m$ at a new equilibrium size for the cell. If solutes then are increased until ψ_o falls to the initial value, the process can be repeated. As presented, this sequence is artificial because the four processes of wall relaxation, water uptake, expansion of the cell wall, and solute accumulation occur continuously and simultaneously. Cellular expansion is discussed and illustrated schematically by Hsiao and Bradford (1983).

The situation is immensely more complicated when one is considering the expansion of an organ, such as a root, in the soil. Not only do the cells in an organ tend to reinforce the constraint of the cell walls, but the adjoining cells, with their cellular membranes, also tend to alter water uptake patterns.

The presence of the soil system further complicates the situation. When an isolated cell is located in a nutrient solution, relaxation of the cell wall is sufficient to initiate a fall in the cell pressure potential with subsequent water uptake. In a root located in soil, relaxation of the cell walls may not result in additional water absorption. First, the soil matrix itself may have an additive constraint on organ expansion. This constraint, called *soil strength* or *mechanical impedance,* is discussed in Chap. 2. Second, the soil may reduce the effect of a given drop in water potential through a reduced transport of water to the organ. This effect is discussed more fully in Chap. 4 on uptake of water by root systems.

Mineral Nutrient Needs

Essentiality: concepts and criteria

Higher plants must have access to N, P, K, S, Ca, Mg, Fe, Zn, Mn, Cu, Mo, B, and Cl in order to meet their essential mineral nutrient needs. Under most natural conditions, soil provides these 13 elements for growing plants. An important exception is the N_2 provided to leguminous plants through their symbiosis with rhizobia. Some mineral nutrients may be supplied directly to plant foliage from the atmosphere, and under some conditions this source may be a major contributor to plant needs for elements such as S and Cl. Without any one of the essential elements, plants cannot complete their life cycles because each element serves some unique vital role. With the exception of B and Cl, a well-defined and unique physiological function has been established for the 13 essential elements.

Five other elements, Co, Na, Ni, Si, and V, are required for good growth of some plants, but recognized criteria for establishing plant essentiality, i.e., serving uniquely for growth, development, or physiological functions, have not been fully satisfied for these five. From the results of many studies using a number of plant species grown with and without Ni, and from detection of this element in plant urease, it has been proposed that Ni should be added to the plant-essential list of elements (Brown et al., 1987).

We will consider here three aspects of the mineral nutrient requirements of plants: (1) the quantities needed, (2) the plant metabolic functions served, and (3) the chemical characteristics of the essential mineral nutrients that account for their unique contributions in plant metabolism. The quantities needed vary widely depending upon plant species and variety, and upon soil and environmental conditions during growth. Values reported in the literature will be given to compare quantities of essential nutrients taken up by different kinds of plants grown under very favorable conditions. Crop plants will be used for most examples because there is more information regarding these than for native species.

The functions essential elements serve in plants may be related to properties they have at the time of uptake, to changes they undergo during assimilation, or to both. Properties that determine whether an element can participate in a metabolic reaction, influence cellular environments, or become linked in a structural component include size, electron configuration, and electrical charge. With the exception of B absorbed as H_3BO_3 and of N_2 entering plants via rhizobia-mediated fixation, nutrients are taken up by plant roots in the form of inorganic ions. Organic forms, for example, amino acids and even larger nitrogenous molecules, can enter plant roots, but these generally are relatively unimportant sources of plant nutrients. Organics, such as atrazine, added to soil as herbicides, may also be absorbed. Chelate-ion complexes, either added as fertilizers or formed by the reactions of nutrient ions with naturally occurring chelates, as for example in the case of Fe (Römheld and Marschner, 1986), aid nutrient transport in soil; cleavage of the chelated ions prior to their uptake may occur, rather than uptake of the complex in toto.

Two or more ions functioning similarly at one reaction site in a soil-plant system may not share the properties necessary for their mutual substitution at some other site in that system. Differences in the manner in which Ca and Mg ions function in soil-plant systems is one example. In their effects on the activity of K in soil, for example (see Chap. 3), the amounts of these two ions have an essentially additive influence; Mg, not Ca, however, links the N of four porphyrin groups together in chlorophyll molecules.

As usually defined, nutrient essentiality for plants is considered with respect to amounts and metabolic functions for physiological purposes, but in a broader sense needs beyond one growth cycle might be included. Survivability and subsequent vigor may depend upon sufficient amounts of one or more mineral nutrients being available to permit the biosynthesis of adequate amounts of all the constituents needed to be stored in seeds and used subsequently for germination and resumption of growth. Also, plants are links in food chains, and in this context essentiality of mineral nutrients might be considered relative to meeting needs of plant consumers. Influences of mineral nutrition on plant composition relative to survivability and crop quality are discussed in more detail in Chap. 6.

Amounts, functions, and chemistry of the essential mineral nutrients

Nitrogen. Nitrogen is the mineral element generally required in greatest amounts by higher plants, typically accounting for 1 to 5 percent of plant dry matter. From its uptake as NO_3^-, the predominant form in most soils except where conditions limit nitrification, to its most abundant form as the peptide linkage in proteins, N undergoes a valence change from $+5$ to -3. The very stable peptide bond is made possible because of an electronic configuration that allows formation of strong covalent linkages with two adjacent C atoms. The energy of dissociation of C—N bonds is 184 kcal mol^{-1} (Chemical Rubber Co., 1983). To completely cleave the C—N linkages between amino acids in proteins by chemical hydrolysis using strong acids (e.g., 6 M HCl) requires heating at elevated temperatures for a minimum of several hours or more, depending upon the protein being analyzed.

All aspects of plant growth and development depend upon enzymes which are proteinaceous complexes. In vegetative tissue of many plants, the enzyme catalyzing the linkage of CO_2 to ribulose 1,5-bisphosphate, ribulose bisphosphate carboxylase oxygenase (RuBPCase), accounts for a significant fraction of the N present. In leaves of potato and of wheat, RuBPCase accounts for 40.8 and 23.7 percent, respectively, of the total soluble proteins (Ku et al., 1979). These values are in contrast to the value of 7.8 percent of total soluble proteins as RuBPCase in leaves of corn, a species with the more efficient C_4 photosynthetic mechanism.

Chemical linkages involving N also account for physiological functions served by nonproteinaceous metabolites. In the reduced form, by donating unshared electrons, N may behave as a fairly strong Lewis base. Thus it can bind metal ions, such as linking to Mg in chlorophyll, and can also produce changes in molecular configuration necessary for certain reactions of intermediary metabolism. Oxidation of NADH can occur by the release of electrons from the reduced N present in the nicotinamide ring. By forming complexes with metal ions, lower molecular weight organic N compounds, such as amino acids, and amides aid ion transport in the xylem (White et al., 1981).

The amounts of N plants need to absorb to meet the requirements for growth and to complete their life cycles vary widely, depending upon the kind of plant and the conditions of growth. High yields of crops growing under favorable growing conditions require amounts on the order of 20 g m^{-2} and more (Table 1.2). Additional data on N uptake by other crops are summarized by Olson and Kurtz (1982).

How well the supply of soil N meets plant needs depends upon soil and plant factors. The readiness with which solid-phase organic N fractions are converted to forms available for plant uptake depends upon their chemical nature and the soil environment in which they occur (Chap. 3).

Plant factors influencing N use efficiency include the effectiveness of N uptake and assimilation mechanisms (Moll et al., 1982) and transport processes. These factors function interdependently and are related to C metabolism. During the vegetative period of growth, N generally accumulates in plants at a greater rate than does the accumulation of dry matter (Fig. 1.6). The accumulation of N in the leaves of plants grown in soils high in available N may extend the vegetative

TABLE 1.2   Seasonal N Uptake into Aboveground Portions of Crops Grown with Nutrient Levels and Growth Conditions Favorable for High Yields

Crop	N uptake, g m^{-2}	References
Alfalfa (3 cuttings)	41	Jenkins and Bottomley (1984)
Bird's-foot trefoil	19	McGraw et al. (1986)
Coastal bermudagrass (4 cuttings)	39	Day and Parker (1985)
Corn	28	Russelle et al. (1983)
Potatoes*	23	Lauer (1985)
Rice	22	DeDatta and Mikkelsen (1985)
Wheat	28	Cox et al. (1985)

*Including tubers.

phase of growth. This accumulation may provide a larger pool of N to be used subsequently during the reproductive stage of growth, but in cereals, for example, it may decrease the physiological efficiency of N use under adverse conditions that impair remobilization and translocation during grainfill. An opposite effect, a delay in the onset of the reproductive stage, may result from N deficiency in some species. At high soil N levels, a lower proportion of the total N absorbed may be partitioned into storage organs or fruit, as shown in Fig. 1.7 for potatoes (Lauer, 1985).

There are large and complex differences both between and within species in the relationship between the acquisition of N and its use by plants. Through breeding and selection, and genetic engineering, genotypes that use soil N more effectively in the production of dry matter are being developed. The influences of genetic differences in maize

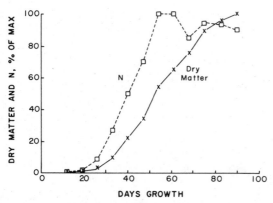

Figure 1.6   Accumulation of dry matter and N by a corn crop. (*Data plotted from B. Bar-Yosef and U. Kafkafi, Soil Sci. Soc. Am. Proc. 36:931–936, 1972.*)

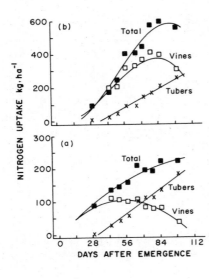

Figure 1.7 Cumulative uptake of N by Russell Burbank potatoes grown with (*a*) adequate (210 kg ha^{-1}) and (*b*) excessive (610 kg ha^{-1}) rates of applied N. (*Reproduced from D. A. Lauer, Agron. J. 77:193–197, 1985, by permission of the American Society of Agronomy, Inc., Madison, WI.*)

plants, and of seasonal factors, on rates of accumulation of N per se and on dry matter per N (DM/N) ratios, are shown in Fig. 1.8. The low N assimilation rates during the 14- to 28-day period in 1970 were attributed to low seasonal rainfall. Nitrogen accumulation rates and DM/N values of the hybrids were about equal to or greater than those of the inbred parents. For comparison with another species, DM/N values for three harvests of 24 rice genotypes ranged from 86 to 126 (Broadbent et al., 1987). Interrelationships between plant parts as sources and sinks during reproductive growth stages are contributing factors in N use efficiency (Crawford et al., 1982).

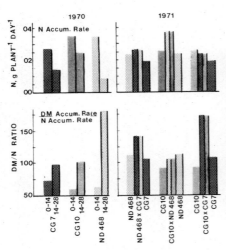

Figure 1.8 Rates of accumulation (Accum.) of N and the dry matter, (DM)/N ratios of inbred and hybrid corn genotypes during the postsilking period. For 1970, the data are from samples collected at 14 and 28 days after silking; for 1971, the data are from samples collected 24 days after silking. (*Reproduced from E. G. Beauchamp, L. W. Kannenberg, and R. B. Hunter, Agron. J. 68:418–422, 1976, by permission of the American Society of Agronomy, Inc., Madison, WI.*)

Factors other than those related to physiological aspects need to be considered in evaluating the performance of newly developed genotypes relative to N nutrition. Traits affecting harvestability, e.g., the propensity of some corn genotypes to lodge, may limit their otherwise high-yield, N-efficient potential (Swank et al., 1982). Constraints relative to choices of feasible cultural management practices and to economic factors also need to be considered (Bock, 1984).

If efforts now being made to incorporate into nonlegumes the capacity to use N_2 through symbiosis with rhizobia are successful, less mineral N will need to be applied to soils to produce high crop yields. It appears unlikely, however, that in the near future the incorporation of a capacity to fix N_2 by nonlegumes will have advanced sufficiently to significantly influence the use of mineral N fertilizers. In order to substitute effectively for applications of fertilizer N, N-fixation by organisms associated with nonlegumes will have to be accomplished at costs of photosynthetic energy lower than the research in this area presently indicates.

Sulfur.   Sulfur is similar to N in some functions it serves in plant metabolism, but there are also important differences. Most often S is absorbed by plants as SO_4^{2-} and, like N when absorbed as NO_3, must undergo an 8-electron change during assimilation in order to serve its quantitatively most important role as a protein component.

Like N, the chemical structure of S permits the formation of stable covalent bonds, especially with C and other S atoms. The bonding to C as in cysteine (—C—SH), methionine (—C—S—CH$_3$), and cystine (—C—S—S—C—) in proteins, accounts for most of the S in plants. Plants deficient in S become chlorotic, similar to N-deficient plants, because of impaired biosynthesis of proteins that form complexes with chlorophyll in chloroplasts.

The C—S linkage is very stable, with an energy of dissociation of 167 kcal mol^{-1} (Chemical Rubber Co., 1983). The S—S linkage is relatively weaker (102 kcal mol^{-1}), and the reversible transformation of the disulfide functional group (—C—S—S—C—) of cystine to the sulfhydryl functional group (—C—SH) of cysteine is an important redox system. Glutathione (L-γ-glutamyl-L-cysteinylglycine) helps to maintain S-containing amino acids metabolically active by keeping them in a reduced form (Duke and Reisenauer, 1986). Sulfur linked to Fe in metalloproteins also serves as a redox system. Reduced S is metabolically active in nonprotein nitrogenous compounds, for example, in the heterocyclic rings of two coenzymes, biotin and thiamin. The presence of S in coenzyme A provides a reactive site for reversible oxidation-reduction reactions.

Oxidized S as SO_4^{2-} also serves metabolic functions. Generally, one-third to one-half of the total S must be present as SO_4^{2-} for the optimum growth of higher plants. For its reduction and assimilation, SO_4^{2-} ions must be present at reduction sites at adequate levels. Sulfate ions along with a number of other cations and anions are necessary in plant tissues for the proper functioning of cells and membranes. Because of its hydrophilic nature, SO_4^{2-} linked to organic metabolites confers greater solubility to these complexes.

Sulfur also occurs in a wide variety of other compounds in plants, but for many of them a general physiological function has not been clearly defined (Thompson et al., 1986). Examples include a number of S-substituted cysteines and S-esters. Some of these impart aroma and taste to plant components, and these characteristics may serve a role in plant survival and competitiveness.

Forage legumes generally have relatively high S requirements to attain maximum growth. An uptake of 5.2 g m^{-2} was found in the aboveground portion of a season's growth (five cuttings) of alfalfa (Rendig, 1956). Comparable values were found in other studies (Nuttall, 1985; Pumphrey and Moore, 1965). In a 3-year study of a nonlegume, cotton, mean yearly S uptake was about 2 g m^{-2} (Kamprath et al., 1957).

Instances of soil S levels too low to meet crop needs are becoming more frequent. In countries or regions in which restrictions have been placed on the uses of fuels containing S, additions of S to soils by atmospheric deposition have decreased. Use of non-S-containing fertilizers such as urea, ammonium nitrate, and ammonium phosphate in place of ammonium sulfate and single superphosphate, which contains about 50 percent gypsum, have also decreased incidental additions.

Phosphorus.   Like S and most N, P taken up by plants from soils is in anionic forms as $H_2PO_4^-$ and HPO_4^{2-}. Each of the anionic forms of these three elements involves linkages to O by covalent bonding. Compared to S and N, P is more electronegative, and its linkage to O is retained in plant tissues. Phosphorus atoms link to C and to each other through O bonds, as in ATP and ADP. These polyphosphate complexes are a vital part of the energy conversion processes in plants. They are water-stable, but when properly configured, and in the presence of an appropriate kinase, P—O linkages are broken and the energy released is used for a number of metabolic reactions. The amounts of energy (8 kcal mol^{-1}) in these P—O linkages, often referred to as "high-energy bonds," are not large compared to most covalent bonds, such as those indicated above for N and S. The effective transfer of the energy in the linkage to drive metabolic reactions depends not only on the amount, but also upon physiological regulation of the rate at which this energy is released. Turnover times for the individual P atoms are very rapid. It has been estimated that each inorganic P ion entering a plant cell makes an average of 60 passages through ATP and the metabolic cycle before it is withdrawn in growth, storage, or transport (Bieleski, 1976).

Phosphorus serves vital functions other than as a component of ADP and ATP. It undergoes reversible esterification with many sugars and other compounds involved in photosynthesis and respiration. Phosphorus atoms provide bridges between the ribonucleoside units of RNA and DNA. The amounts of P in these nucleic acids account for about the same proportion of the total P in vegetative tissue as the amounts in P-esters, typically ranging from 10 to 25 percent of total P. Phosphorus is an essential component of RuDPCase, but this enzyme, with a molecular weight of about 500,000, accounts for only a very small fraction of the total P in plants.

As with S, amounts of P provided for optimum plant growth must exceed the needs for assimilation into organic forms so that a substantial portion of that present in the plant tissues is in inorganic forms. In their review of the metabolism of P, Bieleski and Ferguson (1983) concluded that the cytoplasmic pool of inorganic P (P_i) "appears to be the hub of all cellular P metabolism and of the whole P economy of the plant." Studies with isolated chloroplasts from spinach have shown that RuBPCase activity is impaired if adequate levels of inorganic phosphate are not present, and 3-phosphoglycerate or dihydroxyacetone phosphate will not substitute for this need (Heldt et al., 1978). The ratio of P_i to phosphorylated compounds in the cytoplasm during maturation depends upon reproductive sink demands, indicating an important role of P_i in sink size to source activity relationships (Plaut et al., 1987).

The P needs of roots and shoots during the early stages of plant growth are provided by phytic acid (P-ester of inositol) stored in seeds. This storage form accounts for a major fraction (in some cases over 50 percent) of the total amount of P present in the seeds of many plants. Too few data are available for any generalizations regarding the efficiency with which the P in vegetative parts of plants is used to meet the needs of developing fruits. In studies with peanuts , during the period of rapid accumulation of P in the kernel, stem tissue was found to undergo the greatest decrease in P (Bunting and Anderson, 1960). A much larger fraction of the total amount of P in the kernel apparently was obtained through absorption by the roots.

The amounts of P that crops need to absorb to meet the requirements for growth and development vary widely, and depend upon other conditions of growth as well as on amounts of P in soils. Amounts taken up by several crops grown under favorable conditions are shown in Table 1.3. The reports from which these examples were selected included data on crop responses to P additions, and the uptakes shown were estimated as those needed aboveground to produce maximum yields. Much greater uptakes, e.g., over 7 g m^{-2} by a corn crop, have been reported (Karlen et al., 1988). Extractable (Mehlich I) soil P at the site where this crop was grown was 247 kg ha^{-1}, a very high soil level.

There is currently much interest in seeking ways to improve the effectiveness with which crops use soil P, including that previously added as fertilizers but retained in the soil. The possible contributions of phosphatases and mycorrhizal uptake in aiding the release of P retained in inorganic and organic soil components are being investigated, and are discussed in more detail later (Chap. 3).

Potassium.   The functions served by K in meeting plant needs have little in common with those for N, S, and P. Except under severe K deficiency or saline conditions, K^+ is the main counterion for balancing the negative charges of sulfate, nitrate, phosphate, chloride, and organic ions. The NH_4^+ in plant cells also serves this role, but the quantity generally present is too low to contribute significantly to the maintenance of ionic balance. Unlike N, S, and P, the atomic structure of K is not conducive to covalent bonding and thus does not form stable coordination complexes. Like P, but unlike N and S, K undergoes no change in redox state during assimilation, remaining entirely in the same ionic form as absorbed.

The functions that K serves in plants are much too numerous to review in detail here. Excellent discussions of specific roles of K in enzyme catalysis (Suelter, 1985), protein metabolism (Blevins et al. 1985), photosynthesis (Huber, 1985), structural features (Beringer and Nothdurft,

TABLE 1.3   Seasonal P Uptake into Aboveground Portions of Crops Grown with Nutrient Levels and Growth Conditions Favorable for High Yields

Crop	P uptake, g m^{-2}	References
Alfalfa*	1.0	Nuttall (1985)
Coastal bermudagrass*	1.0	Day and Parker (1985)
Celery	3.0	Lorenz and Vittum (1980)
Corn	2.1	Hanway and Olson (1980)
Corn	2.3	Bar-Yosef and Kafkafi (1972)
Cotton	2.1	Bassett et al. (1970)
Oats	1.1	Hanway and Olson (1980)
Rice	3.0	DeDatta and Mikkelsen (1985)
Wheat	1.1	Hanway and Olson (1980)

*Avge. cut^{-1}.

1985), and assimilate transport (Mengel, 1985) have been published (Munson, 1985). A very thorough review of the roles of K in plant water relations has been published by Hsiao and Läuchli (1986).

With concentrations in plant cell sap commonly in the range of 100 to 300 (Beringer and Nothdurft, 1985), K ions have a marked effect on cell water potentials and turgor. Thus growth by cell extension of bean leaves (Mengel and Arneke, 1982) and of cotton fibers (Dhindsa et al., 1975) is affected by K nutrition. As the major osmotic component in leaf guard cells, the transfer of K into and out of these cells regulates stomatal opening and closing. The identification of this regulatory function as a specific role of K, first described by Fischer (1968), has been supported by the results from research by many other investigators (see Hsaio and Läuchli, 1986). These findings have included both analytical data showing the effects of K nutrition on the amounts of K in the guard cells, and evidence of a more indirect nature such as the effects of differences in plant K nutrition on physiological processes, including loss of water and the uptake of CO_2 through the stomates (Peoples and Koch, 1979; Terry and Ulrich, 1973). Other alkali metal ions, including Li^+, Na^+, and Cs^+, if present in guard cells, can affect the opening and closing of stomates, but the concentrations required may exceed those that are likely to be present in plants growing in soils. The possibility that the movement of K^+ into and out of guard cells is a response to other regulatory mechanisms, such as controlled changes in other cellular constituents and in water flux, has been suggested (Maier-Maercker, 1983). Other important plant species differences influencing the relationship between tissue K levels and stomatal opening include rates at which changes in openings respond to cellular K^+ level changes, and interactions with light and CO_2 (Hsiao and Läuchli, 1986).

Besides their abundance in plant cells, K ions have other attributes suiting them for specific physiological functions. They are relatively small in size even in the hydrated state, and they are very mobile since they do not readily bond to other cellular components. Thus, they are ideally suited to aid the intercellular and intracellular transport of inorganic and organic anions. Sodium and Li ions are also small but move less freely than K^+ because of their higher energies of hydration. Plant species such as sugar beets, in which Na^+ can effectively substitute for a large fraction of K, are called *natrophilic*. Being less sensitive to its possible phytotoxic effects, these plant species can use Na^+ to maintain soil-plant water relationships suitable for growth under saline conditions.

Potassium ions influence the conformation of proteins and thus contribute to the effectiveness of some enzymes in catalyzing metabolic reactions. A lower activity of RuBPCase was suggested as a possible reason for the subnormal rates of assimilation of CO_2 by K-deficient alfalfa plants (Peoples and Koch, 1979). The effects on enzyme function may also account for the relationship between K concentration in ryegrass and the effectiveness with which N is used for protein synthesis (Fig. 1.9). In some instances where K ions activate an enzyme, other ions may also serve in this same role. For example, asparaginase, the enzyme catalyzing the metabolism of asparagine in the biosynthesis of various amino acids, is activated by K^+, but in some plants such as peas Na^+ is also an effective activator; because of other possible adverse effects, however, Na^+ may be less suitable than K^+. Likewise, other enzymes activated by K^+ may be activated by NH_4^+ or Rb^+ in vitro, but the levels needed for greatest effectiveness in vivo are phytotoxic because of adverse effects on other metabolic reactions.

Plants typically require amounts of K similar to needs for N. Some examples for several crop plants grown under favorable conditions are shown in Table 1.4. These values will vary widely with amounts of K in soils in which the crops are grown. The uptake of essential nutrients in excess of plant growth needs ("luxury consumption") when present at high concentrations in the growing medium is particularly well exemplified by K, but this also occurs with other nutrients, particularly some micronutrients. Other conditions of growth also influence the uptake and plant usage of K. Thus, for example, Karlen et al. (1982a) found that much larger total amounts of K (20.9 g m^{-1}) were taken up by the soybean crop in the second than in the first year of a 2-year study, but seed yields were better in the latter. Rainfall was much heavier in the second year and may have produced conditions of low soil O_2 levels that interfered with plant development during the reproductive phase. Varietal differences are also important in the uptake of K.

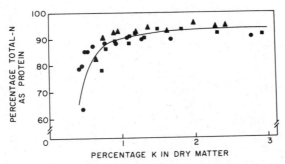

Figure 1.9   The relationship between percentage of K in dry matter of ryegrass and the percentage of total N present as protein. (*Reproduced from R. A. Leigh and R. G. Wyn-Jones, New Phytologist 97:1–13, 1984; used with permission.*)

TABLE 1.4   Seasonal K Uptake into Aboveground Portions of Various Crops Grown with Nutrient Levels and Growing Conditions for Producing High Yields

Crop	K uptake, g m^{-2}	References
Alfalfa (4 cuttings)	38	Rominger et al. (1976)
Bermudagrass	35	Day and Parker (1985)
Corn	25	Rhoads and Stanley (1984)
Cotton	13	Bassett et al. (1970)
Rice	26	DeDatta and Mikkelsen (1985)
Soybeans	21	Karlen et al. (1982)
Wheat	17*	Alley et al. (1983)

*Mean of four soft winter varieties; uptake likely exceeded needs for maximum grain yields.

As also noted for N and P, crop nutrient needs and accumulation of dry matter do not necessarily correspond. In studies by Bassett et al. (1970), a higher proportion of the total uptake of K by a cotton crop occurred in the latter part of the growing period than was the case for N and P (Fig. 1.10). Apparently a larger fraction of the N and P needs during fruiting were met by transfer from vegetative tissue than was the case for K.

Calcium.   Much of the Ca in plants occurs as intermolecular linkages in cell walls and membranes, and it thus contributes to the structural stability and cell-to-cell movement of various metabolites. As much as 50 to 60 percent of the total Ca in plant roots is present in cell walls (Rossignol et al., 1976). The manner in which Ca links molecules, particularly carboxylates and phosphates, in cell walls and membranes is

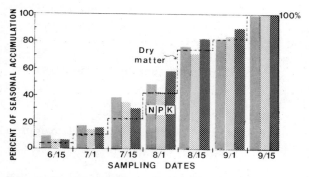

Figure 1.10 Accumulation of N, P, and K compared with dry matter accumulation in cotton grown at six test sites. (*Reproduced from D. M. Bassett, W. D. Anderson, and C. H. E. Werkhoven, Agron. J. 62:299–303, 1970, by permission of the American Society of Agronomy, Inc., Madison, WI.*)

unique and vital, but details of these linkages are not well understood. Adequate Ca helps plants to avoid stress effects due to the presence of heavy metals or salinity. Substitution of Ca by heavy metals can cause structural distortion, resulting in cell walls losing their rigidity, and in the inability of membranes to function properly. Ample Ca helps lessen the adverse effects of the presence of NaCl on both the production and shape of cotton plant root cells (Kurth et al., 1986), and on the integrity of membranes in corn root protoplasts (Lynch et al., 1987). Plant growth under saline conditions is discussed further in Chap. 7.

Calcium also reacts with various other cellular components to form insoluble salts. Thus, under some conditions, a significant fraction of the total Ca in vacuoles and organelles may be present as precipitates of organic acids, particularly oxalates, and as phosphates. In mature sugar beet leaves, up to 90 percent of the total Ca is bound to oxalate (Marschner, 1986).

Soluble Ca also serves a number of important functions in plant metabolism, but some regulatory mechanisms are needed to prevent soluble Ca from reaching levels which can have inhibitory effects. The readiness with which Ca reacts with organic ligands and inorganic P to form highly insoluble products assures very low concentrations in the cytosol of plant cells. These insoluble forms provide a reservoir from which soluble Ca can be derived for metabolic needs. Solubilization of Ca is aided by the presence of malate.

The Ca-activated protein calmodulin, first noted in animals but subsequently also found in pea plants (Anderson and Cormier, 1978), plays a major role in a number of metabolic reactions involving Ca. Its functions include activation of the photosynthetic enzyme NAD-kinase (Dieter, 1984) and roles in protein phosphorylation (Veluthambi and Poovaiah, 1986) and phytochrome responses (Chen and Roux, 1986; Roux et al., 1986). The ATPases involved in the transport of Ca into and out of cellular compartments through membranes have a high degree of specificity for Ca (Gross and Marme, 1978). During senescence, Ca influences membrane deterioration (Leshem, 1984).

The data from field studies for the total amounts of Ca needed for plant growth are limited. Bar-Yosef and Kafkafi (1972) found that, after 90 days of growth, the aboveground portion of a hybrid corn crop grown in field plots receiving the N and P treatments which produced the highest yields contained 5.5 g of Ca per square meter. Similarly, as already noted for the uptake of N and P, Ca accumulated more rapidly than the dry matter. Karlen et al. (1982a) found that at the time of maximum accumulation, prior to leaf fall, an average of 5.7 g of Ca per square meter was taken up by the four determinate soybean cultivars (Fig. 1.11). Like K, more Ca was absorbed by these same cultivars in the second year of the study when, compared to the prior year, much greater vegetative growth but lower seed yields were produced.

Magnesium. Generally, most of the Mg in plants is present as divalent cations. The characteristics of this element relative to its main functions in plants are intermediate between K and Ca. Magnesium is sufficiently abundant and mobile as the soluble ion to serve with K and other cations as an important counterion for various inorganic and organic anions. Thus it is an important contributor to the physiological processes in which properties of cellular environments such as ionic strength and water potential gradients are involved. The resemblance of Mg to Ca is in its divalency and its ability to form chemical linkages that are somewhat stable, but generally Mg bonds are less tenacious than those of Ca. Magnesium in chlorophyll, where it is linked to the nitrogen of four porphyrin groups by partially covalent bonds, accounts for about 15 to 20 percent of the total Mg in plants.

Many reactions of intermediary metabolism involve activation of N bases and phosphoryl groups by linkage to Mg, for example, to aid nutrient flux across the plasmalemma (Leonard, 1984). Formation of an ATP-Mg complex is necessary before the energy in —P—O—P— bonds can be released and then used for driving metabolic reactions

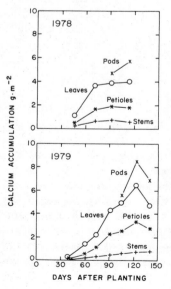

Figure 1.11 Accumulation and distribution of Ca (excluding loss by leaf fall) in irrigated soybeans grown in 1978 and 1979. (*Reproduced from D. L. Karlen, P. G. Hunt, and T. A. Matheny, Agron. J. 74:347–354, 1982, by permission of the American Society of Agronomy, Inc., Madison, WI.*)

and for synthesizing metabolites. Magnesium activates fixation of CO_2 by RuBPCase, but what specific function it serves in this reaction is not understood. Other modulating factors involved in the reaction include light (Seeman et al., 1985) and pH (Heldt et al., 1978). Wheat and corn seedlings differ in regulation of RuBPCase (Rubisco) activity by CO_2 and Mg^{2+} (Gustafson et al., 1987).

In in vitro studies, other ions, e.g., Mn, have been found to be capable of substituting for Mg as enzyme substrate activators; they are generally much less effective, however. Chemical attributes of Mg that account for its uniqueness in serving most effectively in this role are its relatively small size, high energy of hydration, and strong electrophilic properties (Clarkson and Hanson, 1980). Calcium might be expected to behave similarly, but with an ionic radius about 50 percent greater than Mg, its energy of hydration is less and it does not link to O as tenaciously as Mg.

The amounts of Mg taken up for growth of crops are generally somewhat lower than for Ca. In studies with soybeans, Karlen et al. (1982a) found uptakes of Mg by irrigated and nonirrigated soybeans were 5.2 and 5.1 g m^{-2}, respectively. Differences in responses in Mg uptake for the 2 years of the study were similar to those already noted for K and Ca. An average annual Mg uptake of 1.8 ± 0.3 g^{-2} was found for a N- and K- fertilized mixed pasture, with perennial ryegrass and cocksfoot as the predominant species (Reith et al., 1964).

Manganese.   Like Mg, the most abundant form in which Mn generally occurs in plants is as a divalent ion. The amounts of Mn present are low compared to Mg, Ca, and K, so it has much less influence than these three cations on the ionic strength and osmotic properties of the cytosol. If Mn were present at concentrations high enough to be an important contributor to osmotic properties of cells, it would be phytotoxic.

Probably the best-documented role of Mn in plants is its involvement in O_2 evolution during photosynthesis, in conjunction with the transfer of electrons from H_2O (Clarkson and Hanson, 1980). Manganese atoms become bound to proteins at photosystem (PS) II reaction centers through photoactivation (Cheniae and Martin, 1969). The details of this reaction of intermediary metabolism are not yet well enough known to define the attributes of Mn which uniquely suit it for this function. Not only the kinds of linkages formed with protein components but also their stability, as well as the manner of coordination, are probably involved. Iron, Zn, and Cu, the other transition elements essential to plants, may not be suited for this role because they become bound too firmly and are not sufficiently reactive. The complex stability constants of these three heavy metals exceed those of Mn.

The redox potential of Mn is also a likely factor determining its participation in photosynthetic O_2 evolution. Although the occurrence of the reaction is not firmly established, there is evidence that at least part of the Mn in the PS reaction center undergoes a change from the divalent to the trivalent form (Ono et al., 1986). If an ability to undergo reversible oxidation-reduction were not necessary, Mg might be a good substitute to bind the protein ligand in the PS II reaction center. Linkage of Mg or Ca to a "hard" base protein ligand (Lewis acid type reaction) would form a redox stable product (Ochiai, 1977).

Activities of a number of other plant enzyme systems are influenced, in vitro at least, by the presence of Mn. In some of these systems, other elements, most often Mg, can serve equally well as Mn. If Mg is quantitatively interchangeable with Mn, or nearly so, it seems likely that in vivo Mg would serve as the activator. The concentrations of Mn and Mg ions in plant tissues have been estimated at 0.3 and 19 mM, respectively, based on the total amounts of each generally found in plant tissues (McClendon, 1976).

An absolute requirement for Mn was found in a number of those C-4 plant species in which fixed CO_2 is transferred to the bundle sheath cells as aspartate (Hatch and Kagawa, 1974). Activities of the NAD-dependent malic enzymes in leaf extracts of saltbush, two species of amaranth, and millet, were entirely dependent upon the presence of Mn, whereas Mg was ineffective. A need for Mn ions along with biotin as coenzymes for biosynthesis of lipids in plant membranes is possible; however, the lower oil content noted in seeds of Mn-deficient plants may reflect the role of Mn in photosynthesis (Marschner, 1986).

The amounts of Mn required for a season's plant growth are only a fraction of 1 g m^{-2}. In a 2-year study with soybeans which included both irrigated and nonirrigated treatments, the average maximum seasonal Mn accumulation in the crop was approximately 0.030 g m^{-2}, and about one-third of the total Mn was present in the pods (Karlen et al., 1982a). Greater total uptake (0.37 g m^{-2}) was found for a rice crop grown in the Philippines and yielding 9.8 t ha^{-2} rough rice grain (DeDatta and Mikkelsen, 1985).

Iron. One of the best-known visual manifestations of the consequences of a mineral plant nutrient deficiency is the rather distinctive pattern of chlorosis on the younger leaves of Fe-deficient plants. While over one-half of the total Fe present in plants may be present in chloroplasts, just what specific function Fe serves that results in chlorotic leaves is not fully understood. Various ways in which Fe might be directly involved in chlorophyll biosynthesis or in reactions associated with biosynthetic pathways have been proposed, but these have not been well substantiated. From his own results with sugar beets , and from results reported by others, Terry (1980) indicated that Fe-deficiency stress affects not only the amounts of several photosynthetic pigments in the chloroplast, but a reduction in photosynthetic electron transport as well; the Fe deficiency, however, did not impair CO_2 fixation expressed per unit weight of chlorophyll. Other research, also with sugar beets, has shown that in leaves of Fe-deficient plants the biosynthesis of thylakoid galactolipids is impaired (Nishio et al., 1985). It was suggested that this impairment may have an adverse effect on the development of thylakoid membranes, and thus may affect chloroplast function.

The most ubiquitous role of Fe in plants is to undergo reversible oxidation-reduction while linked to a variety of ligands vital to reactions of intermediary metabolism. One large group of such metabolites are the heme and nonheme Fe proteins. The former are also called porphyrins since the skeletal structure to which the protein becomes linked is porphine. Examples of this group are the cytochromes in which Fe is centered in the heme complex linked to four N atoms (Fig. 1.12). In cytochrome f, R consists of a protein linked to a C side chain through S. Another example of a porphyrin, but lacking Fe, is chlorophyll, in which the central linkage is to Mg rather than Fe. Cytochromes function in coupled electron-transfer reactions through which the energy needs of plants are provided, with bound Fe atoms serving as redox loci. The redox potential of Fe in the porphyrin structure differs from that of Fe present as free ions.

Nonheme Fe also performs important physiological functions. In ferridoxin it is linked to S and through this linkage to another Fe atom (Fig. 1.13). The structure of this complex varies among different kinds of organisms. Ferridoxin in plants is involved, in some cases with thioredoxin, in a number of oxidation-reduction reactions, notably

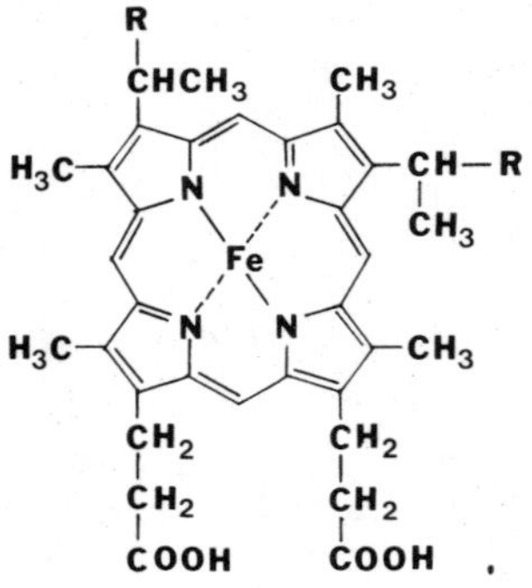

Figure 1.12   The heme structure of C-type cytochrome c.

Figure 1.13   Proposed structure of the ferridoxin in higher plants. (*Reproduced, with permission, from the Annual Review of Biochemistry, volume 42, 1973, by Annual Reviews, Inc.*)

those that are light-activated (reviewed by Buchanan, 1984). Some Fe is present in a soluble form and some is membrane-bound. The latter has a lower molecular weight (ca. 8000) and contains more (4 vs. 2) Fe atoms than the soluble form. In chloroplasts the Fe in ferridoxin is present in both divalent and trivalent forms, and under illumination a portion of the Fe^{3+} accepts electrons and becomes reduced (Boardman, 1975).

Because of its greater solubility and mobility, Fe^{2+} is more metabolically active than Fe^{3+}. Significant amounts of the trivalent form occur as inorganic precipitates. Chelates such as citrate help mobilize Fe from these insoluble forms.

Plant needs for Fe are comparable to those for Mn. In the 2-year study with soybeans, the average total seasonal accumulation by four cultivars ranged from 0.07 to 0.12 g m^{-2}. The higher value was obtained the second year when there was greater production of dry matter but lower seed yields (Karlen et al, 1982b). Total uptake of Fe by a rice crop was the same as for Mn, 0.37 g m^{-2} (DeDatta and Mikkelsen, 1985).

Copper.   Specific unique plant physiological functions of Cu have been identified, but the amount necessary to meet plant needs is the least of any of the essential elements taken up as cations. Copper is a vital component in the functioning of a number of enzyme systems involving oxidation-reduction reactions. Why other metals such as Fe and Mn do not also function in these systems is not known, but likely reasons include constraints of size and of coordination in the complexes in which Cu occurs. Also, the complex stability constant of Cu is greater than that of Mn.

A major portion of the Cu in plants occurs in chloroplasts. This metal provides reducing equivalents to photosystem 1 as a component of plastocyanin, the terminal protein in the electron transport chain during photosynthesis. Plastocyanins of differing molecular weights (10,500 to 21,000) have been extracted from different plant species, and these contain one to two atoms of Cu in each molecule (Boardman, 1975). The essentiality of Cu in photosynthetic electron transport is indicated by the inactivating effects of treatments with Cu-complexing chemicals such as KCN and $HgCl_2$. Another group of Cu-containing enzymes, also present primarily in chloroplasts, are the superoxide dismutases. These enzymes aid in ameliorating the effects of superoxide radicals generated in photorespiration (Sandman and Böger, 1983).

Cytochrome c oxidase, also a Cu-containing enzyme, functions in respiratory processes, catalyzing the transfer of electrons to O_2 to form H_2O. This enzyme accounts for only a small amount of Cu, since there are only two Cu atoms for each two porphyrin-protein complexes (cytochromes). The two Cu atoms show some dissimilarities, but both are not equally involved in reducing O_2.

An assay of the activity of a Cu-containing oxidase enzyme has been suggested as an effective means of diagnosing Cu nutrition in plants. Ascorbate oxidase activities in leaves of subterranean clover, grown in a glass house or in field plots, correlated well with responses in yields and Cu uptake to soil applications of Cu (Fig. 1.14). Activity of another Cu metalloprotein enzyme, diamino oxidase (DAO), also responded to Cu nutrition, but the effect was less marked and its activity was related to N nutrition. Insufficient Cu impairs biosynthesis of the DAO enzyme protein (Delhaize et al., 1986).

Leaves and stems of plants with insufficient Cu show abnormal morphological features. Distortion of leaves is related to the lower

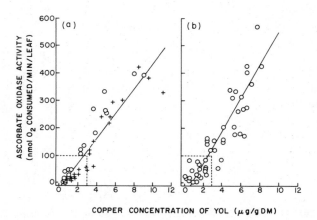

Figure 1.14 Relationship of ascorbate oxidase activity of young folded (YF) leaves to Cu concentration in the youngest open leaf (YOL) of subterranean clover: (a) cv. 'Seaton Park' grown at six levels of Cu supply on a Cu-deficient sand in a greenhouse with N supplied as NH_4NO_3 (+) or by symbiotic fixation (o), and (b) cv. 'Mt. Barker' grown at various levels of Cu supply on a Cu-deficient sand in the field. (*Reproduced from J. F. Loneragan, E. Delhaize, and J. Webb, Aust. J. Agric. Res. 33:967–979, 1982; used with permission.*)

amounts of lignin in cell walls because of reduced activity of phenolase in Cu-deficient tissues (Robson et al., 1981).

Total uptake of Cu by plants generally is the least of the heavy metals. A Cu concentration of 0.026 g m^{-2} was found in the aboveground portion of a high-yielding rice crop (DeDatta and Mikkelsen, 1985) In Cu-deficient wheat plants, much of the Cu absorbed becomes bound in nonmobile forms in vessels, but in the presence of ample external Cu concentrations, a large proportion of the Cu absorbed is transported into the leaves (Loneragan, 1975).

Zinc. Results of early studies showing that plants grown with low levels of Zn in the external medium were stunted and had small leaves, indicated an involvement of Zn in plant auxin functions. One explanation for the responses noted in these studies was that Zn was required for biosynthesis of tryptophan, an auxin precursor. Subsequent evidence regarding Zn serving this function is conflicting. A specific need of Zn for the synthesis of auxin from tryptophan has been proposed (Takaki and Kushizaki, 1970). Zinc deficiency in young corn seedlings was corrected by supplying tryptophan in the nutrient solution in which the plants were grown (Salami and Kenefick, 1970).

Zinc has been implicated in the functioning of a large number of enzymes, mostly in animal systems, but in relatively few have specific functions of Zn been clearly defined (Ochiai, 1977). Establishing with certainty that one or another heavy metal is needed in order for a physiologically vital component to function poses severe analytical problems. Commonly these components have molecular weights exceeding 10^4, and the metals are generally present in amounts of a few atoms per molecule. The propensity of Zn to become bound to organic ligands generally is less than that of Fe or Cu, but greater than that of Mn. Thus Zn tends to be less mobile than Mn but more mobile than Fe or Cu.

One of the plant enzyme systems with which Zn is associated is carbonic anhydrase. This enzyme is found in chloroplasts and catalyzes the following reaction: $H_2O + CO_2 = H^+ + HCO_3$. The reaction proceeds without the enzyme, but at a slower rate. The enzyme activity is severely impaired in some Zn-deficient plants, but the linkage between the metal and the enzyme has not been established. The results of some studies indicate a tight binding of Zn to the enzyme, but Fellner (1963) could find no Zn in a carbonic anhydrase prepared from spinach. If Zn were present in the enzyme, but not tightly bound, it could be lost during the isolation procedure.

In some organisms, including some yeasts and fungi, Zn has been shown to be an essential cofactor for the activity of fructose 1,6-diphosphate aldolase, but its necessity for the functioning of this enzyme in plant or animal systems has not been shown (Ochiai, 1975). This aldolase catalyzes the splitting of hexose into two 3-carbon molecules.

Zinc is essential for the enzyme D-glyceraldehyde-3-phosphate dehydrogenase (GPDH) to catalyze removal of H and addition of a phosphate group to C-1. It is uncertain what characteristic(s) uniquely suits Zn for this role. Its size, capability to form tetrahedra, and resistance to change in redox potential are likely contributing factors (Clarkson and Hanson, 1980).

Generally the amounts of Zn needed to complete a growth cycle of many plants are comparable to those for Mn. In a study with soybeans, Karlen et al. (1982b) found an average maximum aboveground Zn accumulation for four cultivars of 0.015 and 0.022 g m^{-2} for the first and second year, respectively (Fig. 1.15). Vegetative growth was much greater and seed yields much lower in the second year compared to the first. For a rice crop grown in the Philippines, uptake was 0.05 g m^{-2} (DeDatta and Mikkelsen, 1985).

Molybdenum. Molybdenum serves two vital and unique functions in N nutrition of plants. It is a component of nitrogenase, an enzyme necessary for plants that depend upon fixation of N_2 by their symbiotic relationship with rhizobia. To serve this role, Mo needs to be present only in root nodules where N_2 is converted to NH_3.

A second function, for plants using NO_3^- to meet N needs, is as a constituent of a molybdoflavoprotein enzyme, NO_3^- reductase, which catalyzes the reduction of N from $+5$ to -3. There may be other functions that Mo serves in this reaction, but because its redox potential in this enzyme complex is in the appropriate range, it is the likely accep-

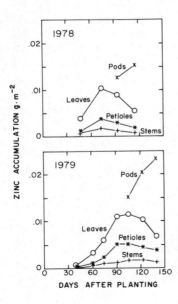

Figure 1.15 Accumulation and distribution of Zn (excluding leaf fall) in irrigated soybeans. (*Reproduced from D. L. Karlen, P. G. Hunt, and T. A. Matheny, Agron. J. 74:297–303, 1982, by permission of the American Society of Agronomy, Inc., Madison, WI.*)

tor of the electrons produced when NO_3^- is converted to NO_2^-. Respiratory mechanisms must function concurrently since this reaction requires that 2 e^- and 2 H^+ must be present for each NO_3^- that undergoes reduction.

The amounts of Mo needed by plants are very low. Based on the concentrations commonly found in plants growing in soils with adequate but not excessive levels of Mo, and a biomass yield of 10^4 kg ha^{-1}, an Mo uptake of 1 mg m^{-2} is sufficient. Plants can accumulate concentrations 10^3 times those needed for growth, but such concentrations, which can be phytotoxic, are rare under field conditions.

Boron. Boron is unique compared to the other essential elements in that under most conditions it is taken up largely, not as an ion, but as undissociated boric acid.

That B is essential for plants can be readily shown in growth experiments, but a vital physiological role has not been clearly defined. Influences of B on metabolism and translocation of carbohydrates have been reported. These effects are generally explained on the basis of the capability of B to link adjacent diols, particularly those with the cis configuration, but complexing B with OH's in other configurations has been suggested (Dugger, 1983). More information on how such a mechanism functions is needed to establish it as a basis for a B requirement. Recent evidence of a need for B in Ca metabolism in animals has been reported.

A need for B in phenol metabolism has been proposed to account for abnormalities in cell walls and membranes, and in root growth elongation, observed in B-deficient sunflower plants (Hirsch et al., 1982). Increases in amounts of phenols in B-deficient plants was related to a lower level of 6-phosphogluconate, an inhibitor of phenol biosynthesis from erythrose-4-phosphate (Lee and Aronoff, 1967). Impaired root development in summer squash growing in a B-nutrient solution was attributed to decreased synthesis of DNA or its precursors (Krueger et al., 1987).

There is an anomaly in the behavior of B in its uptake and movement in plants. The observed influence of transpiration rate on B uptake is consistent with its entry into plant roots as H_3BO_3. Once inside plants, however, much of the B absorbed becomes immobile, not moving readily from older to younger, growing plant parts. Low B mobility may result from complexing in some manner, or because of some other constraint in the phloem. In the sap expressed from plant tissue, much of the B is not dialyzable, indicating the presence of a retention mechanism.

Total uptake of B (0.032 g m^{-2}) by a rice crop is comparable to that for Zn and Cu (DeDatta and Mikkelsen, 1985). Concentrations of B in dicots are generally much greater than in monocots, by about an order of magnitude (Mengel and Kirkby, 1982).

Chlorine. Growth experiments have established Cl as an essential element for higher plants, but a vital physiological function has not been conclusively identified. The amounts of Cl present in plants are highly variable and commonly exceed the low amounts needed for optimum growth. Because Cl is ubiquitous, mobile, and, in some soils, abundant, it can influence physiological processes or reactions of intermediary metabolism that are affected by the ionic strength or water potential of plant cells, such as osmoregulation. Similar physiological effects are also produced by other inorganic ions, so such effects on cellular environments would not be a basis for establishing Cl as a plant-essential element.

There is evidence that Cl^- is necessary for the evolution of O_2 in photosynthesis. Whether this is a general need in the plant kingdom is questionable, however, since the expected impairment of photosynthetic activity was not observed in leaves of Cl-deficient sugar beet plants (Terry, 1977). Also, methods used in preparing experimental material for demonstrating Cl^- essentiality in photosynthesis can affect other plant components and result in artefacts (Andersson, 1984). The in vitro Cl^- requirement for optimal O_2 evolution from a thylakoid vesicle preparation was decreased fiftyfold by the addition of a spinach protein preparation.

In an as yet not fully understood way, low Cl^- levels in soils in which winter wheat is growing increases the incidence of take-all root rot, a disorder caused by the fungus *Gaeumannomyces graminis* var. *tritici* (Christensen et al., 1981). A lowering of the leaf water potential has been associated with the suppressing effects of increased Cl^- concentrations in the plants. By favoring a greater uptake of Cl^-, less damage from take-all occurs when ammoniacal rather than nitrate fertilizers are used as N for wheat (Christensen et al., 1987).

Only a small fraction of the Cl^- taken up may be removed if the vegetative portion is not harvested, and the residues are left on the soil. Amounts of Cl ranging from 5.4 to 24.6 g m^{-2} were found in tops and roots of sugar beets grown on Calciaquoll soils at five dryland sites in the Red River Valley of North Dakota (Moraghan, 1987). Amounts in the roots ranged from 0.8 to 2.0 g m^{-2}. Plant Cl^- leaches readily since binding is neglible.

Phytotoxic concentrations of Cl⁻ are a frequent cause of salinity stress on plants. These are discussed in Chap. 7.

2

Root Growth
and Distribution

For a plant organ to continue growth, new cells must be formed and then expand. This expansion occurs when hydrostatic pressure (turgor) is sufficient to overcome the constraining effects of the cell walls, thus allowing an irreversible increase in volume, area, or complexity. If the growing organs are located underground, they must also overcome the resistance to deformation of the surrounding soil.

Osmotica in the root cells are responsible for causing water to flow from soil to the expanding cells. These osmotica can be maintained only if respiration can proceed. Root growth thus can continue only if continuing supplies of water are present for hydrostatic pressure, of O_2 for respiration, of hormones for cell wall loosening, of calcium for cell wall synthesis, and of carbon and other metabolites for energy and cellular building materials. These concepts were discussed more fully in Chap. 1.

Root Functions

Roots absorb the water and nutrients required to satisfy the shoot's demand. These functions are complex because roots must deliver water and nutrients that have been absorbed simultaneously from deep and shallow soil layers, from moist and partially dry soil, and from soil zones of different biological, chemical, and physical properties. Roots also serve several other functions for the plant. They provide anchorage to keep the plant from being washed or blown away or from being toppled. Anchorage also is necessary for the shoot to emerge through soil crusts or for roots to force a path through a soil matrix.

Fleshy roots, especially of dicotyledonous plants (dicots) such as sugar beets, radishes, and turnips, serve as storage reservoirs for starches, sugars, and proteins in their pith or cortex. Roots of grasses usually have less storage capacity, so this storage is often located in the crown or in rhizomes.

Roots of some plants develop adventitious shoots when the main shoot is killed. Plants able to reestablish shoots by this mechanism often become noxious weeds in cultivated fields or in intensively managed pastures, especially if roots of these species have substantial underground storage capacity for photosynthates and minerals.

Roots are believed to be the primary source for cytokinins and gibberellins and for ethylene in some flooded soils.

Root-Shoot Relationships

Shoots are the initial source for most of the organic metabolites used in growth and maintenance, and roots are the initial source for nearly all the inorganic nutrients and for water. Roots and shoots obviously are interdependent. By themselves, however, these interdependent roles do not explain the close coordination of root and shoot development. When seeds first germinate, much of the metabolite is directed toward root expansion. For a specific environment, genotype, and growth stage, there will be a set fraction of the metabolites directed toward this expansion. If half of the root mass is removed from a seedling, root growth will accelerate, relative to shoot growth, until this set fraction is again achieved (Fig. 2.1). Similarly, if half of the shoot mass is removed, shoot growth will increase, relative to root growth, until the ratio again is achieved. Chemical messengers probably are interchanged between roots and shoots to control growth and development processes.

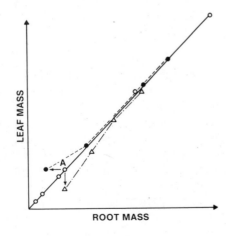

Figure 2.1 Recovery of original root-shoot ratio in beans as affected by removal of half of the roots (closed circles) or half of the leaves (triangles), compared to normal growth (open circles). (*Adapted from Brouwer and deWit, 1969.*)

Many factors affect the relative shoot-root proportions. Tropical (C_4 photosynthesis) grasses have higher shoot-root ratios than temperate (C_3 photosynthesis) grasses. Root growth rate declines during seed filling, thus increasing shoot-root ratios. This decline in root growth can be reversed by removal of fruit. Shoot growth rates are increased, relative to root growth, by increasing soil water availability, by alleviating waterlogging and thus the induced water and ion stress, by increasing a low temperature regime, by increasing the phosphorus and nitrogen supplies to roots, and by defoliating the plant. Conversely, relative root growth is enhanced after damage to roots by tillage or by root-feeding insects, after CO_2 concentration is increased around the shoots, after light intensity is increased, and after soil water content is decreased (Fig. 2.2).

Root and shoot masses are important data in studies of nutrient and carbohydrate redistribution or of respiration. Leaves, however, capture the sunlight energy, and, until leaf area indexes approach a value of about 3, photosynthesis increases with leaf area, other factors being adequate. Similarly, roots absorb the water and inorganic nutrients. As root length or root dispersion increases, per unit of soil volume, absorption increases, other factors again being constant. All factors that alter the ratio of shoot mass to root mass probably alter the leaf area–root length ratios.

It is easy to find out that a sudden hail storm, a mowing operation, or an insect infestation has reduced leaf area, but it is much more difficult to find out if root length has been significantly decreased by cultivation or by root-feeding insects. It should not be assumed that a reduction in root mass or root length necessarily is associated with

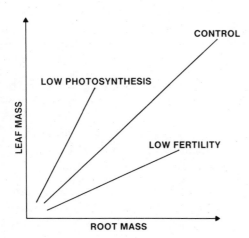

Figure 2.2 General effect of reducing photosynthesis or fertility below the optimal values on root and shoot mass of field bean.

reduced seasonal yield. Final yield will be reduced only if ion, water, or growth-regulating compound supplies are reduced at some critical period.

Root Origin and Distribution

Roots originate from a wide variety of tissues but most often arise from the primary root or its branches, from stem nodes on stolons, bulbs, and rhizomes of grasses, or from the hypocotyl of certain dicots. Roots can arise from more than one type of tissue on the same plant. Root primordia tend to coincide with the presence of xylem vessels near parenchymatous cells capable of renewed differentiation. Initiation of the lateral primordia probably involves complex hormonal responses.

Root systems are classified as fibrous-rooted or taprooted, but there is a continuous spectrum between these two extremes. Monocotyledonous plants (monocots) tend to have fibrous root systems, and dicotyledonous plants (dicots) tend to have some variant of taprooted root systems.

Monocots

Roots of monocots originate at stem nodes except for the radicle. In the grass family, these nodal roots consist of two kinds—the seminal roots that arise from root primordia contained in the seed, and adventitious (crown) roots that arise from the crown, but occasionally arise at the seed depth if a coleoptilar tiller develops there (Fig. 2.3). Generally for the grass family, crown roots begin development by the three-leaf stage (Newman and Moser, 1988), and all support prior to this stage must depend on the seminal root system.

Adventitious roots of monocots arise with time from successively higher nodes. The number and diameter of these roots increase with higher node number for most, if not all, cereals.

Root extension rates for monocots are rapid if conditions for growth are adequate. As an example, Gregory et al. (1978) found that wheat grown in England extended its roots downward at a rate of 6 mm day^{-1} from December to April 8, and then at a rate of 18 mm day^{-1} from April 8 until the end of May. Their wheat plants had a rooting depth of about 2 m by harvest. Köpke et al. (1982) found that the rooting depth of wheat in Germany increased from about 1.0 m on 23 April to about 1.95 m on 18 June, 56 days later, for an extension rate of 17 mm day^{-1}. Cholick et al. (1977) found that each of five cultivars of winter wheat penetrated to the 3.0-m depth by harvest in Colorado.

Both rooting depth and root length density (meters of roots per cubic

Figure 2.3 Photograph of a wheat plant grown in soil at Pendleton, Oregon. Seminal and crown roots are clearly visible. (*Photo courtesy of R. W. Rickman, USDA.*)

meter of soil) increase with time during the vegetative phase, and roots do not completely stop growth even when seed sinks develop. Root length density usually decreases with depth, but values of root length density at a specific depth in the profile vary widely. As an example, wheat plants growing in England and transpiring at the potential rate had 2.4×10^4 m of roots in an average square meter of land area (Gregory et al. 1978), while wheat in South Africa, also transpiring at the potential evapotranspiration rate, had 3.5×10^3 m of roots in a square meter of land area (Proffitt et al., 1985), or 15 percent of the Gregory et al. (1978) value. There also were differences in root length among cultivars of wheat, when growing in the same soil (Köpke et al., 1982).

Dicots

As a result of both genetic background and environment, dicot root systems vary greatly among species. Soybeans are used here merely as an example of a dicot root system (Fig. 2.4).

The radicle of soybean emerges from the seed and soon develops into

Figure 2.4 Photograph of the root systems of a group of soybean plants. Nodules of *Rhizobium* are clearly visible on the roots. (*Photo courtesy of R. R. Allmaras, USDA.*)

a taproot that is positively geotropic and grows downward at a rate of 25 to 50 mm day^{-1} (Kaspar, 1982). The taproot can penetrate at least to the 1.5-m depth, but often terminates downward growth at lesser depths due to adverse soil conditions (Kaspar, 1985). Soybean taproots are tetrarch, so laterals emerge at 90° around the taproot circumference. Diameters of these laterals average 0.65 to 0.75 mm.

A large proportion of the soybean root system consists of four to seven extensively branched roots that originate near the base of the taproot. These basal roots are 2 to 3 mm in diameter. They grow outward at a characteristic angle, which depends on the cultivar and soil temperature (Stone and Taylor, 1983). These basal roots grow laterally for 200 to 360 mm, then abruptly turn downward and rapidly grow to a 1.8-m or greater depth (Mitchell and Russell, 1971). Their diameters, even at a 1.5- to 1.8-m depth, are about 1 mm. They often grow faster than the taproot.

Second-order roots are smaller in diameter than the basal roots, and higher-order roots are even smaller than second-order ones. The average functioning life of higher-order roots may be 10 to 20 days. These higher-order roots form when environmental conditions are appropriate and die when water nutrients are depleted in their immediate vicinity. Up to 80 percent of the root length can senesce when soil water potential in a particular layer decreases to below −0.2 MPa for a week to 10 days.

The rates of both new root formation and old root death vary with time and environmental conditions. The net result is that root length density and root length per plant fluctuate rapidly during the season (Fig. 2.5). Root growth does not cease during pod filling but continues at least at half the rate achieved during vegetative growth. If soil conditions are satisfactory, increases in soybean rooting depth continue slowly until the first pods cease filling their seeds (Kaspar, 1985).

Influence of Carbohydrate Supply

Reduced root growth during seed fill implies that the photosynthate supply for root growth is limiting during that period. Presumably, anything that decreases seed demand for photosynthates or increases photosynthate supply should increase root growth during seed filling. Depodding, increased CO_2 concentration within the canopy, and increased photosynthetic irradiance increase root growth relative to shoot growth. Defoliation decreases root growth with respect to shoot growth.

Factors Affecting Root Distribution

The principal factors that affect root distribution within a field soil profile are (1) genetic differences among and within species, (2) flows of photosynthates and growth-regulating compounds from the shoots,

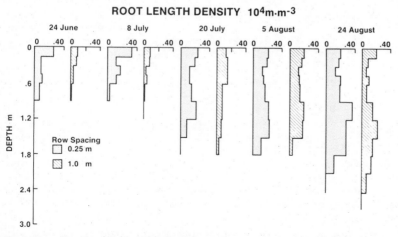

Figure 2.5 Root length densities as functions of soil depth and time for Wayne soybeans grown in two row spacings on Ida silt loam (a loess) soil at Castana, Iowa, during 1976. (*Data of Taylor, 1980; used with permission.*)

(3) seasonal shifts in root primordia, and (4) soil chemical, physical, and biological factors.

Genetic differences

When grown in an "ideal" environment, plant root systems grow in a form and shape dictated by their genetic makeup. These forms and shapes vary extensively from one species to another and often from one line to another within the same species. These characteristic forms and shapes may be approached in a mist chamber (Smucker and Erickson, 1976), but almost never are fully expressed when plants are grown in a field soil with its ever-changing environment.

Lore Kutschera (1960) published an extensive atlas of root growth of various plants growing in soils, and J. E. Weaver published, either as the sole or as the senior author, 23 manuscripts (listed by Böhm, 1979) that describe root growth under a wide variety of conditions. Taylor and Terrell (1982) published a list, for many species, of maximum rooting depth, working rooting depth, lateral spread, and soil characteristics at the site where the studies were conducted. The wide differences can be illustrated by comparing rooting patterns of onion, cacti, and mesquite trees. Onion has a maximum rooting depth of 1.0 m, but most of the roots are located above 0.80 m. Onion has a lateral spread of about 0.30 m (Weaver and Bruner, 1927). The fact that onions intensively root a small volume of soil is one reason that onions respond so well to intensive irrigation. Cacti have a high proportion of their roots in the upper 0.30 m of soil with a lateral spread 10 to 15 m from the plant base (MacKey, 1980). This rooting habit allows cacti to absorb water from small rains very efficiently. Some mesquite plants have taproots that penetrate as deep as 53 m (Phillips, 1963). These deeply penetrating roots allow mesquite plants to survive during long droughts.

Chemical environmental effects

Large areas of each continent, except Antarctica, are dominated by acid soils (Van Wambeke, 1976). Soils are acid because their parent materials were initially low in basic cations (Ca^{2+}, Mg^{2+}, K^+, and Na^+) or because the basic cations were removed by normal rainfall leaching or by plants being harvested. Even the normal growth of a clover pasture for 50 years decreased the pH of an Australian soil from 6.0 to 5.0 at a 0.3-m depth (Williams, 1980). Soil acidification is intensified by the use of acid-forming nitrogenous fertilizers (Pierre et al., 1971) and by acid deposition in rainfall (Ulrich et al., 1980).

Acid soil injury to plants is insidious and may be mistaken for drought effects, herbicide injury, low temperature damage, plant disease, soil physical problems, or ordinary nutrient deficiencies. Extreme acidity in subsoils is harmful because it can cause shallow rooting, denying plants access to the water and nutrients located there.

Farmers have limed soils for many centuries, but liming was placed on a scientific basis only during the nineteenth century, when the concept of soil pH was developed. Liming to change soil pH alters the availability or activity of all ions in the soil solution. This fact has caused much confusion to persist in the soil liming literature because in many experiments only initial and final soil pH, amount of lime added, and final yield were measured and concentrations of all ions, other than hydrogen, were not measured.

Chemical toxicities

H and Al   Two adsorbed ions, hydrogen and aluminum, are largely responsible for the toxic effects of soil acidity on root growth and function. Although excess Mn often is toxic to top growth, Mn usually affects root growth to a lesser extent than top growth.

In most soils, Al^{3+} toxicity is much more important than H^+ toxicity to root growth in higher plants, particularly to nonlegumes. However, H^+ ion toxicity may restrict the survival and activity of soil microorganisms including rhizobia (Wood et al., 1984). The effects of H^+ concentrations on root growth in soil are difficult to separate from the effects of Al because Al^{3+} concentration increases significantly when soil pH falls below the pH range of 5.0 to 5.5 (Fig. 2.6).

Because the effects of H^+ ion are confounded with the effects of other factors in soil, scientists have used solution or sand culture media to characterize root response to low pH. Roots of plants damaged by pHs lower than 4.0 are shortened, thickened, fewer in number, and dull brown or gray (Islam et al., 1980). Root hair lengths are decreased with decreased pH from 7.2 to 5.5 (Ekdahl, 1977). Cotton primary root length was decreased when solution pH was decreased below 4.2 (Howard and Adams, 1965). Excess H^+ ions compete with cations for absorption sites, interfere with ion transport, and cause root membranes to become more leaky. Because of these effects on membrane permeability, excess H^+ ions can increase the Ca^{2+} requirement. Lund (1970) found that soybean primary roots growing in the nutrient part of a split root system required higher Ca^{2+} levels at a pH of 4.5 than at 5.6. Excess H^+ ions can also decrease the uptake of Mg^{2+} (Blamey et al., 1982).

Any substantial increase in Al^{3+} concentration (Blamey et al., 1982) or Al activity (Adams and Lund, 1966) in the soil solution will cause root growth to slow or stop (Fig. 2.7). This slower root growth

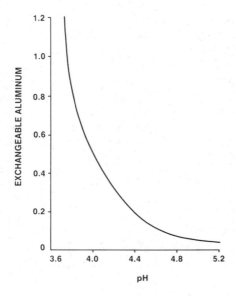

Figure 2.6 Relationship between pH (1 mol dm^{-3} KCl) and exchangeable aluminum (cmol kg^{-1}) on an Avalon sandy loam. (*Drawn after Blamey and Nathanson, 1977.*)

occurs because both cell division and cell elongation are affected. If the decreased root growth causes the plant to undergo additional stress at some critical stage, seed yield also may be decreased.

In addition to its effect on cell division and root elongation, Al^{3+} concentration affects root morphology and function. Aluminum-injured roots are stubby and distorted with patches of brown cortical tissue. The roots generally lack fine branching. Binucleate cells occur

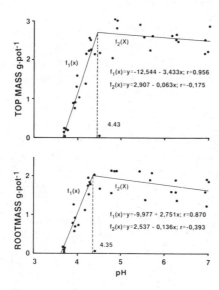

Figure 2.7 Relationship between soil pH (1 mol dm^{-3} KCl) and the yield of sunflower seedling tops and roots. (*After Blamey and Nathanson, 1977; information from Agrochemophysica reproduced under copyright authority 8755 of 30 September, 1987, of the Government Printer of the Republic of South Africa.*)

more frequently in Al-injured roots than in normal ones. Root cells in the pericycle may be damaged. Ion and water uptake rates (per unit weight or length of root tissue) are lower in Al-damaged than in normal roots.

Aluminum concentrations in the soil solution can be measured directly, and Al activity can be estimated using the Debye-Huckel equation for single ion activity (Adams and Lund, 1966). Because the soil solution concentrations of Al and the percentage of Al saturation of the soil exchange complex are closely linked, many experiments have shown that root growth is decreased as the percentage of Al saturation is increased.

Aluminum effects of root growth and function are discussed more completely by Adams (1974, 1984), Foy (1974, 1984), and Blue and Dantzman (1977).

Allelopathic toxicants. Plants, including microorganisms, produce many chemicals that escape into the immediate environment. The term *allelopathy* refers to the interactions among plants that are caused by these escaping chemicals. In this context, allelopathic effects depend on the addition of a chemical to the environment and are separate from competition effects, which involve the reduction of some factor from the environment.

There are many examples in the literature where the increased prevalence of one species has reduced the growth of another species. Obviously much of that reduction can be attributed to competition, and many experiments have not separated the competitive and allelopathic effects. However, some experiments have shown direct allelopathic effects on plant growth. For example, velvetleaf reduced the growth of corn and soybean (Bhowmik and Doll, 1979). Quackgrass reduced the yield of corn, wheat, peas, and alfalfa. Purple nutsedge reduced the yield of strawberry despite the fact that all the purple nutsedge tops were cut back at short intervals to prevent shading, and the strawberry plants were regularly watered and fertilized (Rice, 1984). At least 50 species of weeds have been identified as having allelopathic effects on crop growth (Rice, 1984).

It has been shown that allelopathic agents sometimes (1) affect hormonal synthesis or utilization, (2) inhibit nitrogen fixation and nitrification by bacteria, (3) prevent seed decay during germination, (4) alter division, elongation, and ultrastructure of cells, (5) affect membrane permeability, (6) reduce mineral uptake, (7) inhibit photosynthesis, (8) inhibit respiration, (9) inhibit protein synthesis, and (10) decrease stem conductance for water (Rice, 1984).

Growers frequently encounter "replant" problems with peaches, apples, lettuce, and papaya. Replant problems usually have been resolved by moving to land not previously planted to the same crop.

However, Ko (1971) solved the papaya replant problem by digging a hole about 10 cm deep and 30 cm in diameter, filling the hole with virgin soil, and then planting the papaya plants in that virgin soil. Lynch (1983) discusses several other techniques that have proved useful in overcoming allelopathic or pathogenic problems.

Many compounds are phytotoxic when present in sufficient concentrations. Often, the concentrations required for phytotoxicity are greater than those found in the soil; therefore, the phytotoxic properties of the compound are ignored by field-oriented scientists. Many synergistic effects have been noted, however, where two or more compounds, each present in concentrations too low to affect plant growth, have acted in conjunction to drastically reduce growth.

Many opportunities seem to exist for increasing the growth of plants through eliminating allelopathic reactions; however, much greater research efforts are required before these opportunities can be realized in practical plant production.

Salinity. Saline soils exist in many parts of the world. Soluble salts contained in the soil solution cause both direct and indirect effects on root growth. First, these soluble salts reduce the total water potential of the soil solution, thus tending to reduce the potential difference between soil water and the atmosphere. If plant roots do not absorb enough salts to adjust their osmotic potentials to that of the soil solution, uptake of water will be reduced.

Second, increases in soil salinity reduce root elongation rate. In a split root experiment, Leo (1964) showed that tomato root tips subjected to a 1% NaCl solution elongated at 26 percent of the rate that roots of the same plant elongated in control nutrient solutions. Cotton radicles progressively reduced their elongation rates as total water potentials, as modified by NaCl solutions, were reduced (Fig. 2.8).

Third, increases in soil salinity increase suberization and reduce root permeability. Salinity affects the width of casparian strips, the suberized strips on endodermal cell walls. In halophytes, the casparian strips cover almost all of the endodermal end walls, but cover a much smaller proportion of the walls in nonhalophytes.

Fourth, increases in salinity may upset hormonal balances, which control many plant responses such as membrane permeability to water and ions, cell wall plasticity, and transpiration rates.

Fifth, increases in salinity alter the ionic composition of the soil solution and, in turn, affect the nutritional balance of the plant.

Sixth, increases in salinity usually increase soil pH, thus affecting solubility of many nutrients.

Finally, increases in soil salinity may alter soil structure, affecting soil strength, aeration, and hydraulic and ionic conductivities.

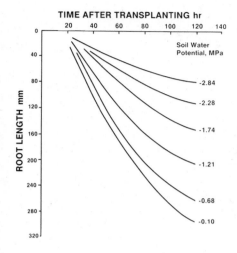

Figure 2.8 Cotton seedling radicle length during a 120-h growth period as affected by soil water potential. Soil water potential was varied using NaCl solutions. (*Data of J. E. Box and H. M. Taylor as given by Taylor, 1983.*)

There are substantial research programs devoted to increasing crop production on saline soils, principally through plant selection programs (Epstein, 1983).

Other toxic agents.   Un-ionized NH_3, NO_2^-, Be, Cd, Pb, Cu, Cr, Fe, Hg, and Zn all reduce root growth to a much greater extent than shoot growth in nutrient solutions. It seems likely that each of them will reduce crop growth rate and yield, especially if the roots encounter them while the plants are seedlings. Differences among plant genera in toxicity responses certainly occur, and differential tolerances among genotypes for each of them probably occur (Foy et al., 1978).

Many pesticides alter root growth without affecting top growth under minimal stress conditions. Ideally, a pesticide controls its intended target without affecting nontargets. Ashton and Crafts (1973) examined 16 classes of herbicides and found that 10 of them contained at least one compound that affected root growth in nontarget species. Some herbicides affect geotropic response; others affect root initiation, cell wall formation, mitosis, protein synthesis, cell wall lignification, and integrity of cellular membranes. As one example, trifluralin reduces lateral root initiation and nodulation (Kust and Struckmeyer, 1971).

Chemical insufficiencies.   Some acid soils are infertile because root growth and subsequent nutrient and water uptake are restricted by toxic quantities of H, Mn, Al, or allelopathic biochemicals. Some acid soils are infertile because the roots absorb sufficient quantities of certain toxic ions that harm top growth. Some acid soils are infertile because the concentration of some essential ion is too low or too unavailable throughout the profile. These conditions are discussed in other sections of the book.

Some acid soils are infertile because roots must have minimal concentrations of Ca and B in their immediate vicinity to grow (Loneragan, 1979). No other ions are required in the immediate soil environment surrounding the elongation zone because the other essential ions can be translocated from other parts of the root system. If Ca and B are supplied to one part of a root system growing in solution culture, other parts of the root system located in solutions minus Ca or B will not grow (Haynes and Robbins, 1948).

The concentrations of Ca^{2+} required to permit some growth of roots varies with species and with H^+ levels. At Ca^{2+} concentrations of 0.5 to 1.0 μM, roots of beans, tomatoes, and flax develop normally and roots of corn develop at even lower concentrations (Neales, 1960, 1964).

Physical environmental effects

Many experiments have been conducted during attempts to define the "ideal" physical environment for plant roots. Often, however, the researcher has evaluated the effect of changes in a single measured variable without considering the accompanying changes in other, unmeasured, variables. This section first reviews experiments that evaluated the soil physical variables of water, air, heat, or strength under conditions where it was presumed that no interactions occurred with other environmental factors that affect root growth. Later in the section, some problems associated with effects of interactions are discussed.

Soil water.   For roots to grow, defined here as the irreversible increase in length, water must be present in sufficient quantities within the meristematic zone for cells to divide. In addition, sufficient water must be present within the elongating cells to overcome cell wall constraints (Pfeffer, 1893). Key factors that control root growth rate, therefore, are the presence of continuing supplies of water to maintain hydrostatic pressure in the elongating cells of the root, of metabolites for cell wall construction, and of growth hormones to loosen the bonds within the cell wall constituents (Lockhart, 1965).

Root elongation.   Cells in the elongating zone must maintain osmotic potential sufficiently low to absorb water radially from the surrounding soil or longitudinally from more mature regions of the root. Water flows radially into the elongating cells when their total water potential is lower than the combined osmotic and matric potentials of the soil. When the combined potentials of the soil are lower than the total water potential of the root, water flows outward and elongation will cease unless water is supplied from the more mature root tissue. The rate at which water moves radially to the root cells depends on the combined values for conductivity of the liquid water and diffusivity of water vapor through the soil pore spaces. For elongation to continue after the root encounters dry soil, sufficient water must move longitudinally within the root to the elongation zone to overcome the outward flux of water from the root to the dry soil. Thus, some root growth can occur with tomato and corn at water potentials of -4.0 MPa, but for all practical purposes, root growth ceases at -5.0 to -10.0 MPa potentials (Portas and Taylor, 1976). However, alfalfa and guayule roots grew into soil drier than wilting point, and some corn roots grew into air-dry soil with estimated potentials from -27.5 to -90 MPa (Hunter and Kelley, 1946a, b).

Most experiments relating root growth to soil water content have not separated the direct effects of soil water from its indirect effects on oxygen, temperature, or strength of soil. Taylor and Ratliff (1969b), however, conducted an experiment, using cotton and peanuts as test crops, in which root elongation rates were determined as functions of soil water potential and soil strength. This experiment was conducted under temperature-controlled conditions, and air-filled porosities were great enough so that soil aeration was adequate. Soil matric potentials between -0.017 and -0.7 MPa did not directly affect the root elongation rates of cotton (Fig. 2.9), and those between -0.019 and -1.25 MPa did not directly affect the root elongation rates of peanuts when neither crop was actively transpiring. It is not known what

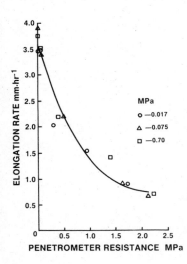

MPa

o —0.017
△ —0.075
□ —0.70

Figure 2.9 Effect of penetrometer resistance and soil water potential on cotton root elongation for the period 40 to 80 h after transplanting. (*Data of Taylor and Ratcliff, 1969; used with permission.*)

would have happened to root elongation if the plants had been transpiring.

Root diameter. Root diameters are much more sensitive than root elongation rates to changes in soil water potential. Decreases in either soil matric or osmotic potentials cause roots to shrink in diameter, sometimes to only 40 percent of their hydrated value (Fig. 2.10). Roots grown in loose soil at a − 0.5- to − 1.0-MPa matric potential are thinner than those grown in loose soil at less negative potentials.

Root death. Root death also seems to be quite sensitive to soil water content. When the matric potential of a soil layer drops to a − 0.1- to − 0.2-MPa value, root length density often decreases if other parts of the root system are located in soil with a higher potential. In field situations where annual plants are undergoing meteorological drought, rapid shifts in root length density can occur because more roots will die than are being formed in the drier surface soil layers, but more roots will form than will die in the wetter deep layers (Fig. 2.11).

Root hair. Some of the epidermal cells of many plants develop tubular outgrowths called *root hairs*. These root hairs increase the surface area of the root and the volume of soil exploited by the root. The root hairs increase nutrient uptake, especially of phosphorus. The yield of white clover increased with root hair length in three populations grown in soil with a low phosphorus level. There is controversy on the root hair effects on water uptake (Rosene, 1943; Cailloux, 1972; Jones et al., 1983), but root hairs are known to be important in the formation of symbioses between legumes and *Rhizobium* spp. (Dart, 1974). Root hairs may help anchor roots and may help maintain contact between root and soil during soil drying (Tinker, 1976).

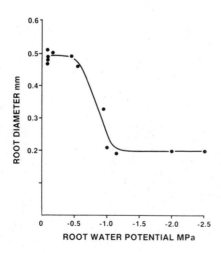

Figure 2.10 Relationship between root water potential and root diameter. (*Data of Cole and Alston, 1974; used with permission.*)

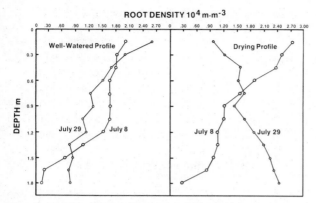

ROOT DENSITY $10^4 \, \text{m} \cdot \text{m}^{-3}$

Figure 2.11 Root length density profiles at two dates in a soil profile that remained moist and one that was allowed to dry. (*After Klepper et al., 1973; used with permission.*)

Plant species differ in their length and spatial density of root hairs. Dittmer (1949) found that the root hair length in 34 species varied from 0.08 to 1.5 mm with most being less than 0.5 mm. Caradus (1980) found that root hair lengths of 10 grasses varied from 0.4 to 1.0 mm and from 0.17 to 0.29 mm for 11 legumes. Itoh and Barber (1983) found differences in length (0.04 to 0.6 mm) and spatial density (560 to 1819 cm^{-1}) in 6 contrasting species. Root hair length varies with species, with cultivar, with pH, with concentrations of phosphate, nitrate, calcium, and potassium, and with soil water content.

Soil air.   Respiratory energy is necessary for many plant processes and reactions to occur. The plant obtains this energy by using molecular oxygen to convert carbohydrates to carbon dioxide and water. This reaction releases about 300 kcal of biologically useful energy per mole of carbohydrate substrate, about 19 times as much as that released by the anaerobic (absence of free oxygen) pathway (Russell, 1977). For aerobic respiration to occur in roots, the oxygen must be relatively free to move through air-filled spaces, either in soil or in root tissue.

Soil oxygen.   Movement of oxygen to the roots through soil occurs through interconnected air-filled pores. If water content or soil bulk density is great enough to cause partial blockage of air-filled pores, oxygen diffusion rates are reduced substantially. The diffusion coefficient of oxygen in water is approximately 10,000 times smaller (at 26°C, 0.26×10^{-4} cm^2 s^{-1}) than that in air (0.23 cm^2 s^{-1}).

   Oxygen in the air-filled pores diffuses through a water shell around the root and then through root tissue to the point of use. Increases in soil water content increase both the thickness of the water shell around the root and the root diameter. Both of these factors decrease the oxygen supply to the root cells.

Plant roots also contain interconnected air-filled passages for gaseous diffusion. These pores allow sufficient oxygen movement for the roots of even sensitive plants to penetrate short distances into zones of low oxygen content (Fig. 2.12). Root systems of many kinds of plants respond to waterlogged soils by increasing their internal porosity through development of large continuous air-filled channels called *aerenchyma*. These channels increase gaseous diffusion downward toward the root tips. Under certain conditions, sufficient oxygen can move into flooded soils to create aerobic conditions in a shell of soil that surrounds each root.

Molecular diffusion in response to a concentration gradient is the major source of oxygen for respiration. However, oxygen can be supplied by mass flow due to pressure changes induced by air turbulence at the soil surface, by temperature changes, and by barometric pressure changes. In addition, some dissolved oxygen can be supplied as water infiltrates into soil.

Oxygen concentration in the soil pore space decreases when oxygen is supplied at rates lower than that required for the respiration of roots and microorganisms. These respiration rates increase with soil temperature. Currie (1970) showed that the oxygen consumption from bare soil was $0.7 \text{ g m}^{-2} \text{ day}^{-1}$ in January and increased to $11.6 \text{ g m}^{-2} \text{ day}^{-1}$ in July. When kale was grown in this well-drained soil, oxygen

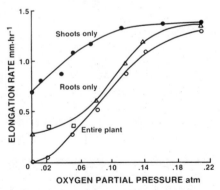

Figure 2.12   Effect of varying oxygen partial pressure on pea seedling root elongation rate when the entire plant was held at different oxygen partial pressures and when the roots only or shoots only were held at different oxygen partial pressures while the other part of the plant was held at 0.21 atm. Each data point represents five plants. (*After Eavis et al., 1971; used with permission.*)

consumption was 2.0 g m^{-2} day^{-1} in January and increased to 23.7 g m^{-2} day^{-1} in July. Lemon and Wiegand (1962) calculated from the data of Machlis (1944) that the oxygen consumption of barley roots was about 1.4×10^{-5} of oxygen per cubic millimeter of root volume per day at a distance of 10 mm from the tips. Oxygen consumption rates also depend on the genetic background and physiological age of the root material.

Several methods have been used in attempts to predict the effects of a reduced soil oxygen supply of root growth and function. The most commonly used methods are (1) oxygen diffusion rate, (2) oxygen concentration in the soil air, (3) air-filled porosity percentage, (4) redox potentials, and (5) air permeability. All of these techniques contain inherent difficulties because the measurements are not taken at the mitochondrial surface, the site of O_2 use.

Oxygen diffusion rate measures the chemical reduction of elemental oxygen at the surface of a platinum wire electrode maintained at a constant potential difference, usually -0.65 V, between the reference and the platinum electrodes. Numerous factors affect the oxygen diffusion rate values that are obtained. However, a value of about 10×10^{-10} g of oxygen per square meter of electrode surface per minute is often accepted as the threshold below which roots will not grow. Values between 20 and 40×10^{-10} g mm^{-2} min^{-1} often cause retarded shoot growth.

Air composition is another traditional way to monitor oxygen status of the soil. It usually is assumed that a problem exists when oxygen concentration in the soil air drops below 10 percent at a specific site. However, Tackett and Pearson (1964a) showed that other soil factors interacted with the O_2 concentration in controlling the root penetration of cotton (Fig. 2.13). Gas chromatographs or membrane-covered

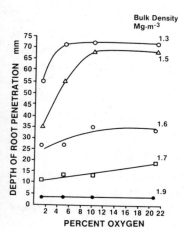

Figure 2.13 The effect of O_2 concentration and bulk density on depth of root penetration into compacted subsoil. (*After Tackett and Pearson, 1964a; used with permission.*)

electrodes (Willey and Tanner, 1963) are used to determine the O_2 percentage at various times and soil profile depths. Oxygen percentages of 14 percent (Eavis et al., 1971), 5 percent (Cannell and Jackson, 1981), 2.5 percent (Greenwood and Goodman, 1971), or less than 1 percent (Armstrong and Gaynard, 1976) have been estimated as the value below which elongation is slowed. The fact that oxygen percentage is a static measurement, as well as genetic differences observed among plants, may help explain such large differences in threshold values.

Air-filled porosity is another way to monitor the oxygen status of the total soil volume. Because part of the soil volume is occupied by mineral particles and part by water, diffusion of oxygen is greater in bulk air (D_o) than in soil (D_s). Various relationships between the ratio D_o/D_s and air-filled porosity have been proposed. Grable and Siemer (1968) found that the ratio of D_o/D_s fell to about 0.02 when air-filled porosity decreased to 10 percent. Baver and Farnsworth (1940) found that the number of live sugar beet plants and yield decreased when air-filled porosity decreased below 10 percent. This 10 percent value is often considered as the threshold, but diffusion of oxygen differs for various soils and various ratios of air to water.

The *redox potential* of a soil system is a measure of its tendency to accept or donate electrons. Under oxygen deficiency, soil microorganisms may use electron acceptors other than oxygen for their respiratory oxidations. This fact results in the conversion of several soil compounds to a reduced state and lowers the soil redox potential. Redox potentials commonly are measured using a platinum microelectrode. Despite various procedural difficulties and theoretical limitations, redox potential measurements are widely used and generally accepted as indicators of conditions where anaerobic pathways of respiration are likely. Redox potentials of $+400$ to $+700$ mV indicate oxidizing conditions and $+150$ to -400 mV indicate reducing conditions.

Air permeability is a measure of the mass flow of air in response to a total gas pressure difference. This method uses either constant pressure or falling pressure air permeameters to obtain a comparative value. In general, air permeability increases with air-filled porosity and with the proportion of large to small pores.

Many theoretical and practical problems occur in air permeability studies; this technique is seldom used now to study aeration effects on plant root development and function. Each of the other techniques discussed in this section is used frequently.

Other effects of anaerobic soil conditions. The restriction in oxygen supply to roots is not the only potential cause of injury to root growth and function when anaerobic conditions develop. Many complex changes occur, but only accumulations of CO_2, ethylene, and organic acids are considered here. More complete discussions of anaerobic soils are given in soils textbooks such as Russell (1973) or Taylor and Ashcroft (1972).

Carbon dioxide is produced during both the aerobic and anaerobic respiration of carbohydrate substrates. This CO_2 accumulates in the root zone if its escape is prevented by high soil water contents.

Carbon dioxide contents as great as 17.5 percent have been reported for soil air (Jackson, 1979), but these levels do not reduce root growth very much unless all other root growth factors are nearly optimum (Fig. 2.14). Nitrogen fixation by *Rhizobium* in leguminous plants, however, may be inhibited by CO_2 concentrations as low as 3 percent.

The concentration of *ethylene* usually is low in well-aerated soils. When anaerobic conditions occur, ethylene production increases and its diffusion to the soil surface decreases. After 7 days, concentrations of ethylene in 0.75-m-tall cylinders of sandy loam soil were 0.14 ppm at the 0.60-m depth when the top of the cylinder remained open, but ranged from 9.3 to 10.6 ppm when the cylinder top was sealed. Most of the rise in ethylene concentration occurred during the first 3 days (Smith and Russell, 1969). Concentrations of 10 ppm almost completely prohibited root elongation in barley (Fig. 2.15).

Ethylene present in the soil air probably does not cause root death because the ethylene is a growth regulator rather than a toxin. Ethylene accumulation, however, inhibits elongation, cambial activity, and stelar differentiation in roots, but stimulates lateral branching and root hair formation (Fig. 2.16). Ethylene concentrations as low as 0.4 ppm can inhibit nodule formation on roots of legumes. Long-term exposure to ethylene can severely affect the pattern of root growth of plants. In some cases, small increases in ethylene can increase the length of rice roots grown in water.

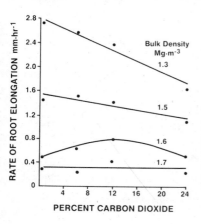

Figure 2.14 Effect of CO_2 level on rate of cotton seedling root penetration of subsoils compacted to different bulk densities. Oxygen was maintained at 21 percent. (*After Tackett and Pearson, 1964b; used with permission.*)

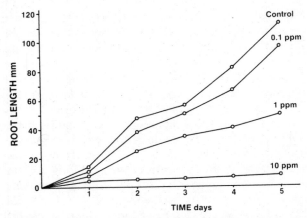

Figure 2.15 The effect of different concentrations of ethylene on the increase in length of barley roots. (*After Smith and Russell, 1969; copyright Martinus Nijhoff, Publ., Dordrecht, (The Netherlands; used with permission.*)

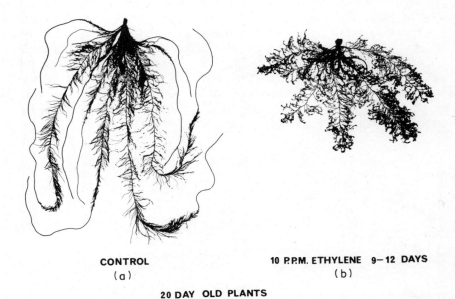

CONTROL
(a)

10 P.P.M. ETHYLENE 9–12 DAYS
(b)

20 DAY OLD PLANTS

Figure 2.16 The root systems of 20-day-old barley seedlings grown in solution culture: (a) control, (b) exposed to 10 ppm ethylene in air for the final 11 days of growth. (*After Crossett and Campbell, 1975; copyright Martinus Nijhoff, Publ., Dordrecht, The Netherlands; used with permission.*)

Ethylene promotes the collapse of cells in the cortex of roots, leading to the development of aerenchyma. Kawase (1978) postulated that a deficiency of oxygen triggers the anaerobic formation of ethylene, which causes an increase in cellulase activity and leads to the formation of aerenchyma. The transport of oxygen is enhanced by the aerenchyma. When plants were waterlogged, then treated with ethylene gas or with cellulase, aerenchyma formation occurred. Some factor other than the concentration of ethylene, however, controls the formation of aerenchyma in rice (Jackson et al., 1985).

Even though 66 percent of the radial pathway across the cortex of corn roots was interrupted by air spaces (Fig. 2.17), nearly as much $^{86}Rb^+$-labeled potassium was translocated to the stele in the aerenchymatous roots as in the normally aerated roots when both were placed in aerated solutions (Drew et al., 1980). Several factors contribute to the overall uptake of an ion, with the structure of the roots being only one of these factors. The conclusion is valid, however, that roots modified by the development of aerenchyma can effectively absorb and transport cations when returned to aerated media.

Soil temperature.   Each species of plants has a minimal soil temperature below which no growth of roots will occur. Above that minimal temperature, root mass accumulates almost linearly with temperature (Fig. 2.18) to a maximal rate at an optimal temperature, and then decreases rapidly until a high temperature is reached where no accumulation occurs. There are differences among cultivars in growth rates (Stone and Taylor, 1983).

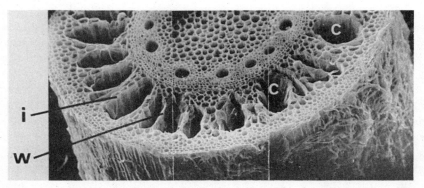

Figure 2.17   Scanning electron micrograph of nodal (adventitious) root of *Z. mays* grown in nonaerated culture solution. Micrograph shows a freshly cut, lyophilized, transverse section in zone 8 to 10 cm from root tip. c: Cortical air space; w: wall residues of collapsed cells; i: intact cells linking inner and outer cortex. Bar indicates 500 µm. (*After Drew et al., 1980; copyright © American Society of Plant Physiologists; used with permission.*)

Figure 2.18   Bean seedlings grown for 8 days (following germination at 20°C) at the root temperatures 5, 10, 15, 20, 25, 30, and 35°C (from left to right). (*After Brouwer and Hoagland, 1964; used with permission.*)

Root diameters often decrease with increasing soil temperatures. The diameter of corn averaged 0.6 mm at 17°C, 0.5 mm at 23°C, and 0.44 mm at 30°C (Anderson and Kemper, 1964). As a result of this trend, the root mass of corn was greater at 23°C than at 17 or 30°C, but root length was greatest at 30°C (Anderson and Kemper, 1964). Shoot-to-root ratios also were greater at 30°C than at 17 or 23°C.

The optimal root temperature decreases with time. Ten hours after being placed in a controlled temperature environment, cotton radicles elongated faster at 36°C than at 28 or 32°C. The situation later changed, however, because at 70 h, cotton radicles were longer at both 28 and 32°C than at 36°C (Fig. 2.19).

Root temperature affects the angle at which lateral roots grow from the central axis. The angle of growth of maize roots (relative to the horizontal) was a minimum (10°) at a constant 17°C and was more vertical at either lower or higher temperatures (Onderdonk and Ketcheson, 1973). Soybean lateral root inclination also is affected by root temperature, but there are differences among soybean cultivars in the temperature at which the penetration angle of the lateral roots is most vertical (Kaspar et al., 1981).

Different parts of the root system of a single plant experience widely different temperatures. When part of the root system is located in warm, moist, and well-aerated soil, shoot growth usually will not be

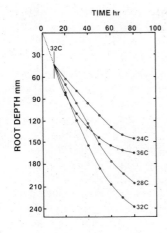

Figure 2.19 Cotton root tip location during the first 70 h after differential soil temperatures were applied. Each data point represents an arithmetic mean of 16 plants. (*After Taylor et al., 1972; used with permission.*)

affected by cooling the rest of the root system. Inflows by phosphate into rape roots were independent of temperature within the range of 23 to 10°C but were halved at 5°C. Both the root extension rate and the phosphate inflow were unaffected by the temperature of the rest of the root system (Moorby and Nye, 1984). Chilling collards grown at 25°C, to 5°C did not affect the leaf water potential during the first 24 h, but chilling all of the roots of cotton severely reduced leaf water potential (Fig. 2.20).

Soil temperatures vary with soil depth, with time during the growing season, from 1 year to the next, and with soil management. These variations in soil temperatures can be extremely important in controlling rooting depth in northern latitudes where growing seasons are

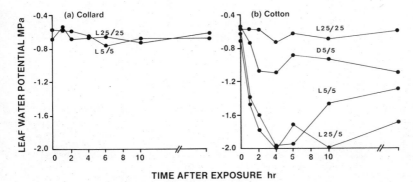

Figure 2.20 Water potentials of the primary leaves of (*a*) collard and (*b*) cotton seedlings measured at various times during the first 24 h after exposure of the whole plants or of the roots alone to 5°C. Plants were in light (L) or dark (D) during the exposure period. (*After McWilliams, 1982; used with permission.*)

short. Mason et al. (1982) measured soil temperatures as functions of time, soil depth, and row spacing. They found that the depth of soybean rooting coincided with the depth of the 15 to 17°C isotherms for the period 42 to 98 days after planting. Stone et al. (1983) used data developed in temperature-controlled water baths located in the greenhouse (Stone and Taylor, 1982, 1983) to predict rooting depth in a field soil where soil temperature and rooting depth were measured. The depth of the lateral root wave was described reasonably well (Fig. 2.21). At 76 days after planting, Kaspar (1982) found that taproot depth of Beeson and Hawkeye 63 cultivars averaged 2.04 m. According to Stone et al. (1983), a 1°C decrease in temperature would have decreased the taproot depth to 1.86 m, and a 1°C increase would have increased the depth to 2.22 m. In their experiment, lateral root depth should have been altered about 0.15 m by the 1°C change.

Soil strength.   Excessive soil strength, sometimes called mechanical impedance or physical impedance, can severely affect the plant's ability to emerge from crusted soils, to extend its root system into unexplored soil volumes, to transport photosynthates from shoots to roots, to transport water from roots to shoots, to bury its seeds for a greater probability of emergence, or to allow below-ground expansion of root crops such as turnips, sugar beets, or radishes.

The excessive soil strength can arise as a result of increased soil bulk density, increased friction between soil particles, increased cohesion between particles, or reduced soil water contents.

Root growth into impeding layers.   Roots grow because the new cells that are formed in the meristematic region lengthen in the cell elongation region. This cell elongation tends to push the root cap and meristematic region forward. If the root cap encounters a hole or pore larger than the root's diameter, the root can grow forward with little resistance from the soil. If, however, the root encounters no such hole, the cell turgor pressure in the elongation zone must be sufficient to

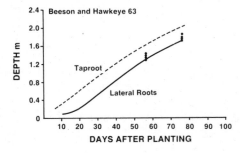

Figure 2.21 Depth of root penetration vs. time for Beeson and Hawkeye 63 soybeans. The data points are means for maximum rooting depth from Kaspar's 1982 field experiment. (*After Stone et al., 1983; used with permission.*)

overcome wall pressures within the cells and the resistances of the soil matrix.

The maximum pressure that roots can exert on the surrounding soil matrix ranges from 900 to 1500 kPa. Much smaller root growth pressures reduce elongation rates substantially, however. Impeded roots are thicker in diameter and much more distorted in shape (Fig. 2.22).

Greacen and Oh (1972) postulated that osmotic regulation in the elongating cells of roots can account for the differences among plants in their reactions to mechanical constraints. If this postulate were correct, one should expect different species to exert different maximal root growth pressures. The maximal root growth pressures are somewhat different (Pfeffer, 1893; Stolzy and Barley, 1968; Eavis et al., 1969; Taylor and Ratliff, 1969a). Russell and Goss (1974) questioned the Greacen and Oh postulate by pointing out that root elongation rates could differ among species if hormones located in the root cells alter cell wall constraints differentially among species. Oosterhuis (1985) has shown that water stress affects solute accumulation in roots of cotton plants. In addition, concentrations of various plant hormones vary with the species, age of tissue, and environmental conditions (Gardner et al. 1985). The question remains open about the relative roles of osmotic adjustment and of cell wall bond loosening in

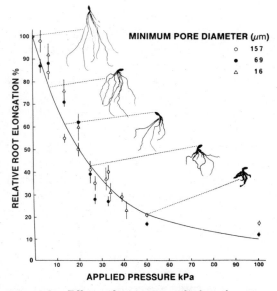

Figure 2.22 Effects of pressure applied to the outside surface of a flexible container on relative root elongation and shape of barley roots. (*After Russell and Goss, 1974; used with permission.*)

explaining differences among species in root elongation through restraining soil.

Measuring soil strength. Many different devices have been used to apply force to the soil in order to obtain a soil strength value. Some of the more common ones are penetrometers, shear vanes, shear rings, triaxial shear cells, and unconfined compression cells. Soil behavior under applied load is a passive process if the soil does not yield under load and is a dynamic process if the soil does yield. A rigid mathematical framework has not been worked out using fundamental parameters to predict soil yielding under load.

Soil penetrometers have been used to a greater extent than the other devices for measuring effects of soil strength on root penetration. The three main groups of penetrometers are (1) those that measure the pressure required to push a tip a specific distance into the soil volume (called a static-tip penetrometer); (2) those that measure the pressure (or force) required to move the tip through the soil at a more or less slow constant rate (called a moving-tip penetrometer); and (3) those that record the number of blows required to drive the penetrometer tip through a specific depth of soil (called an impact penetrometer). Freitag (1971) has published a procedure for using the Cone Index Penetrometer, a moving-tip device useful in field compaction studies.

Because no unifying theory exists relating soil strength to fundamental soil parameters, one cannot use the values obtained with one specific device as appropriate ones for another type of strength measuring device. For example, Taylor et al. (1966) compared values obtained with a static tip penetrometer to those obtained with a shear vane. For five soils, the values were linearly correlated ($r = 0.93$), but a penetrometer value of 1.5 MPa represented the same soil condition as a shear vane value of 0.058 MPa.

Interactions among soil physical and chemical factors affecting plant rooting. Many of the experiments quoted in this chapter have evaluated the effects of a single physical or chemical variable on root growth. In nature, however, the situation usually is much more complicated. The effects of increases in soil bulk density are discussed as an example.

When soil bulk density is increased, more soil particles are packed into a unit soil volume (by definition, more soil mass). The increased volume of soil particles occurs at the expense of air-filled porosity, so air storage capacity and transmission rates are reduced. More soil surfaces are present in the unit volume after compaction, so frictional and cohesive components of soil strength are increased. The reduced total porosity after compaction results in reduced saturated hydraulic conductivity, but the increased surface area may result in increased unsaturated hydraulic conductivity. Water storage capacity is also altered, sometimes increased and sometimes decreased, by soil compaction. The increased surface area results in greater inorganic ion retention in the compacted soil volume, but ion movement results both from diffusion and mass flow so changes in ion movement often are unpredictable. Finally, water and soil particles require more heat than does air to increase temperature by a stated amount. In addition, increases in water cause increases in thermal conductivity. All of these factors interact to reduce the precision with which one can predict the effects of soil compaction on root growth. A similar case can be made for effects of changes in soil water content on root growth.

The Rhizosphere

Soil in its natural state is extremely heterogeneous (Fig. 2.23), consisting of minerals, organic matter, water, salts in solution, gases, roots of plants, small animals, and microorganisms.

Minerals comprise the major component of most soils except peat. These minerals are derived from the physical and chemical weathering of the parent material. The organic matter originates as vegetation produced by green chlorophyll-containing plants and consists of cell wall fragments, mucilages, and soluble compounds released from root cells (Rovira, 1979). These residues can be decomposed by actions of insects, earthworms, and other soil animals, but most of the decomposition occurs through activity of bacteria, actinomycetes, and fungi. These microorganisms not only decompose the organic residues, but also secrete carbohydrate slimes and gels. These polysaccharides constitute 10 to 20 percent of the soil organic matter and hold soil particles together to form soil aggregates. These aggregates, in turn, are loosely bound into soil crumbs by the hyphae of fungi and actinomycetes and by plant roots and root hairs.

About 80 percent of the organic matter that remains after these biological processes have occurred is humic materials, made up of complex polymers of carbohydrates, polyphenols, and amino acids. The morphology of these materials depends on the parent materials from which they were derived and on the types of organisms acting on these materials.

Growing plants constantly produce new roots, while at the same time older roots die. Cells in the elongation zone of the new roots have hydrostatic pressures that range from 0.9 to 1.5 MPa. These pressures strain the cell walls, forcing the root cap and meristematic zone forward through the soil matrix. This forward passage must occur through soil voids, or the root must deform the soil crumbs, which

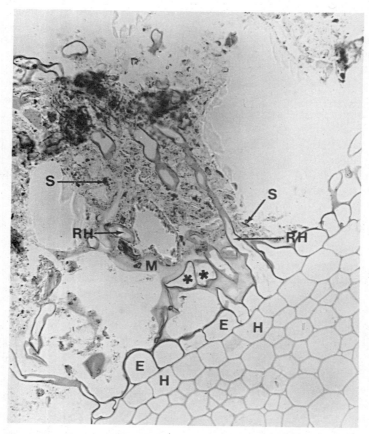

Figure 2.23   A 2-μm-thick section of corn root embedded in plastic. Mucilage (M), sloughed root cap cells (asterisks), root hairs (RH), and soil particles (S) are resolved in the photograph. The root epidermis (E) and hypodermis (H) were intact and live. (*Photographic credit, M. E. McCully; used with permission.*)

tend to resist passage of the root tip. Soil particles abrade the cells in the root cap, emptying some of them of their contents. These cell contents help lubricate the passage of the root cap, which compresses and shears a soil zone around the root epidermis. X-ray analyses have shown particles that are oriented parallel with the root surface. This oriented, compressed zone has physical properties, such as hydraulic, heat, and gaseous conductances, substantially altered from those of the bulk soil matrix (Greenland, 1979).

The *rhizosphere* is the interfacial volume between plant roots and the bulk of the soil (Russell, 1973). Chemical properties in this zone of soil modified by the presence of the root are also altered considerably.

Ions are carried to the roots by the mass flow of water. Some ions are more concentrated and others are less concentrated than in bulk soil during periods of high transpiration. Some salts precipitate at the root surface, forming tubules around smaller roots. These tubules tend to damp the diurnal oscillations in ionic concentrations, but osmotic potentials can still differ substantially from those of bulk soil.

The pH of rhizosphere soil also can differ substantially from that of bulk soil. The uptake of anions, such as nitrate, in excess of cations often causes the roots to secrete bicarbonate ions in order to maintain electrical neutrality, thereby raising the pH. The uptake of cations, such as potassium or ammonium, in excess of anions can cause the roots to exude hydrogen ions, thus lowering the pH. Both processes cause rhizosphere pH to change, thereby altering solubilities of compounds located there.

The rhizosphere also can differ in O_2 and CO_2 concentrations from that of bulk soil, thereby altering root respiration rates and possibly ethylene, phenol, and terpene concentrations that may affect either root or microorganism growth. A number of these compounds are phytotoxic to seedlings.

Organic matter contents and properties in the rhizosphere also differ from those of bulk soil. The root cap exudes a carbohydrate-rich gel, and root epidermal cells are mechanically ruptured as roots grow through the soil. These gels, root cell contents, and root exudates are chemically diverse, but serve as excellent substrates to support a great diversity of life and large numbers of microorganisms. These rhizosphere microorganisms include bacteria, fungi, viruses, yeasts, actinomycetes, algae, mites, arthropods, and amoebas. These microorganisms, along with the root, comprise a soil ecosystem that is vastly different from that outside the rhizosphere.

Mycorrhizae

Roots of most healthy plants growing throughout the world, either in natural or cultivated conditions, are intimately associated with one or more species of fungi. These colonized roots are termed *mycorrhizae*. The fungal associates usually cause little or no damage to the host, other than a relatively small carbon drain. In return, the fungus often increases nutrient supplies to the plant root system.

Mycorrhizae traditionally have been classified into two types, *ectotrophic* and *endotrophic*. This classification is based on the arrangement of the vegetative filaments, or hyphae, in relation to the root epidermis of the host plant. Fungi of ectotrophic mycorrhizae enclose the root in a dense sheath and penetrate the host cells to a very limited extent. In contrast, endotrophic mycorrhizae form only a loose network of hyphae on the root surface but develop extensively within the root tissues. The types within the ectotrophic mycorrhizae are included in the endotrophic group—the *Ericales,* the *Orchidaceae,* and the *vesicular-arbuscular.*

Lewis (1973) has suggested that, functionally, mycorrhizae should be classified into four clearly defined groups—sheathing, vesicular-arbuscular, orchidaceous, and ericaceous. The ericaceous group is further subdivided into *ericoid* and *arbutoid* types.

The mycorrhizal fungus usually lives with its plant partner in a balanced, intimate association in which both partners benefit. The fungus obtains all or most of its carbon supply and energy directly from its partner. In return, the fungus helps keep its partner supplied with inorganic minerals, which it extracts from the surrounding soil. This association is *mutualistic symbiosis.*

A very different type of relationship has evolved in orchids and some members of Ericales. These plants contain no chlorophyll for part (or in some cases, all) of their lives. They are able to obtain their carbon supplies only from the fungus. Movements of inorganic minerals and of carbon both occur from the fungus to the plant. The "higher" plant thus is parasitic on the fungus, a curious situation.

This discussion shows the difficulty of generalizing about mycorrhizal associations. It is likely that the intermediate situation between mutualistic symbiosis and parasitism occurs quite often. It is known that many fungi can switch from symbiosis to parasitism to pathogenism, depending on environmental conditions. These interrelationships are discussed further by Scott (1969) and Deverall (1981).

Types of mycorrhizae

Sheathing mycorrhizae. The sheathing mycorrhizae are one of the most common mycorrhizal associations. They occur with the great majority of trees in the northern temperate countries, e.g., spruce, pine, poplar, willow, oak, and fir. In southern temperate countries, sheathing mycorrhizae occur on *Eucalyptus* and southern beech (*Nothofagus*). Their hyphae have many different colors and diameters.

A number of sheathing mycorrhizae synthesize growth-regulating compounds, even in axenic culture. It seems likely that the changes undergone by short roots during conversion into mycorrhizae roots are induced by auxin-related compounds exuded by the symbiotic fungi.

The shortest roots of trees usually are the ones that become mycorrhizae. A loose web develops over the surface of these short roots, and then the web gradually thickens as it develops into a sheath enclosing the entire root so that no direct contact exists between the root and soil. Root hair growth may be suppressed entirely. The mineral nutrients being absorbed by the plant must pass through the sheath.

Behind the root meristem, hyphae from the sheath grow between the root cortical cells. The hyphae penetrate to varying depths in the roots. The network of hyphae between the cortical cells is called a *Hartig net.* The depth of the Hartig net varies from a few cortical cells to the endodermis, but never beyond.

Roots of young trees growing on adverse sites, such as coal mine spoils, kaolinite dumps, and ore tailings, have very few types of mycorrhizae, probably due to selection pressure, but these mycorrhizae can be very effective in promoting colonization of the site by higher plants.

Vesicular-arbuscular mycorrhizae. Vesicular-arbuscular (VA) mycorrhizae occur commonly on a wide range of plants including gymnosperms, angiosperms, and occasionally bryophytes. There are only a few families of angiosperms, such as Cruciferae, Chenopodiaceae, and Resedaceae, where VA mycorrhizae are absent or rare. VA mycorrhizae commonly are found in association with most agricultural crops and may be of major economic importance in crop production.

VA mycorrhizae are characterized by a coarse mycelium growing through the soil and connected at a few points to a mycelium growing in the roots of the host. The mycelium in the root grows within and between cortical cells and gives rise to two types of structures. *Arbuscules,* found in the cortical cells, are formed of frequently branched hyphae, the size of which decreases with branching. The other structures, *vesicles,* develop later than arbuscules and are intercellular or intracellular spherical or ovoid-shaped bodies. It is assumed that the vesicles serve as storage structures and sometimes as survival propagules when the colonized root disintegrates and that the arbuscules serve as an exchange mechanism between the fungus and the host.

Ericaceous mycorrhizae. The Ericales plants are any of a large genus (*Erica*) of the heath family of low-growing, much-branched evergreen shrubs. The persistence and success of heathland plants probably is due to their specialized mycorrhizal associations. Penetration of the hyphae is usually intercellular and confined to the outer layer of cells. If no fungal sheath is present, the mycorrhizae are termed *erocoid.*

Some of the ericaceous mycorrhizae have a well-developed sheath and a Hartig net from which extensive host cell penetration occurs. These mycorrhizae are termed *arbutoid.* As much as 80 percent of the total root volume of heavily colonized hair roots may be occupied by the endophyte. The intracellular hyphae cause minimal damage to the host tissue but do disturb the host cell's nuclei, which become enlarged.

Orchid mycorrhizae.   Under natural conditions, nearly all orchids have an obligate dependence on colonization by mycorrhizal fungi. The exact stage at which colonization is required varies with the orchid species. In some orchids, germination is initiated by penetration of the fungus through the testa into cells at the attachment of the embryo. The embryo cells then enlarge and rupture the testa. In other orchids, germination occurs when enough water is absorbed to rupture the testa; however, the seedling soon depletes the very small amount of seed reserves, and further growth cannot occur without fungal colonization. In still other orchids, germination and growth occur in aseptic conditions, but growth is accelerated in the presence of mycorrhizal fungi. *Rhizoctonia solani* is one of the mycorrhizal fungi of orchids. Strains of this fungus are pathogenic to a wide range of plant species, including tomato and cauliflower. Sometimes, an environmental change will alter a symbiotic fungus into a parasitic one, even on an orchid plant.

Factors affecting formation of mycorrhizae

The main factors affecting the susceptibility of the host's roots to the colonization of sheathing mycorrhizae seem to be photosynthetic activity and soil fertility. In general, conditions that cause an accumulation of soluble sugars increase colonization. Thus, long days and high light intensities increase colonization. Moderate levels of soil fertility are conducive to abundant colonization. Low soil fertility reduces the overall growth of host plants, while high levels of nitrogen and phosphorus reduce the quantities of soluble sugars.

It is quite possible that auxin level may also affect colonization levels. Many rhizosphere organisms accelerate auxin synthesis by supplying symbiotic fungi with extracellular substances, and some of these organisms produce auxin directly. By contrast, some host plants produce inhibitory substances, which reduce or completely stop fungal growth.

Soil temperature affects both the growth rate of the roots of the host plant and the growth rate of the fungus. Although mycorrhizal formation proceeds at relatively low temperatures, increases in temperature generally increase fungal infection. Soil temperature also affects the amount and composition of root exudates. Any changes in root physiology obviously affect fungi colonization.

Soil water contents, either too high or too low, affect mycorrhizal fungal growth. At low water potentials, the sheath and outer layers of mycorrhizae shrink and new root growth slows or ceases. Some fungal hyphae can persist and absorb nutrients at water potentials too low for root elongation. If the soil is too wet, the soil oxygen status is too low for aerobic respiration. Under these conditions, mycorrhizae are limited in extent.

Hydrogen ion concentration affects sheathing mycorrhizal formation. Many of the sheathing fungi species require an acid soil for good development, while others form abundant mycorrhizae in alkaline soils. The sheathing fungi vary in their hydrogen and hydroxyl ion tolerances just as higher plants vary.

Isolation of mycorrhizal fungi

The distribution and relative frequency of sheathing mycorrhizae are poorly known. These fungi are difficult to isolate from the roots and to identify. The VA mycorrhizae have not been successfully grown in pure (axenic) culture. The nearest thing to pure culture has been cultures of the fungus and seedlings of host plants. One consequence of the obligate nature of VA mycorrhizal symbiosis for the fungus is that it is impossible to study the physiology of the fungus independently of the host plant.

Fungal symbiont and host plant interaction

The host plants derive the benefits of (1) increased nutrient uptake; (2) increased water uptake and drought resistance; (3) resistance to certain root pathogens; (4) increased tolerance of toxins, temperature extremes, and adverse pH. The fungal symbionts obtain carbon and energy requirements from their hosts and have access to nutrients with little or no competition from other rhizosphere microorganisms.

Many experiments have shown that associations between VA mycorrhizal fungi and roots will increase phosphorus absorption and often will increase yield. This principle has been established over a wide range of crops and soils. However, field inoculation with VA fungi to enhance plant growth has not been predictable or long-lived, especially for annual crops, unless the soil has been fumigated or has undergone long fallow periods.

There are two situations where inoculations with efficient strains of VA mycorrhizal fungi seem particularly appropriate. The first is where tree seedlings are grown in a nursery for later transplantation. These trees are started in sterilized soil. Inoculation of the soil will resupply VA mycorrhizal fungi that have been killed by sterilization. The second situation is where field or vegetable crops are started in the greenhouse or hotbeds for later transplantation. Here, inoculation can be sufficiently intense for successful colonization. In most other situations, too much inoculant is required or the colonization rate is too slow for economical field inoculation.

Nitrogen-Fixing Microorganisms

Rhizobium fixation

Rhizobium is a genus of gram-negative, rod-shaped, motile, heterotrophic bacteria that selectively infects legume roots and then reduces N_2 molecules to ammonia, which then becomes immediately available to the plant for growth. The infection process is very selective for certain combinations of *rhizobium* bacteria and legume. This high degree of selectivity forms the basis for one system to classify the various species of *Rhizobium*. For example, *R. trifolii* infects clover root hairs and *R. meliloti* infects alfalfa root hairs. Neither *Rhizobium* species infects the root hairs of the other legume. Many *Rhizobium* bacteria, however, nodulate hosts of more than one cross-inoculation group.

Rhizobium bacteria normally will grow aerobically but require low oxygen levels if they are to fix nitrogen. There are countless strains, with a few thousand strains being maintained in cultures. Strains can be distinguished by growth characteristics, by immunological reactions, and by the ability to nodulate different legumes.

For a large part of their existence, *Rhizobium* bacteria survive as free-living bacteria before the process of nodulation is possible. As free-living bacteria, *Rhizobium* numbers are affected by soil temperature, dessication, pH, soil type, and soil texture (Ham, 1980).

The infection process starts with bacterial attachment to a root hair, then curling of the hair and its penetration. Confined to a tubular infection thread, the *Rhizobium* bacteria are transported to the base of the root hair, where they penetrate into the root cortex and form nodules that restrict oxygen and fix nitrogen gas into ammonia. Some *Rhizobium* bacteria also penetrate the cortex where lateral roots have emerged.

The rate of nitrogen fixation depends on two parameters, nodule mass and the specific N_2 fixing activity (N_2 fixed per gram of nodules). Both of these parameters vary widely with the photosynthate supply and soil environmental factors, including the soil nitrogen supply.

One important feature of nodule formation in annual legumes is the time required for nodules to appear and become functional in N_2 fixation. This time lag depends on a series of interconnecting factors: (1) the effectiveness and efficiency of the *Rhizobium* strains present in the inoculum or soil, (2) the competitive ability of the introduced *Rhizobium* bacteria in relation to the native population, (3) the ability of the host to supply the *Rhizobium* bacteria's nutritional needs, and (4) the environmental factors, especially limiting factors in soil, that act on the bacteria and its host root. Fixation rates of 500 to 600 kg ha^{-1} year^{-1} have been estimated for *Sesbania cannabina* and *Leucaena leucocephala,* but rates of 50 to 60 kg ha^{-1} are much more common.

Some evidence exists that soils contain inhibitors that affect root-nodule bacteria. It has been proposed that toxin-producing microorganisms, which proliferate at the expense of the organic matter that remains from the original vegetation, generate inhibitors that affect the *Rhizobium* bacteria.

Fungicides applied to seeds represent a severe stress for *Rhizobium*. Such fungi are designed to inhibit the activity of pathogenic fungi that affect the seed or seedling. At the same time, these fungicides kill *Rhizobium* bacteria. A benefit is obtained from the fungicide-suppressing pathogens, but harm is being done to the nitrogen-fixing ability of the legume. Screening for fungicides with less toxicity toward *Rhizobium* and screening *Rhizobium* strains for tolerance to the existing fungicides are obvious avenues to alleviate the fungicide-*Rhizobium* problem.

Other diatrophs in the rhizosphere

Although the *Rhizobium*-legume symbioses are by far the most important nitrogen fixers, or *diazotrophs,* several other nitrogen-fixing associations exist.

Azospirillum is a genus of gram-negative, mobile bacteria that are about 1.0 μm in diameter and 2 to 4 μm in length. Cysts can form, especially in older cultures. The *Azospirillum* genera are widespread in nature, having been isolated from soils of Europe, Africa, and North and South America. The organisms seem to associate preferentially with grasses, but there are numerous exceptions (Hubbell and Haskins, 1984).

Azospirillum inoculations into soil may benefit grasses by several mechanisms. Following inoculation, *Azospirillum* adsorbs to and proliferates on the rhizoplane and probably invades root internal parts. When adsorbed on the roots, *Azospirillum* may (1) promote root hair development, (2) alter cell arrangement of root cortical cells, (3) increase mineral uptake by the inoculated roots, (4) increase dry matter accumulation in plant parts, (5) improve plant water status, (6) enhance biological nitrogen fixation activity, mainly at flowering, and

(7) in many cases improve the yield of cereal and forage grasses and of legumes (Okon and Kapulnik, 1986).

Much more information is required before scientists will be able to predict the effectiveness of inoculating seed or soil with *Azospirillum* to enhance nitrogen fixation or yield.

Free-living, nitrogen-fixing bacteria have been known since the beginning of the twentieth century. The classic examples of the aerobic diazotrophic ones are the *Azotabacter* spp. They are found in low numbers in humid temperate soils with almost neutral pH and frequently are suppressed in the rhizosphere. *Azotabacter* may occur abundantly in soils of warm arid regions (Vancura et al., 1965). Other examples are from the *Bacillus* spp., Enterobacteriaceae, *Herbaspiillum* spp., and *Pseudomonas* spp. (Dobereiner and Pedrosa, 1987).

Another nitrogen-fixing symbiosis is that of actinomycete-induced nodules that occur on 175 known plant species. The endophyte is of the genus *Frankia.* One nodulated nonlegume that may be important in food production is *Rubus ellipticus,* a relative of the common raspberry, *Rubus idaeus.* The economic importance of other nonleguminous nodulated species is associated with their capacities to increase the nitrogen status of land that is very poor in nitrogen. For example, extensive use has been made of alder (*Alnus glutinosa*) to reforest rubbish heaps and severely eroded lands. Other *Alnus* sp. are valued highly for wood production, both in temperate and in tropical forests.

Much more knowledge is required before humans can inoculate soils or seeds to obtain consistent yield increases for cropped plants other than by using the legume-*Rhizobium* association.

Models of Root Growth

Many of the current plant production models require a quantitative description of the root system and its location within the soil profile. A large supply of labor is required to adequately sample the soil-root system at various times during the growing season. It would be extremely useful to have models that simulate root length and root mass distributions as functions of plant genotypes, time, and soil properties. It also would be desirable to be able to generate locations of root initiation, aging, and senescence for their effects on suites of root pathogens. This section describes some approaches used in existing models of root growth and functions.

Several different types of root growth models are currently available. The simplest are models of root distribution with depth (Gerwitz and Page, 1974) and of rooting depth with time (Borg and Grimes, 1986) or with soil temperature (Stone et al. 1983).

Models that partition carbon between the aboveground and below-ground biomass are more complex than the simple ones. The partitioning coefficient sometimes is assumed to be a constant fraction of the daily photosynthate production or of an amount that remains after shoot requirements are met. One generalized model assumes that roots grow on the reserve carbohydrate pool (Coughenour et al., 1984). Another model allocates 10 percent of the carbohydrate to roots (Johnson, 1983). A slightly more physiologically based concept partitions photosynthate based on the root-shoot mass ratios (Fishman et al., 1984; Skiles et al., 1982).

One type of model involves both carbon and nitrogen nutrition (Davidson, 1969; Reynolds and Thornley, 1982). The Reynolds and Thornley (1982) model partitions photosynthate between root and shoot on the basis of the nitrogen-to-carbon ratio in the plant's labile pool. Johnson and Thornley (1985) created a grass crop model that divides root structure into four categories (growing, newly expanded, medium-aged, and senescing roots). These divisions allow calculations of "live root structural dry weight" and permit separate uptake rates and respiration costs to be used for different ages of roots. Nitrogen uptake by roots depends on the root content of soluble carbohydrates.

Porter et al. (1986) have taken a different approach in their model WHTROOT. They describe cereal root system growth and development in terms of growing degree days (GDD). Each model axis develops at a set point in GDD and grows vertically at a constant rate when measured as millimeters per GDD. Their GDD base is 0°C. Each model axis branches after 250 GDD have elapsed. The model assumes different rates of elongation and different diameters for vertical axes, first-order and higher-order laterals. The model contains no restrictions on root growth from soil stresses.

Jones et al. (1989) have included some soil stress factors in a model of root growth. They specifically include reductions in root growth associated with aluminum toxicity and calcium deficiency by including soil-specific parameters. They include soil textural effects by reducing root growth proportional to the fraction of the soil mass that occurs in soil fragments greater than 2 mm in diameter. They include soil strength effects which reduce root growth through inputs of soil water content, bulk density, and sand content. Lack of adequate aeration is included by considering the amount of water-filled pores and a plant-dependent sensitivity factor for flooding. Soil temperature effects are included for each soil volume by incorporating a species-dependent value for minimum and optimum soil temperature for root growth. Root senescence is handled by assuming that 1 percent of the dry weight of root dies each day in each layer, but low soil water content or poor aeration increases root senescence to 2 percent each day.

Diggle (1988) has developed a model called ROOTMAP, which uses three-dimensional coordinates to describe the growth and structure of a fibrous root system. Root growth is specified in terms of the growing time, number of axes, initiation time of axes, growth rates and branching characteristics of the roots, and characteristics governing the direction of root growth. Soil conditions and growth and branching characteristics are static during a simulation run unless the operator changes them manually.

The ROOTMAP model uses a temperature dependence that functionally is equivalent to that of Porter et al. (1986). In a manner similar to the models of Rose (1983) or Porter et al. (1986), ROOTMAP uses the root elongation rate, branching density, and duration of apical nonbranching as the basic attributes affecting root growth.

In each time step of ROOTMAP, the direction that a root tip grows depends on the direction that the tip grew in the last time step and an amount and angle of deflection from the old direction. The initial heading of a subbranch is 90° to the orientation of the main branch. The subbranch emerges randomly around the main branch.

The user of ROOTMAP specifies a seeding depth, a time of germination, a maximum number of pairs of nodal axes, and a maximum number of seminal axes pairs in addition to the initial seminal axis. ROOTMAP is potentially useful for making inferences about the effects of geotropism and deflection on the distribution of roots, on the effects of root deflection in structured soils (Dexter and Hewitt, 1978), on the variability of root distributions, and on the efficiency with which various root distributions can intercept and exploit soil pockets of nutrients or water.

The ROOTMAP model developed by Diggle (1988) cannot simulate the entire root system of a mature plant on a personal computer because it requires too much storage capacity. However, the trend toward increased capacities in microcomputers should soon remove this constraint.

Some readers may desire to model growth in individual root apices. Such a model has been described by Gandar (1983). In that model, root growth is assumed to be one-dimensional with new length being generated as a result of cell division and expansion in the apical growth zone. Gandar (1983) presents two different viewpoints of root tip growth. The first viewpoint focuses attention on activity at fixed distances from the tip of the apex. Data on cell production rates and on growth deformations at various distances along axes are obtained with this focus. The second viewpoint is one where a particular cell or group of cells is identified and behavior is observed with time. Data on the proliferation and expansion of cells as they migrate through the growth zone are provided through this focus.

We have provided a sparse sampling of some root growth and function models. It his hoped that models of root growth and function soon will include more soil and plant factors that affect rooting and will be less expensive and easier for the novice computer scientist to use.

3

Plant Essential Mineral Nutrients in Soils

Sources of Plant Nutrients

The demands for mineral nutrients by plants were described in Chap. 1. Many complex and interacting physical, chemical, and biological factors must be considered when evaluating the capability of soils to meet these demands. The soil solution is generally the primary source of immediate mineral nutrient needs, but generally to maintain good growth for longer periods, plants must draw from the much larger nutrient pool in the solid phase. Evidence that some nutrients in the solid phase fraction are directly accessible for uptake by roots (contact exchange) has been reported, but this concept of nutrient accessibility has not been generally accepted. As better techniques are developed so that the nature of the soil-plant root interface can be more clearly defined, the likelihood of direct accessibility to plant roots of nutrients in the solid phase can be more rigorously assessed.

Under some circumstances, sources other than the solid phase may contribute to replenishing nutrients in the soil solution. While most of the atmospheric N fixed by rhizobia enters directly into the host legume, a portion is released into the soil as soluble N through leaching and microbial degradation of nodules and roots. Some replenishment of the soil solution also occurs for those nutrients, especially N, S, and Cl, which at some stage of their cycling in the biosphere are in a volatile form and brought to earth in precipitation. When crops are irrigated, dissolved salts in irrigation water can contribute significantly to the nutrient supply. Fertilizers added as liquids, or as solids that at least partially dissolve, increase concentrations of nutrients in the soil solution.

The following discussion focuses on the kinds of bonding forces and mechanisms that are involved in nutrient retention by the organic and inorganic solid phase components of the soil, and on reactions by which these nutrients are solubilized. The nature of these bonds, and how susceptible they are to disruption, determines how readily solubilization occurs. Knowledge of the kinds and strength of bonding forces involved is needed to develop parameters that define the effectiveness with which the solid phase provides plant nutrients. Interactions between nutrients, both in the soil solution and in the solid phase, also can have important effects on nutrient uptake.

Occurrence of Nutrients in the Solid Phase

The solid phase of soil contains plant essential mineral nutrients in various chemical and physical states that differ in the readiness in which they become solubilized. Nutrients that occur as structural elements in soil minerals and in the more biologically inert organic components are the most difficult to solubilize. Compared to the chemical bonds in easily dissolved salts, the strong chemical bonds in highly insoluble precipitates are difficult to disrupt. Intermediate in readiness of dissolution, between the very refractory and readily dissolved states, are nutrients present in various adsorbed states. The relative importance of chemical bonding on dissolution, as a factor in nutrient acquisition and use by plants, depends upon other factors, including total nutrient supply and plant requirements.

Many plant nutrients occur as structural elements of the layer silicate minerals. Some silicates, such as feldspars and micas, are primary minerals, while the clay minerals, such as smectites and vermiculites, are secondary in origin, being derived as products of weathering and chemical reactions. Nutrients present as ions with the required configuration and size can occur in octahedral coordination in the 2:1 clay minerals. Of the essential mineral nutrients, Fe and Mg most often occupy these octahedral sites. Ions can also fit in cavities that result from the structure and relative positions of the Si–O tetrahedra in contiguous silicate layers. Of the plant essential nutrient ions, K^+ and NH_4^+ have the most suitable size and electronic configuration to occupy these interlattice spaces. Interlayer ions are not retained so tenaciously as ions in octahedral coordination, but more so than those associated with electrostatic surface charges.

Linkages of O to mineral nutrient elements result in the formation of very stable oxides, oxyhydroxides, and salts that occur in rocks from which soils are derived, or that form in situ. Iron as hematite (Fe_2O_3) and goethite (FeOOH), and Mn as pyrolusite ($MnO_{1.8}$) are examples of commonly occurring oxides and oxyhydroxides that serve as sources of plant nutrients. Apatite in the fluoro-$[Ca_{10}(PO_4)_6F_2]$ and hydroxy-

$[Ca_{10}(PO_4)_6(OH)_2]$ forms are common primary sources of plant needs for P.

Secondary sources of plant nutrients include products of reactions between solute ions to form insoluble precipitates. Iron and Mn may precipitate as hydroxides but in time convert to oxides and oxyhydroxides. Phosphates are very susceptible to precipitation, especially with Ca, Fe, Mn, Zn, and Cu ions. Some mineral nutrients form highly insoluble precipitates in the presence of CO_2. Of particular significance relative to soil-plant relationships is the reaction with Ca^{2+} under alkaline conditions to form $CaCO_3$.

Cations are attracted to the charged surfaces of various inorganic solids by electrostatic and coulombic forces. The charged sites occur in interlattice spaces as a result of isomorphous substitution, and on the broken edges of clay particles. The forces of attraction are weaker than those that bind metals in oxides or those in other insoluble precipitates. Generally, ionic species with lower valences are not attracted as strongly as those of higher valences, but other factors such as the concentration (activity) of each species, their degree of hydration, and the ionic strength of the solution influence relative affinities.

Anions can also be retained by inorganic components in the solid phase at positively charged sites that result from protonation. With greater acidity in a soil, more H ions become attached to basic functional groups of soil components, including some groups with negative charges. This attachment creates positively charged sites and lessens anion repulsion. The result is a greater capacity to retain anions such as $H_2PO_4^-$ and SO_4^{2-}. This type of anion retention is nonspecific. A stronger anion adsorption, the specific type, results from ligand exchange or anion penetration. These involve reactions of anions, particularly $H_2PO_4^-$ and HPO_4^{2-}, but also AsO_4^{3-}, SeO_3^{2-}, and MoO_4^{2-}, with OH^- groups present in solid phase soil components such as oxides. The availability of protons to effectively neutralize the displaced OH^- groups favors these reactions.

Ions associated with charged colloidal surfaces cannot be clearly distinguished from those associated with soluble ions of opposite charge in the bulk soil solution; the adsorbed and soluble forms exist in a dynamic state. According to the diffuse double layer concept, there is a continuous gradation in the concentration of ions from the colloidal surface outward into the solution further away from these surfaces (Fig. 3.1).

Soil organic matter plays a major role in plant nutrition, both as a source of all essential nutrients and by providing functional groups that can retain ions. Several kinds of chemical linkages are involved. Most of the N and a large portion of the S are linked to C by covalent bonds in both microbial and plant residues. This kind of bonding also

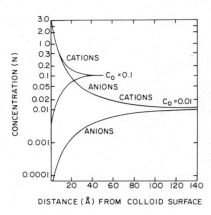

Figure 3.1 Calculated ion distribution in the vicinity of a negatively charged colloid surface. (*Reproduced from Soil Water, 1972, pages 21–63 in Chap. 3, "Theoretical analysis," edited by D. R. Nielsen et al., by permission of the American Society of Agronomy, Inc., and Soil Science Society of America, Inc.*)

links much of the P in plants and microorganisms to C through O, as in $H_2PO_4^-$. Oxygen is also covalently linked in SO_4^{2-} and NO_3^-.

The organic N in residues undergoes marked chemical changes during biological decomposition in soils. While well over 90 percent of the N in fresh residues is present as amino acids and amides, this fraction accounts for about 30 to 50 percent of the organic N found in the extracts from soils after treatment similar to the conditions used for hydrolyzing proteins. These proteinaceous components must be constrained by some binding mechanism, however. If the measured amino and amide N were present as such or as free proteins in soil, the organic N fraction should mineralize much more rapidly than is usually the case. Some organic N can be converted to amino sugars by microbial activity and serve as a source of N for plant use.

Biological degradation of plant and microbial residues also results in production of some very refractory forms of organic N. Humic acids, a heterogeneous group of complexes with molecular weights as great as 25×10^4, are formed by polymerization of reaction products of amino N with polyphenols and quinones. These complexes could become bound to clay minerals by a mechanism like that shown in Fig. 3.2. Existence of a humus-clay complex having this exact structure is difficult to prove, but some of the observed chemical behavior of soil organic N is consistent with that expected if the proposed structure accurately represents N retention mechanisms. An extensive review of the quantities, chemistry, and decomposition of nitrogenous compounds in soil organic matter has been published by Haynes (1986).

Organic matter contains functional groups that can, like the inorganic components discussed above, retain ions by electrostatic forces. At least for a time after plant residues are deposited on the soil, and prior to their being much decayed, essential mineral nutrients are retained in the soil organic fraction by chemical bonds like those in liv-

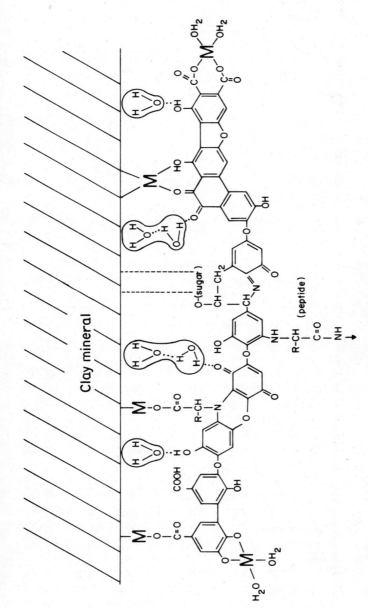

Figure 3.2 Schematic diagram of clay–organic matter–metal complexes in soil. (*Reproduced from F. J. Stevenson and M. S. Ardakani, "Organic matter reactions involving micronutrients in soils," in Micronutrients in Agriculture, 1972, edited by J. J. Mortvedt, P. M. Giordano, and W. Lindsay, pages 79–114, by permission of the Soil Science Society of America, Inc.*)

ing tissue, such as by —O⁻ in carboxyl and hydroxyl groups. Similar linkages are present in microbial residues. At soil pH levels near neutral and above, hydroxyl and carboxyl groups can dissociate and attract cations. Under very acidic conditions, protonation of amino groups could provide positively charged exchange sites that could retain anions.

Also present in both fresh and weathered organic matter are compounds such as organic acids that can serve as chelating agents. The essential mineral nutrients most often associated with these chelate complexes are Ca, Fe, Mn, Cu, and Zn. Some Mg may be chelated, but monovalent ion-chelate complexes are too unstable to be an important nutrient fraction.

Solubilization of Solid Phase Mineral Nutrients

Principles of soil solution chemistry

How well mineral elements, present in the solid phase, serve as plant nutrients depends in part upon the nature of their occurrence, as just briefly described, but their chemical properties and the reactions they may undergo as solutes are also very important factors. Thus, prior to considering solubilization processes further, a review of some basic principles of soil solution chemistry and terminology is in order.

The composition of soil solutions is the net result of a number of factors: (1) the nature of the soil materials with which the solutions are in contact; (2) temperature and moisture effects on the physical, chemical, and biological processes involved in solubilization and immobilization; and (3) the extent of solute removal by root uptake and leaching. Our present interest for this discussion is the abundance and behavior in soil solutions of the elements essential for plant growth, but principles considered apply also to other soluble constituents, including some that may be phytotoxic. The greatest proportion of the soluble essential elements generally are present as ions, except for B as boric acid and for chelated metals.

There are large differences between soils in the concentrations of soluble mineral nutrients (Table 3.1). Several different techniques are used to obtain soil solutions, but for the data shown, sources were chosen in which solutions were extracted at or near field capacity. This is desirable for purposes of comparison, but it is recognized that under field conditions, soluble nutrient concentrations change. Increases in soil water content decrease the concentration of solutes simply by dilution, but this may be only temporary if there is a reserve supply of solutes in a form readily dissolved. Similarly, a decrease in soil water

TABLE 3.1   Mineral Nutrient Concentrations in Soil Solutions, μmol dm^{-3}

	Data source		
Nutrient	Barber (1984)	Murrman and Koutz (1972)	Reisenauer (1964)*
Ca	1500–3300	750–7500	< 1200*–12000†
Mg	500–2500	200–2000	< 1000–8700
K	150–700	25–250	< 250–5000
NO$_3$–N	1000–20,000		< 1800–14,000
SO$_4$–S		1500–15,000	< 800–3000
PO$_4$–P	1.0–1.6	0.06–1.0	< 1–5
Mn		2–20	
Cu		0.5–5	
Zn		< 0.01	
Fe		< 0.01	

*Maximum levels for a group of samples containing the lower concentrations of the nutrients indicated.
†Some higher concentrations included in original tabulation, but in toto they accounted for less than 10 percent of the samples reported.
SOURCE: Data compiled from sources indicated.

content may result in an increase in concentration, but this too may be only temporary for those solutes already present at a saturation level.

It is apparent from the very wide variation in concentrations for each of the nutrients shown in Table 3.1 that one cannot quantitatively define a "typical" soil solution. With regard to differences between nutrients, particularly noteworthy is the very low concentration of P compared to the other major plant nutrients. This reflects the readiness with which soluble P reacts with other soil components, particularly various forms of Al and Fe, to form refractory precipitates or to become tenaciously adsorbed. In soils where such reactions are present, soil solution P may be present at concentrations lower than those of some micronutrients. Precipitation and adsorption of P with various forms of Ca also occurs, but results in products with solubilities somewhat greater than those formed with Al and Fe.

The chemical behavior of soluble ions in soil solutions involves more than their concentrations, however. Constraints imposed by the presence of other ions lower the chemical activity of each ion present in soil solutions. Such effects become significant in soils or at sites in soils when solute concentrations are at relatively high levels. Activities a of ions are calculated products of their activity coefficients γ and their concentrations c in molar units:

$$a = \gamma c \qquad (3.1)$$

Several ways of calculating γ have been proposed. The simplest is from the Debye-Huckel "limiting" expression:

$$- \log \gamma = 0.5\, Z_i^2\, \Omega^{1/2} \tag{3.2}$$

where Z_i = charge of the ion, and Ω = ionic strength of the solution in which the ion is present = $1/2\ \Sigma\ c\ Z_i^2$.

The units in which γ and a are expressed is a matter of choice. If γ is unitless and c is in mol dm^{-3}, a also is in mol dm^{-3}. If γ is in units of mol dm^{-3}, then a is unitless. From the relationships of the parameters shown in Eq. 3.2, values of γ for polyvalent ions are expected to be more sensitive to changes in Ω than are values of γ for monovalent ions.

In soil solutions having high concentrations of total soluble ions, there are very significant differences between the concentrations and activities of individual ions because of ionic strength and ion pairing. The differences are much greater with divalent species. Thus for a displaced soil solution with Ca^{2+}, Mg^{2+}, and SO_4^{2-}, present at concentrations of 15.2, 5.5, and 11.0 mmol L^{-1}, respectively, calculated activities of the three ions are 5.4, 2.2, and 3.3, respectively (Adams, 1971). The dominant ion species in the solution was NH_4^+ (69 mmol L^{-1}) and Cl^- (95 mmol L^{-1}). The calculated activities of these two ions were 49 and 68, respectively. In contrast, in six Ultisol subsoils in which the mean Ca concentration was 0.50 mmol L^{-1}, the mean Ca activity was 0.37 (Adams and Moore, 1983). The dominant soluble ions were Ca^{2+}, Mg^{2+}, and K^+. Other variables, including temperature and ion volumes, also need to be taken into account in applying Eq. 3.2 to solutions more concentrated than those typically found in soils.

Activities of individual ion species in solutions extracted from soils cannot be determined exactly, but useful estimates of these values can be made using highly sensitive ion specific electrodes. Most commonly used are electrodes responding to H^+ activity to obtain estimates of soil pH. These values have helped greatly in advancing the basic concepts of soil chemistry and soil-plant relationships and are also important tools in developing effective crop management practices. More accurate and rapid measurements of other ions, including Na^+, K^+, NH_4^+, NO_3^-, and Cl^- are now possible using appropriate ion-specific electrodes. With miniature-sized electrodes, ion activities at soil-plant root interfaces can be determined.

Information about other attributes of soluble ions can be obtained if their activities can be determined. The change in free energy ΔG, or the difference between the chemical potential at some chosen condition μ and at some standard state μ^o, are related to $\ln a$:

$$\Delta G = \mu - \mu^o = RT \ln a \tag{3.3}$$

where R = the gas constant, and T = Kelvin temperature.

Equation 3.3 expresses mathematically a principle with regard to changes in solutions when their concentrations change, i.e., free energy decreases as solutions become more dilute. The effectiveness of this expression for characterizing soil solutions relative to soil-plant relationships depends upon the accuracy with which measurements can be made at microsites where plant roots and soil solutions interface. This limitation of accurate analytical techniques also applies to its use in estimating μ values for sorbed species in contact with the soil solution. Adding to the complexity of applying thermodynamic principles to quantitative studies of soil-plant relationships are the continual changes in solution composition as ions are taken up by plant roots. For detailed discussions of the thermodynamics of soil solutions, publications by Bohn (1983) and Sposito (1981) should be consulted.

Nitrogen and sulfur

Nitrogen is the nutrient element most often limiting the growth of nonleguminous plants in soils. To obtain the maximum growth of high-yielding crops, N as fertilizer, manure, waste, etc., must be added because under most field conditions the amounts of soluble and readily mineralized soil N are insufficient. Complete uptake of NO_3–N from a soil in which it is present at a solution concentration of 25 mg L^{-1} (Table 3.1) provides less than 20 percent of the N needs of high-yielding crops (Table 1.1). Ammoniacal N is also readily accessible for plant uptake, but under the conditions usually present during the growth of the crops listed, except for rice, NH_4–N is normally present at levels much below that of NO_3–N. Fertilizer N additions depend upon desired yield levels, organic N solubilization rates, and N losses through leaching and volatilization. The discussion here will focus on the mineralization of organic N.

Soluble organic N decomposition products can serve as N sources for plants, but the effectiveness of soil N in meeting plant needs generally depends upon their rates of conversion to the ammoniacal form. In most well-aerated soils the rate at which ammoniacal N is produced is slower than the nitrification of NH_4^+ to NO_3^- by the ubiquitous autotrophs *Nitrosomonas* and *Nitrobacter*. Ammoniacal N accumulates only under conditions of low temperatures and abundant soil water.

The effectiveness of NO_3^- as a plant N source is strongly influenced by soil water conditions. Being very soluble and usually adsorbed only slightly if at all by the solid phase, NO_3^- is readily leached. If aeration is restricted by abundant soil water, and substrates to supply energy are present, denitrifiers will convert NO_3^- into volatile forms, with a loss of gaseous N into the atmosphere.

The specific reactions and processes that limit the conversion of organic N into the ammoniacal form are difficult to identify. Soil organic N is too resistant to biological degradation to exist in soils as free protein, even though amino acids are released when soils are subjected to chemical treatments similar to those used for hydrolyzing proteins. Both physical and chemical factors contribute to resisting breakdown. Smaller proteins and peptides may be protected from biological attack by becoming less accessible through binding to soil clay minerals, but such associations do not necessarily decrease vulnerability to mineralization (Ladd and Jackson, 1982).

The linkage of N to C in humic acids is more stable than C—N peptide bonds, and thus less susceptible to degradation by enzymic reactions. Details of the chemical structures involved are not yet well enough understood to define their quantitative relationship to biological activity. The presence of polypeptidases and proteinases in soils can be demonstrated, but the complexity and variability of the medium complicates accurate determination of the parameters that are needed for kinetic analysis of the system (Haynes, 1986). If some simplifying assumptions are made, the Michaelis-Menten enzyme catalysis model, discussed later in Chap. 5, may be applicable. Attempts to correlate N mineralization rates with soil biochemical properties, such as CO_2 evolution, or with microbial biomass, as indicated by differences between mineralization in fumigated and unfumigated soil, generally have not been successful (Ross et al., 1984).

The products of the early and later stages of plant residue decomposition differ in their N mineralization rates. The distinction between the labilities of newly immobilized and resident organic N can be made by incubating soil samples treated with a readily decomposed plant residue, commonly straw, along with mineral N containing ^{15}N in an amount differing from the normal abundance. From the amounts of N immobilized and then released as soluble N, as determined by isotope abundance, the fraction that came from the freshly formed organic N and that from organic N present prior to the treatments can be calculated. Such studies have shown that freshly formed organic N is much more labile than that existing in the soil for longer time periods (Fig. 3.3). This concept implies that organic N synthesized at soil-plant root interfaces by microorganisms, using inorganic N, root exudates, and residues as substrates, has a relatively rapid turnover.

The C/N ratio has a very strong regulatory role in the release of

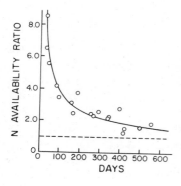

Figure 3.3 Changes in availability ratios of immobilized N over time. (*Reproduced from F. E. Broadbent, "Plant use of soil nitrogen," in Nitrogen in Crop Production, 1984, edited by R. D. Hauck, pages 171–182, by permission of the American Society of Agronomy, Inc., Crop Science Society of America, Inc., and Soil Science Society of America, Inc., Madison, WI.*)

mineral N from the solid phase. Results from experiments conducted under controlled conditions indicate that additions of readily decomposable, low-N organic materials to soils with C/N ratios at or near steady state in the range of 9:1 to 12:1, generally increase C/N ratios and decrease soluble N levels temporarily. Both the direction and extent of change produced when organic residues are added, however, varies greatly with different soil conditions. Results from a recent study showed that soil N and C/N ratios had to reach levels ranging from 0.30 to 1.83 percent and 167:1 to 27:1, respectively, depending upon the tree species producing the litter, before mineral N was released in decomposing forest litter (Haynes, 1986).

Low C/N ratios may be found in subsoils because of a high proportion of the N present in the ammoniacal form relative to the amount of organic matter. Thus, for studies involving determination of subsoil N mineralization, the ratio of organic C to organic N rather than the total C to total N may be a more informative parameter. Characterizing organic matter in terms of energy (E) rather than an amount of C in the substrate, and calculating an E/N ratio, also has been proposed as an alternative to C/N to help predict responses of soil N to additions of different kinds of organic matter (Jansson and Persson, 1982).

Chemical fractionation techniques have been used to identify a portion of the organic N that is relatively more susceptible to mineralization. These studies involve comparisons among different chemical forms of N in a number of soils before and after being cropped. Generally the analytical methods used to characterize the N are similar to those employed for fractionating proteins. These studies indicate that the fraction yielding amino N when the soil is subjected to acid hydrolysis is somewhat more labile for crop removal than other N fractions. The techniques are too involved, the analytical results too variable, and the changes in amounts of the fractions relative to amounts present too small, to encourage this approach to characterize mineralizability of soil N.

Rates of release of mineral N by chemical reagents have been proposed as another means of characterizing soil organic N. A small, more readily mineralizable fraction of soil organic N was indicated by kinetic analysis of amounts of NH_4^+ released from soils by acidified $KMnO_4$ and by $CaCl_2$ solutions (Carski and Sparks, 1987).

Biological vulnerability has been used more often than chemical solubilization to identify the most mineralizable fraction of soil organic N. In the procedure developed by Stanford and Smith (1972), this labile fraction is called the potentially mineralizable N, N_o. The rate of mineralization of N_o is assumed to follow first-order kinetics, i.e., $dN/dt = -kN$, where N is the mean amount of potentially mineralizable N present in the soil during the time interval dt, and k is the mineralization rate constant. A log transformed integrated form of the first-order equation, $\log (N_o - N_t) = \log N_o - kt/2.303$, was proposed to estimate, by iteration, values of N_o that provide the best linear fit for the regression of $\log (N_o - N_t)$ vs. t. The term N_t designates the cumulative amount of N mineralized in time t during incubation under controlled conditions. As a test of the model, 39 different soils, representing five orders, were collected from all parts of the United States. Values of N_o ranged from 20 to 300+ ppm and the fraction of the total N as N_o ranged from 5 to 40 percent. Except for 2 of the 39 soils, the value of k ranged from 0.040 to 0.090 week^{-1}, with an estimated mean of 0.054 ± 0.009 (Stanford and Smith, 1972).

More accurate estimates of potentially mineralizable N by interpreting soil incubation data using nonlinear regression rather than log-transformed linear regression have been suggested (Talpaz et al., 1981). The error term included in the nonlinear model takes better account of the variability of the analytical data throughout the incubation period than does the linear model. Nonlinear regression analysis of the Stanford and Smith (1972) data gave a mean k value of 0.086 ± 0.023 week^{-1}, exceeding that found by the analysis involving log transformation of the data.

Modifications of the nitrification potential concept have been suggested to take into account differences in microbial vulnerability of various organic N fractions. A more precise description of release of available N during incubation may be possible if both the inorganic and organic N in the leachate are included (Smith et al., 1980). Characterization of soil organic N solubilization may be improved if two (Deans et al., 1986), three (Dendooven et al., 1986), or more (Juma et al., 1984) fractions differing in decomposition rate constants are included. Air-drying samples used for incubation studies and a cropping history of the sampling site can also affect organic N mineralizability (Beauchamp et al., 1986).

Environmental conditions affect biological activity and thus influence N mineralization rates. The relationship of soil water regime to mineralization is variable. Cassman and Munns (1980) found this relationship to be linear in the intermediate soil water range for a Yolo silty loam (mixed, nonacid, thermic typic Xerorthent), but not over the low or high soil water content ranges (Fig. 3.4). These results were obtained using pressure membrane extraction of wetted soil to achieve the desired water content in the soil prior to incubation, rather than the water addition method used with the procedure of Stanford and Epstein (1974). When this latter procedure was used by Cassman and Munns in their study with the Yolo soil, the relationship of mineralization to moisture content was fairly linear, except at high moisture contents. During plant growth, the soil moisture content in the root zone is more often decreasing than increasing, so the technique of water removal by pressure extraction more nearly simulates changes in the water regime associated with soil water uptake than does the water addition method. Temperature differences also affect biological activity and thus influence mineralization rates (MR). Values for Q_{10} [MR at temperature $t°$ C/MR at temperature $(t - 10)°C$] of 2 are sometimes assumed (Smith et al., 1977), but soil conditions other than temperature influence the rates at which organic N is solubilized and mineral N immobilized (Tabatabai and Al-Khafaji, 1980).

No one mechanistic model will likely be found that accurately describes the kinetics of organic N mineralization in all soils. Expressions based on empirical models may more accurately describe experimental data (e.g., give lower mean square values) than those based on mechanistic models (Broadbent, 1986). The rates of release of plant

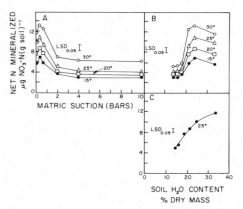

Figure 3.4 Effects of soil moisture and temperature on net N mineralization in Yolo surface soil. (*Reproduced from K. G. Cassman and D. N. Munns, Soil Science Society of America Journal, volume 44, 1980, pages 1233–1237, by permission of the Soil Science Society of America, Inc.*)

available N by a number of different soils tested in a greenhouse study conformed more closely (lower root mean square values) to a parabolic model ($Y = At^B$, where t = time and A and B are constants of proportionality) than to a first-order equation. Values A and B ranged from 1.23 to 13.6 and 0.246 to 0.672, respectively.

The results from research using incubation studies contribute toward a better understanding of soil organic N and the factors involved in its mineralization, but the use of these techniques to help develop better fertilizer management practices is limited by cost and time factors. For N fertility diagnosis, the more usual approach is to estimate from greenhouse and field studies the soil levels of total N, nitrate N, or nitrate plus ammoniacal N, below which there are responses to additions of fertilizer N. Plant tissue tests can be used as diagnostic aids. Details of these approaches to improve N fertilizer management can be found elsewhere (Walsh and Beaton, 1973).

Soil S reactions relative to plant uptake and growth resemble in some respects those for N. The organic fraction contains over 90 percent of the S in most noncalcareous soils (Tabatabai and Bremner, 1972; Tisdale et al., 1985). Based on data from a number of soils differing in origin, S occurs relative to C and N in the ratio 1.3:140:10, respectively (Williams, 1975). The N and S in plant residues become more vulnerable to mineralization as the amino acids in which both occur in their most abundant forms are released through hydrolysis of proteins by polypeptidases and proteinases. The chemical similarity of N and S as plant protein constituents lessens as residues from the plants undergo decomposition. Generally, soil N/S ratios are lower than those in plants. Partitioning S into different humus fractions differs from that of N and C (Bettany et al., 1980). Most of the N in humus is linked to C, as in plants, but during residue decomposition a sizeable portion of the S undergoes changes that result in its becoming bonded to C through O, as in ester sulfates, for example. The reactions involved in forming these S—O bonds and the subsequent linkage to C in soil organic matter are not well understood. That a significant fraction of soil organic S is linked to C through O is indicated by the amount of sulfide formed by reacting soil with hydriodic acid (HI) under conditions of acidity and elevated temperatures such as those used for S analysis by the reduction method (Johnson and Nishita, 1952). Too little free SO_4–S is present in soils to account for the amounts of sulfide generally produced, and S linked directly to C as in amino acids will not be released by the HI treatment.

Sulfohydrolase (arylsulfatase), the enzyme which catalyzes the breakage of C—O bonds in C—O—S linkages and releases SO_4^{2-}, has been measured in a number of soils. This kind of SO_4^{2-} release is called *biochemical mineralization* to distinguish it from *biological mineralization,* in which organisms use the C as an energy source and release the S by breaking C—S bonds (McGill and Cole, 1981). More biological mineralization is found nearer the surface in forest soils where microbial activity is greater than in the deeper soil layers (David et al., 1983). The biochemical type of mineralization should show greater end product inhibition than the biological type. Sulfohydrolase activity may indicate a greater need of S than C by the organisms involved (Freney, 1986).

That fraction of organic S not reducible by HI and not showing the chemical behavior of S in amino acids is least well characterized. This poorly defined fraction can account for over 50 percent of the organic S in some soils. The S it contains differs from that of cystine, cysteine, and methionine in not being susceptibile to reduction by reaction with a Ni—Al alloy (Raney Ni).

Mineralization rates during incubation are different for organic N and S (Fig. 3.5). A higher proportion of the organic S than of the organic N was mineralized in 12 Iowa soils, but the actual amount of mineral N formed was greater than for S. There were also temperature effects. During the 26-week incubation period at 20°C, mean amounts of N and S mineralized were 75 and 22 μg g^{-1}, respectively. At 35°C these values were 332 and 64 μg g^{-1}. Sulfur mineralization was less sensitive than N mineralization to temperature differences, as indicated by about a 30 percent lower Q_{10}. Results obtained at 20°C are more pertinent to conditions under which plant root systems most often function. At temperatures of 35°C, only very likely at or near the surface, the soil is too dry for roots to remain active. The more linear relationship between N mineralization vs. time shown in Fig. 3.5 than

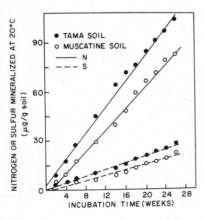

Figure 3.5 Cumulative amounts of N and S mineralized in Tama and Muscatine soils at 20°C in relation to incubation time. (*Reproduced from M. A. Tabatabai and A. A. Al-Khafaji, Soil Science Society of America Journal, volume 44, 1980, pages 1000–1006, by permission of Soil Science Society of America, Inc.*)

in results reported by Stanford and Smith (1972) may be at least in part due to differences in soil water conditions in the samples prior to incubation (Beauchamp et al., 1986).

In flooded soils, sulfide-S is formed by decomposition of organic S and reduction of SO_4^{2-}. The poor growth of rice on soils high in organic matter is attributed to the adverse effects of the presence of H_2S and a low amount of solubilizable Fe (Green, 1957). This plant disorder is called *akiochi*. Soils derived from marine sediments, such as Katteklei (cat clay), are difficult to reclaim because of the high acidity resulting from the oxidation of sulfide (Fleming and Alexander, 1961).

Chemical fractionation procedures have been used to determine differences between organic soil S fractions in the readiness with which they release plant available mineral S. Results indicate that this approach is not likely to be successful for predicting how well different soils provide S needs for plant growth. Freney et al. (1975) found that in newly formed soil organic S (from S^{35} added as a fertilizer), the fraction not reducible by HI was more important than the reducible form in contributing to S needs for the growth of sorghum. In more aged soil, the reverse was true. Also, less organic S was mineralized in soils left fallow than in those in which plants were growing. In another greenhouse study, no consistent relationship was found between changes in amounts of various organic S fractions during the 30 days tomato (var. 'Marglobe') plants were growing in 16 California soils (Arkley, 1961). There was a good correlation between S uptake, as well as plant growth, and the amounts of soluble SO_4^{2-} initially present in the 16 different soils.

Significant amounts of SO_4^{2-} are adsorbed in highly acidic soils. Amorphous hydrated oxides of Al and Fe are the most effective adsorbents, but edges of aluminosilicate clay particles also retain SO_4^{2-} (Bohn et al., 1986). Concentrations of adsorbed SO_4^{2-} and soil Al are generally correlated. Phosphate ions are retained more strongly than SO_4^{2-}, and electrostatic forces are more of a factor in the latter retention mechanisms (Marsh et al., 1987). In some areas, weathering and removal of other soil components have resulted in accumulations of large amounts of soil gypsum, and S in the soil solution may contain more than enough S to meet plant needs. Water percolating through areas of gypsum accumulation, and subsequently used for irrigation, can provide adequate S for crops.

In regions with acidic, highly weathered soils, the SO_4^{2-} adsorbed by kaolinite and hydrous oxides may be a major source for replenishing soil solution S. Less organic matter accumulates in such soils and thus does not contribute as much S for plant needs as soils of more temperate areas. Adding sufficient lime to increase soil pH decreases positive charges and precipitates soluble Al, thus resulting in a release of SO_4^{2-}. Increases in soil pH have a greater effect on release of S than of P.

Phosphorus

Of all the essential macronutrients in soil solutions, P is most often present at the lowest concentration, typically in the range of 0.5 to 1.5 μm (Table 3.1). Orthophosphate ions react very readily with a number of cations and ionic complexes to form highly insoluble salts. In most soils, reactions with Fe, Al, and Ca account for the major portion of the insoluble phosphate precipitates, but reactions involving some less abundant cations, e.g., Zn, can be very important in plant nutrition. Orthophosphate ions are involved in ligand exchange and are held electrostatically by positively charged sites on Fe and Al oxides. Some P is released during organic matter decomposition, but in most soils a lower proportion of the total plant growth needs comes from this source than for N and S. Under natural or cultural conditions favoring organic matter accumulation organic P is an important source of this nutrient.

Satisfactory P nutrition of plants depends upon the presence of sufficient quantities of soluble $H_2PO_4^-$ and HPO_4^{2-} ions accessible to plant roots. The very low amounts of these ions in soil solutions are readily depleted if they are not replenished from solid phase sources. Thus, knowledge of mechanisms and rates of replenishment are important in understanding P nutrition of plants. These aspects will be considered here. Two other important aspects of P acquisition by plants, ion transport and buffer capacity, will be considered later (Chap. 5).

The release of solid phase P into soil solutions involves five types of reactions: (1) solubilization of insoluble minerals and salts; (2) electrostatic anion exchange; (3) ligand exchange; (4) biological decomposition of organic matter; and (5) action of phosphatase enzymes. Results of laboratory studies provide evidence for the occurrence of the these reactions in soils, but clearly distinguishing the separate contributions of each to plant growth needs in soil-plant systems is virtually impossible. Of the first three reactions involving inorganic components, release of P by ligand exchange is generally of least importance relative to plant nutrition.

Information needed to quantitatively relate soluble soil P to specific inorganic solid phase P components includes the amounts and properties of various forms of solid phase P, and of various ions that react with soluble P and influence physicochemical properties of the soil solution. The reactions involved are highly pH-dependent. and a change in acidity may increase or decrease soluble P, depending upon what soil components in a particular soil regulate or affect reactions involving P. Concentrations of soluble P in association with particular solid phase P components can be estimated using equilibrium solubility constants (K^o) (Lindsay, 1979). As an example, assuming that Fe solubility is regulated by an amorphous form of $Fe(OH)_3$, $[Fe(OH)_3(soil)]$ $(K^o = -2.70)$, soluble P derived from strengite $(FePO_4 \cdot 2H_2O)$ $(K^o = -6.85)$, a commonly occurring soil component (Simard et al., 1986), can be described as follows:

$$FePO_4 \cdot 2H_2O + 2H^+ \rightleftharpoons Fe^{3+} + H_2PO^{4-} + 2H_2O \qquad (3.4)$$

$$Fe^{3+} + 3H_2O \rightleftharpoons 3H^+ + Fe(OH)_3(soil) \qquad (3.5)$$

$$FePO_4 \cdot 2H_2O + H_2O \rightleftharpoons H^+ + H_2PO_4^- + Fe(OH)_3(soil) \qquad (3.6)$$

$$(H^+)(H_2PO_4^-) = 10^{-9.55} \qquad (3.7)$$

$$\log H_2PO_4^- = -9.55 + pH \qquad (3.8)$$

Under actual soil conditions, it is doubtful that the quantitative relationship between increasing pH and the increasing equilibrium solubility of strengite P is as precise as these calculations indicate. For example, while an amorphous form of $Fe(OH)_3$ such as that proposed above may serve a regulatory role, it is unlikely that over the soil pH range its chemical properties relative to its influence on P remain unchanged.

Anaerobic soil conditions influence interactions between Fe and P, an important aspect of P nutrition of rice (Sah and Mikkelsen, 1986). Upon flooding, the pH of acidic soils generally increases and the presence of more reduced species of Fe is favored [e.g., Fe_3O_4 instead of $Fe(OH)_3$]. A lower Fe^{3+} activity results in greater solubility of strengite and thus more soluble P. Conversely, as flooded soils are drained, soluble P concentrations decrease.

Calculations based on expressions similar to those shown above with Fe can be made to show that at least over a portion of the pH range of soils, soluble P concentrations associated with Ca-phosphates decrease as acidity decreases. For example, assuming a second-step ion dissociation of orthophosphate of 6.23×10^{-8} and a solubility product of 2.77×10^{-7}, the relationship of soluble $H_2PO_4^-$ in association with $CaHPO_4 \cdot 2H_2O$ is described as follows:

$$\log H_2PO_4^- = 0.63 - pH - \log Ca \qquad (3.9)$$

Thus, a decrease in $H_2PO_4^-$ concentration is predicted as the pH increases. Under conditions near to and above pH 7, however, effects of CO_2 and changes in soluble Ca^{2+} assume more importance. Soluble P concentrations may remain virtually unchanged or respond positively to increases in pH.

Solubility diagrams help to visualize the relationships between soluble P and pH, as determined from calculations using formulas such as Eqs. 3.8 and 3.9 (Lindsay, 1979). Using solubility product principles, the predictability of the effects of pH may be improved if activity values for solid phase P, other than unity, are included in the calculations (Blanchar and Stearman, 1984). From experiments involving eight soils representing several different orders and textures, and with pH values ranging from 4.2 to 6.4, a very good correlation was found between measured and calculated P activities based on amounts of P added, assuming that the regulation of P solubility involves reactions with variscite.

Phosphate electrostatically attracted to surfaces of solid phase soil components is an important pool of the P needed by plants. The positively charged sites necessary for attraction of phosphate, or any other anion, can be created when, for example, Fe atoms on the surface of iron oxide or oxyhydroxide particulates coordinate with water molecules instead of OH^- groups. The water molecules constrained in this configuration may either gain or lose protons, depending upon the pH at the reaction site. Thus, under acidic conditions, protonation will occur and the possibility of phosphate retention is increased.

Plots of data for soluble vs. adsorbed P, as well as for other components, are called *adsorption isotherms*. The designation Q (quantity)/ I (intensity) plots has been proposed as more appropriate, since in most systems including soils, processes other than adsorption may be involved and temperature may not be the only variable (Barrow, 1985).

Many attempts have been made to develop mathematical models expressing a general relationship between soluble and adsorbed P. One of the most commonly used, the Langmuir model, is based on an expression derived for the relationship between the amounts of nonsorbed gas in association with different amounts of gas of the same species sorbed on a solid phase. Three assumptions are made in this derivation: (1) the energies of all adsorption sites are equal and do not change as sites are occupied by adsorbate; (2) there is no interaction between the individual ions or molecules adsorbed; and (3) at maximum adsorption the adsorbate forms a complete monolayer.

A common linear form of the Langmuir equation when applied to P adsorption by soils is

$$\frac{c}{q} = \frac{1}{K_L B} + \frac{c}{B} \tag{3.10}$$

where c = equilibrium concentration of soluble P

$\quad q$ = weight of P per unit weight of soil

$\quad K_L$ = Langmuir constant

$\quad B$ = maximum amount of P that can be adsorbed as a complete monolayer

In the derivation, the term K_L is substituted for the ratio of the adsorption-desorption reaction rate constants, and its magnitude has been interpreted as a measure of the strength of binding of P to the adsorbent. The linearity of data points with c/q plotted vs. c indicates conformity to the Langmuir model. The slope of the plot then equals B^{-1}, and its intercept with the ordinate equals $(K_L B)^{-1}$. In order to improve the common lack of conformity, many modifications of Eq. 3.1 have been proposed. Regressions of c/q vs. c data that are best fitted at different P concentration ranges by two or more regression lines with differing slopes, indicate the presence of heterogeneous adsorption sites having different binding strengths and adsorption maxima.

The Freundlich equation is the mathematical description of the other model which is most often used to describe adsorption phenomena:

$$q = K_F c^{1/n} \qquad (3.11)$$

where K_F = the Freundlich constant, n = an empirical constant, and the other terms are the same as indicated for Eq. 3.10. In contrast to the Langmuir model, the Freundlich model assumes that the energy of the adsorption sites is heterogeneous, and there are no adsorption maxima. Particularly when used in a log-transformed mode, regression of q vs. c, based on calculations of P absorption data using the Freundlich equation, may give a better linear fit than if based on the Langmuir equation.

For quantitatively describing o-phosphate adsorption by hydrous oxides and 44 noncalcareous soils with pH values ranging from 4.9 to 7.6, Goldberg and Sposito (1984) applied the modified constant capacitance model proposed by Stumm et al. (1980). This model assumes ligand exchange of o-phosphate with surface hydroxyls bound to metal cations, mainly of Fe and Mn. The recognition of differences between soils in the manner and strength with which o-phosphate becomes complexed, enhanced conformity of the model to experimental data.

Solubility products and absorption isotherms provide a means of relating fundamental physicochemical processes to the occurrence of P in various forms in soils, and the latter have been used, for example, to estimate amounts of P fertilizer to apply in order to attain a desired level of soluble soil P. In the context of plant needs for P, however, other aspects of soil P behavior are involved. Hysteresis effects are generally shown in the relationship between adsorbed and soluble P. In the rooting zone, transient conditions, rather than the equilibrium states required to quantitatively evaluate reaction substrates and products associated with dissolution and adsorption, more likely prevail. Thus, rates of dissolution and release of solid phase P, along with the effectiveness of diffusion and transport mechanisms, need to be considered.

That diffusion plays an important role in the movement of P in soil systems is indicated in the data of Mack and Barber (1960). The amounts of soluble P released per unit weight by four soils incubated for 9 months and then leached are linearly related to time$^{-1/2}$ (Fig. 3.6). The leaching water was applied slowly enough to minimize anoxic conditions in the soil. The importance of ion diffusion as a regulating factor in P acquisition by plant roots is discussed later (Chap. 5).

In many soils the organic fraction provides a large part of plant P needs. During growth, plants synthesize various kinds of organic P compounds and subsequently some of these become soil organic matter components. Dry microbial tissue contains as much as 2 percent P and thus is a significant contributor to the soil organic P pool (Stevenson, 1982a). During residue decomposition these compounds undergo various chemical modifications, and their original identity is lost. Because of the many alterations that can occur, and the difficulties of extracting P-containing components from soil and purifying them, the bulk of soil organic P generally cannot be accounted for as specific compounds.

Biochemical mineralization like that discussed for S also is applicable to organic P. In plant tissues all P is linked to C through O, and, upon incorporation into soil, action of hydrolase enzymes results in the release of inorganic phosphates. Possible sources of phosphatase activity in soils are plant roots and microorganisms, including mycorrhizae, and this activity may be in the soil solution. Purified and processed to exclude any observable microbial activity, a soil extract was capable of releasing P, using an assay with p-nitrophenyl

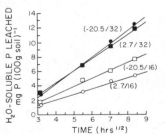

Figure 3.6 Effects of soil temperature conditions on removal of soil P by leaching. Line labels indicate (preconditioning-leaching) temperatures (°C). (*Data from A. R. Mack and S. A. Barber, Soil Sci. Soc. Am. Proc. 24: 381–385.*)

phosphate (Gosewinkel and Broadbent, 1986). Phosphorus deficiency enhances phosphatase activity in plant cell walls (Dracup et al., 1984).

Like N and S in the organic fraction, organic P can react with other soil constituents to decrease vulnerability to microbial attack. These reactions may help explain why some forms of P accumulate and others do not. Inositol phosphates (IP), esters of hexahydrohexahydroxy benzene, account for a high proportion of the organic P in many soils. These heterogeneous and ubiquitous compounds have many different stereoisomeric forms and degrees of phosphate esterification. One form of IP, the Ca salt of *myo*-inositol hexaphosphate, phytin, is the main organic P compound in seeds of many plants, particularly cereals. Because seeds are the primary source, IP is more likely to accumulate in soils of natural ecosystems than in soils used for agricultural crops. However, accumulation also depends upon the activity of microorganisms that have the capability of synthesizing these compounds and to the extent that IP becomes stabilized by reactions with other soil components. Greater resistance to biological degradation results from sorption by inorganic soil components and reactions with heavy metals.

Other soil organic matter compounds may indirectly influence accessibility of organic P to plants. Organic acids, for example, may contribute to P solubility by chelating metals, in particular Al and Fe, that may otherwise react with soluble phosphate to form very insoluble products. Organic acids differ in their effectiveness as chelators. Citric acid can form a stable complex with Al, so that this metal will not react with phosphate ions to form insoluble salts (Traina et al., 1986). Complexes of Al with tartaric or formic acids are much less stable. Microbial activity or root exudation are possible sources of chelating agents in the rhizosphere, but the quantities provided from these sources are uncertain (Stevenson, 1986). Quantitative determination of their relative contributions are complicated by possible influences of mycorrhizae on P uptake.

Potassium, calcium, and magnesium

In most soils, the K, Ca, and Mg held in exchangeable form by soil colloids are the most readily accessible sources for replenishment of these elements in the soil solution as they are removed by plant uptake and leaching. Generally, retention of the cations is mostly by inorganic colloids, but carboxyl and hydroxyl groups of organic residues, particularly during early stages of decomposition, are also significant binding sites.

In young soils, solubilization during weathering of primary minerals is an important soil solution cation replenishment mechanism. For example, over one-half of the K released by resin extraction from three coarse-textured Hapludult soils was from sand fractions (Sadusky et al., 1987). More intensive agricultural use as well as aging of soils tends to reduce soluble soil K concentrations. Data compiled by Barber et al. (1962) showed that over 90 percent of the samples from 142 midwestern soils contained less than 40 mg of K per liter in the soil solution, but a compilation of similar data including a higher proportion of soils from less severely weathered and cultivated areas showed that less than 50 percent of 155 samples had soluble K concentrations below 40 mg L^{-1} (Reisenauer, 1964). In calcareous soils, $CaCO_3$ (calcite), in some cases intermixed with $MgCO_3$ as in dolomite, may dissolve and contribute soluble supplies of both Ca and Mg. Dissolution is aided by HCO_3^- excreted by plant roots and generated by microbial activity. In some less weathered soils, gypsum is an important source of Ca. The Ca in irrigation waters may also be an important contributor to plant needs for Ca.

Because of the size of the ion, K^+ produced by weathering or added as fertilizers may become entrapped between the lattice layers of certain 2:1 types of clay minerals, especially vermiculites and some secondary micas that undergo alternate periods of wetting and drying . This so-called fixed K is more inaccessible as a source of replenishment of soluble K than the exchangeable K on colloid surfaces. Differences between surface and subsoils in solution–fixed K ratios may be related to past fertilizer management. The relatively greater K fixation capacity in the deeper parts of the profiles of five southern California soils was attributed to saturation of the surface fixation capacity by additions of K fertilizers (Shaviv et al., 1985). Similar in size to K ions, ammonium ions can by replacement enhance the release of fixed K into solution.

The nature of the mechanisms involved, and the quantitative aspects of the relationships between the exchangeably adsorbed and the soluble K, Ca, and Mg, has been the subject of much research. The addition of a soluble salt of K^+, Ca^{2+}, or Mg^{2+} to a moist soil changes not only the soil solution concentration of the cation added, but also the concentration of that cation in the exchangeable form and the concentrations of all other cations in both the soluble and exchangeable forms. Replacement of adsorbed cations by the soluble cation added is stoichiometric, but differing amounts (on a chemically equivalent basis) of various cations are required to produce the same amount of replacement of an adsorbed cation. Generally, cations of higher valence are held more strongly and, on a chemically equivalent basis, are more effective than cations of lower valence in replacing adsorbed cations. However, factors other than valence differences are involved. Cations of the same valence also differ in their strengths of adsorption and displacement effectiveness. Generally, NH_4^+ and K^+ are similar in these respects, and both are retained more strongly than Na^+ or Li^+, but less strongly than Rb^+ or Cs^+. For the divalent cations, Ca^{2+} generally is retained more strongly than Mg^{2+}, but less so than Ba^{2+}. Exceptions to these generalizations occur, however, since other factors, including the nature of the adsorbent and the state of ion hydration,. influence the strength of retention.

A number of mathematical models have been proposed to express quantitatively the distribution of cations between the adsorbed and soluble phases. According to one model, as expressed by the Gapon equation, Ca adsorbed by soil component X can be replaced by soluble K as follows:

$$Ca_{1/2}X + K^+ = KX + \frac{1}{2} Ca^{2+} \tag{3.12}$$

and

$$K_g = \frac{(KX)\,[Ca^{2+}]^{1/2}}{(Ca_{1/2}X)\,[K^+]} \tag{3.13}$$

where K_g = the Gapon exchange constant or selectivity coefficient, and the exchangeable ( ) and soluble [ ] cation concentrations are expressed in terms of $cmol(p^+)\ kg^{-1}$ [or meq $(100\ g)^{-1}$] and mol kg^{-1}, respectively.

An expression similar to Eq. 3.13 has been applied in describing the replacement of Na^+ by Ca^{2+} in the reclamation of saline soils. The value of K_G is fairly constant for part of the range over which exchangeable Na^+ is present in such soils. The value of K_G increases as the strength of retention of Na^+ increases.

The concept of ion exchange represented by the Gapon equation is pertinent to mineral nutrition of plants, but its applicability to quantitatively describe redistribution of ions between the sorbed and solution phases when nutrients are withdrawn by plant roots is difficult. Over the short term, precision of analytical methods limits detectability of changes occurring, and over longer periods reactions other than exchange have important influences on ion properties. Several other mathematical models for describing the thermodynamics of cation exchange are discussed by Bohn et al. (1985) and Sparks (1987).

Adsorption isotherms, like those already discussed above for P, are also used to quantitatively describe the relationships between soluble K and the solid phase K fraction (often referred to as *labile* K) most responsive to changes in the concentration of soluble K. The change in quantity Q of labile (exchangeable) K per unit soil weight relative to the change in concentration (intensity, I) of soluble K, as shown on the isotherm, expresses the buffer capacity. The change ratio, $\Delta Q/\Delta I$, generally is not constant over the entire concentration range and varies widely in different soils (Fig. 3.7).

All cations compete for exchange sites, and this competition affects the distribution of K in soluble and exchangeable forms. At intermediate pH ranges, effects of Ca and Mg are most likely. Several expressions have been proposed to take cation competitive effects into account in defining soluble/exchangeable ion distribution. The concept of the activity ratio AR as a measure of soil K intensity was first introduced by Schofield (1947) and further developed by Beckett (1964). This ratio is defined in the following expression:

$$AR^K = \frac{a_K}{(a_{Ca} + a_{Mg})^{1/2}} \qquad (3.14)$$

where a_K, a_{Ca}, and a_{Mg} are the activities of soluble K, Ca, and Mg, respectively. The plot (Q/I) shown in Fig. 3.8 was constructed from data obtained by treating a soil with solutions ranging in AR^K values, and determining the changes in exchangeable K (ΔK) resulting from the treatments (Beckett, 1964). In some studies in which this concept is used, ratios are calculated in terms of concentrations CR rather than activities. Differences between AR and CR values are small in solutions of low ionic strength.

Parameters defined from the Q/I plot as shown in Fig. 3.8 provide another means of soil K characterization that can help to describe quantitatively influences of management practices and changes in soil properties that may affect plant K nutrition. The equilibrium activity (concentration) ratio AR^{Ke} (CR^{Ke}) is the value of AR^K (CR^K) at which ΔK is zero. The linear buffering capacity PBC^K is estimated from the slope of the regression. In a study by Evangelou et al. (1986), samples

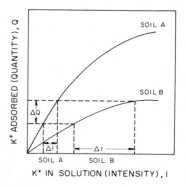

Figure 3.7 Relationship between K^+ intensity and K^+ quantity for two soils with different adsorbing capacities. (*Reproduced from K. Mengel and E. A. Kirkby, Principles of Plant Nutrition, Third Edition, 1982, page 74, by permission of the International Potash Institute.*)

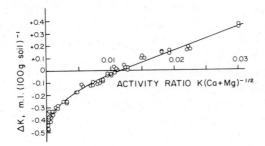

Figure 3.8 Immediate Q/I relation of a Lower Greensand soil measured at laboratory temperature. (*Reproduced from P. H. T. Beckett, Journal of Soil Science, volume 15, 1964, pages 1–23, by permission of Blackwell Scientific Publications, Inc.*)

of Maury (fine-silty, mixed, mesic, Typic Paleudalfs) silt loam soil, collected from a site where management in the prior 14 years involved annual N fertilization with no-tillage (NT), had a mean CR^{Ke} value of 19.6 $(mol\ L^{-1})^{1/2} \times 10^{-3}$. A much lower value (6.6) was obtained with data from a nearby site where no N fertilizer had been applied and conventional tillage (CT) used during the same time period. The higher value, indicating that a higher proportion of the K is more readily extractable, was attributed to a higher level of organic matter at the NT site. The PBC^K values were similar at the two sites, indicating that the two management practices had similar effects on K buffering capacities. The mean values of CR^{NH4} and PBC^{NH4} were also higher with the NT treatment than with CT. Results of other studies have shown the influences of soil organic matter on plant K availability indices (Uribe and Cox, 1988). Oxalic and citric acids, which may be produced by the decomposition of plant residues and released by roots especially in forest soils, are effective in releasing structural K from K-bearing aluminosilicate minerals (Song and Huang, 1988).

The effects on AR^K values have been used to evaluate the effects of various soil treatments on soil properties. The influences of K fertilization and liming treatments on these values have been associated with differences in K fixation mechanisms at various depths in a soil profile (Sparks and Liebhardt, 1981). In high K-fixing soils sampled at various depths, CR^K (designated as PAR) values were found to be linearly related to the ratio of adsorbed K to adsorbed Ca plus Mg (Shaviv et al., 1985). Gapon selectivity coefficients K_G and CR^K were inversely related.

The basic concepts regarding the chemistry of ion exchange as discussed for K also apply generally to Ca and Mg as well, but, as with K, testing these concepts in soil-plant relationships is limited by a lack of techniques for making the necessary analyses at microsites where soils and plant roots interface.

Calcium and Mg ions generally account for the major portion of the positive charges needed to balance the negative charges of soil colloids, but since Ca and Mg limit plant growth much less frequently, there have been fewer studies than with K concerning the relationships between their sorbed and soluble states relative to plant nutrition. Calcium ions are retained more tenaciously than Mg ions in most soils, but the magnitude of adsorption differences depends upon the chemical properties of the clays and colloidal materials present. Differences in the affinity of organic matter and of inorganic soil clays for Ca may influence the distribution of ions between the adsorbed and soluble states (Sposito and Fletcher, 1985). The distribution is also altered in soils containing high levels (> 20 percent of total exchangeable cations) of exchangeable Na. Mineral nutrition of plants growing in saline soils is discussed in Chap. 7.

Iron and manganese

Four traits of Fe and Mn influence their solubilization: (1) they both occur predominantly as oxides or oxyhydroxides in soils; (2) their redox potentials allow them to undergo reversible oxidation-reductions; (3) they are both much more soluble in acidic than in alkaline soils; and (4) they both form chelates with naturally occurring organic ligands, but the stability of at least some of the complexes formed, especially those of Mn, is relatively weak. As oxides, they provide adsorbing surfaces and thus influence the solubility of other mineral nutrient ions, in particular those of other heavy metals. In some quantitative aspects, however, there are large differences between Fe and Mn. Iron is the fifth most abundant element in the lithosphere, and mean values of its total concentration in soils are about 50 times those of Mn. Despite this great abundance of Fe, insufficient amounts are present in accessible forms in many soils to meet plant needs. The amounts of Mn taken up by plants are of the same order of magnitude as those for Fe, but deficiencies of Mn are much less frequent.

In parent material, Fe occurs mostly in various oxides and in aluminosilicate minerals, particularly certain micas. Amounts and rates of dissolution of solid state Fe are highly dependent upon soil pH and redox potential. In its most hydrated form, soluble ferric iron occurs as $Fe(H_2O)_6^{3+}$, but with increasing pH, hydrolysis results in the production of more hydroxylated forms such as $Fe(OH)^{2+}$ or $[Fe(OH)(H_2O)_5^{2+}]$ ($pK \approx 3$). Under less acidic conditions, $Fe(OH)_2^+$, $Fe_2(OH)_2^{4+}$, and $Fe(OH)_4^-$ are formed, and finally $Fe(OH)_3$ and $FeOOH$ precipitate.

Under reducing conditions, soluble soil Fe concentrations are enhanced since the divalent forms are more soluble than the trivalent. The extent of reduction depends upon the relative amounts of electron donors and acceptors in the system. Electron availability, represented by the symbol Eh, is generally expressed in volts or millivolts. More recently, the negative logarithm of the electron activity, $\ln e^-$ (pe), has been used to express the tendency for chemical reduction to occur in a system (Lindsay, 1979). The two expressions for reducing conditions are related as follows, in units of millivolts:

$$pe = \frac{Eh}{59.2} \qquad (3.15)$$

The derivation of this relationship is shown in the appendix.

The prediction of concentrations of soluble Fe in soils from solubility product and equilibrium rate constants is complicated by the uncertainty as to what form(s) of Fe regulate(s) the concentration of the soluble species. Very low concentrations of soluble Fe in most soils are to be expected, since the solid phase Fe-containing species most often present generally have very low solubility product constants. The following equation was derived as a means of estimating the concentrations of soluble Fe in soils as values of pe and pH changed (Lindsay, 1979):

$$\log Fe^{2+} = 15.74 - (pH + pe) - 2\,pH \qquad (3.16)$$

The derivation of this expression is shown in the appendix. The regulator of Fe solubility was assumed to be a modified amorphous phase of $Fe(OH)_3$, [$Fe(OH)_3$-(soil)]. Solubility diagrams based on Eq. 3.16 indicate Fe concentrations (activities) in the range of 10^{-7} to 10^{-16} μM in moderately to well drained soils with pH's ranging from 4 to 7 (Fig. 3.9). In such soils, pe + pH values generally range from 15 to 17.

Ways of quantitatively defining effects of pH and pe on soluble Fe in soils help provide a means of predicting responses to soil treatments, but there are important limits to applying formulas such as Eq. 3.16. One limitation is the accuracy of the measurement of pe. Methods involving platinum (Pt) wire electrodes, most commonly used to determine soil redox potentials, give reasonably reproducible values under some conditions, but not in others (Blanchar and Marshall, 1981). Another limitation in applying Eq. 3.16 to the Fe nutrition of plants is that such thermodynamic models provide no information about the rates at which equilibrium is reached.

The presence of other soil components that affect Fe solubility need to be taken into account. Compounds that chelate Fe, such as organic acids, are present in plant residues and formed as products of residue decomposition. Their effectiveness in aiding Fe solubilization depends upon the chemical properties of other ions present in the soil, as well as on the kinds of ligands with which they chelate. With the synthetic chelate EDTA, Fe forms a complex with a stability constant greater than that formed with other common soil ions, but with citrate or

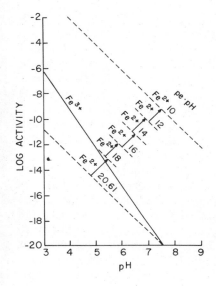

Figure 3.9 The effect of redox and pH on the Fe in equilibrium with soil-Fe. (*Reproduced from W. Lindsay, Chemical Equilibria in Soils, page 140, by permission of John Wiley & Sons, Inc., copyright ©, 1979*).)

oxalate, Al and Ca form more stable complexes than Fe (Norvell, 1972). In the presence of Ca malate, a small amount of MnO_2 aids in dissolving Fe coated on a calcareous sand, but Fe reduction is inhibited in the presence of larger amounts of the oxide (Jauregui and Reisenauer, 1982).

Plant root activity can alter the rhizosphere to enhance solubilization of Fe. Responses of plant roots to conditions of limited available Fe include (1) greater release of reductants; (2) enhanced activation of an ATPase-driven proton efflux pump; and (3) increased production and release of chelating agents (Römheld and Marschner, 1986). These mechanisms may function simultaneously and interact. Besides having effects on Fe solubility by affecting pe and pH in a manner analagous to that represented in Eq. 3.16, release of reductants and protons may increase susceptibility of chelated ferric Fe to reduction, and thus enhance its plant availability. Microbial activity may also influence and be influenced by the operation of the three mechanisms.

There are differences between plant species and varieties in the manner and extent to which their roots enhance Fe solubility. Generally, dicots enhance Fe solubility more effectively than monocots by altering rhizosphere pH and releasing reductants, as well as by having greater activity of reductases in their roots. Some grasses help overcome a lack of sufficient Fe by excreting a variety of nonproteinogenic amino acids, such as mugineic and avenic acid, collectively termed *phytosiderophores* (Takagi et al., 1984). Formation of uncharged organic complexes with Fe aid plant uptake not only by helping to elevate Fe concentrations in the soil solution, but also by contributing to Fe mobility in the root zone.

Solubilization of soil Mn has received less attention than Fe because Mn limits plant growth less frequently than Fe. Concentrations of soluble Mn, like those of Fe, are related to pH and Eh (pe), and to the kinds of oxides that are present in the solid phase. All three factors are involved in regulating the concentrations of Mn retained by electrostatic forces on colloidal surfaces. Desorbed Mn contributes to replenishment of Mn removed by plant uptake or leaching.

Unlike Fe, Mn occurs in the tetravalent as well as the divalent and trivalent forms. The trivalent and tetravalent forms can coexist, so the ratio of O to Mn in oxides can range from 1.5:1 to 2:1. An intermixing with a variety of other elements, including Al, Si, Fe, Ca, and Ba, also affects this ratio in Mn oxides (Taylor et al., 1964). The minerals pyrolusite and birnessite, represented by the chemical formulas MnO_2 and $MnO_{1.8}$, respectively, are not likely to be present in soils. The uncertain composition of Mn oxides, and the presence of variable levels of CO_2, complicate any attempt to estimate soluble soil Mn concentrations using equilibrium activity constants (K^o). Calculations using these constants can, however, give some indications of mineral species whose solubilities are compatible with the levels of soluble soil Mn under different conditions. Manganite (§MnOOH), a likely species at normal atmospheric CO_2 concentrations (0.003 atm), could react as follows:

$$\S MnOOH + 3\,H^+ + e^- \leftrightharpoons Mn^{2+} + 2\,H_2O \qquad \log K^o = 25.27 \qquad (3.17)$$

and result in a Mn^{2+} activity of 2.23×10^{-2} mM. This assumes that the same equation (3.16) used previously for Fe also applies to Mn and that pe + pH = 16.62, a level typical for moderately to well drained soils (Lindsay, 1979). Near plant roots, carbonates are likely reaction products. Possible reactions include

$$Mn^{2+} + CO_2(g) + H_2O \leftrightharpoons MnCO_3^0 + 2H^+ \qquad (3.18)$$

or

$$Mn^{2+} + CO_2(g) + H_2O \leftrightharpoons MnHCO^{3+} + H^+ \qquad (3.19)$$

Equilibrium solution Mn^{2+} activities associated with these reactions are difficult to estimate, since their $\log K^o$ values are vastly different (-18.87 and -6.02, respectively, at 25°C) (Lindsay, 1979).

Except at low soil pH and Eh, solubilization of Mn from oxides, oxyhydroxides, and carbonates is necessary to meet Mn needs of plants growing in low organic soils. In slightly acidic, neutral, and alkaline soils, sorbed Mn occurs in very low amounts (Sims, 1986). Adsorption of Mn on $CaCO_3$ surfaces can lower Mn solubility below that of precipitated $MnCO_3$ (McBride, 1979). Slow diffusional processes may limit accessibility to the mineral and precipitated forms of soil Mn.

The Mn associated with organic matter is also an important source of soluble Mn. Increases in soluble Mn concentrations when soils are dried have been attributed to releases from organic fractions. Increases in soluble Mn sometimes noted with oxidizing treatments have been attributed to changes similar to the effects of drying. This may not be an entirely correct interpretation, however, because treatment of soils with H_2O_2, for example, also releases Mn from oxides (Taylor et al., 1964). Some Mn retention by chelation with compounds present in soil organic matter is possible, but the stability constants of such complexes are lower than those of some other heavy metals, particularly Cu (Fig. 3.10). Other kinds of binding also are indicated by nuclear magnetic resonance (NMR) spectra (Bloom, 1981).

Zinc, copper, and nickel

These three elements have several similarities relative to their solubilization in soils. All three (1) occur in divalent forms under most circumstances, an exception being Cu_2S under very reducing conditions; (2) adsorb on Fe and Mn oxides; (3) substitute, although not equally well, for Fe, Mn, and Mg in certain aluminosilicates; (4) un-

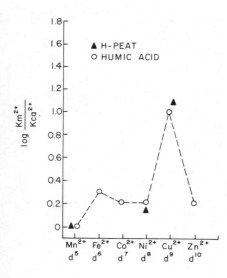

Figure 3.10 Binding constants for d^5 to d^{10} divalent ions relative to the constants for Ca on H^+ peat and humic acid. (*Reproduced from P. R. Bloom and M. R. McBride, Soil Science Society of America Journal, volume 43, 1979, pages 687–692, by permission of the Soil Science Society of America, Inc.*)

dergo hydrolysis to the $M(OH)^+$ form; and (5) form chelate complexes. There are differences among the three in the extent to which each undergoes the reactions indicated by similarities (2) to (5). When compared to Zn and Cu, Ni undergoes little hydrolysis below pH 8. When compared to Zn and Ni, Cu forms much more stable chelate complexes.

Like other cations, Zn^{2+}, Cu^{2+}, and Ni^{2+} are attracted electrostatically to negatively charged colloids, and these adsorbed forms exchange readily with soluble Zn, Cu, and Ni. Their total soil concentrations are highly variable, and the ranges of concentrations of the three overlap in different soils. Of the three, Zn is most often present in highest concentration, with occasional levels greater than 100 $\mu g \, g^{-1}$. Nickel concentrations also may exceed this level in young soils derived from basic rocks.

Zinc, Cu, and Ni present as structural components of aluminosilicate minerals or bound by Fe and Al oxides are the most difficult fractions to solubilize. For example, an average of over 70 percent of the total soil Zn resisted extraction by treatments that would remove the soluble, exchangeable, organic matter–bound, and Mn oxide–bound forms in 19 soils from various areas of the eastern United States (Iyengar et al., 1981). An oxalic acid–oxalate solution (Tamm's reagent) removed about one-third of the remaining Zn, indicating that Zn was bound by Fe and Al oxides. The Zn solubilized by aqua regia–HF was assumed to have been present as aluminosilicate minerals.

Generally a higher proportion of the total Zn, Cu and Ni in soils is soluble under acidic rather than under alkaline conditions. Low pH increases alteration and breakdown of aluminosilicate minerals with the release of Zn, Cu, Ni, and other elements. As soil pH increases, Zn^{2+} hydrolyzes, producing $Zn(OH)^+$ and highly insoluble $Zn(OH)_2$. In the presence of CO_2, some $ZnCO_3$ may be produced but, if so, probably exists as the amorphous form, because the crystalline form (smithsonite) occurs only at a pH exceeding 8 (Harter, 1983). With increasing alkalinity, the HPO_4^{2-}–$H_2PO_4^-$ ratio increases, favoring formation of the highly insoluble $ZnHPO_4$. When Cu^{2+} hydrolyzes, the product is $Cu(OH)_2$, with little or no monovalent Cu being produced. The formation of $Ni(OH)^+$ is not likely at a pH below 8.

The relationship between soluble and insoluble Zn, Cu, and Ni is affected by the amount and kinds of organic matter present. By providing organic acids as chelating ligands, organic matter plays a major role in solubilizing and maintaining soluble levels of all three elements. The presence of an active soil organic fraction has a particularly marked effect on the amount of soluble Cu because Cu ions form very stable complexes with chelating ligands (Fig. 3.11). Over 90 per-

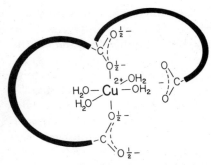

Figure 3.11 Possible chemical binding site for Cu^{2+} in soil organic matter. (*Reproduced from P. R. Bloom, "Metal-organic matter interactions in soil," in Chemistry in the Soil Environment, 1981, edited by R. H. Dowdy, J. A. Ryan, V. V. Volk, and D. E. Baker, pages 129–150, by permission of American Society of Agronomy, Inc., and Soil Science Society of America, Inc.*)

cent of the soluble soil Cu may chelated. While this enhances the mobility of Cu in soil, because of the stability of the complex, chelation may compete with plant uptake for soluble soil Cu. The nature of the binding mechanisms is related to pH. At a pH < 6, carboxylates and H_2O molecules are involved, but at a pH 6 to 7 binding by O- and N-containing ligands is more prevalent (Sposito et al., 1988). Rapid (within 24 h) changes in retentiveness of Cu added to soil is attributed to differences in the energy of binding sites (Lehman and Harter, 1984).

Chelation is also an important aspect of Zn solubilization. Under conditions where complexing is favorable, the proportion of uncharged (complexed) Zn is greater under alkaline conditions than under acidic conditions (McBride and Blasiak, 1979).

When reducing conditions become severe enough in flooded soils for H_2S to form, ZnS precipitates. This reaction may regulate the level of soluble soil Zn in flooded soils and result in an insufficient level for plant growth (Gilmour and Kittrick, 1979). The precipitation reaction competes effectively with the chelating mechanisms for soluble Zn.

Boron

Total B concentrations in soils range from less than 10 to over 200 mg kg^{-1}. Boron is associated with silicate minerals, in the borosilicate tourmaline (3 to 4 percent B), and as a substituent for Si in other minerals. Organic matter is an important source of the B required for plant growth. Aluminum hydroxy compounds, particularly when freshly formed, retain relatively large amounts of B (Keren and Bingham, 1985), and the reactions involved probably account for the appearance of plant B deficiencies following additions of lime to acid soils. Iron hydroxy compounds, broken edges of aluminosilicate minerals, and organic matter are sites of B adsorption. The Al and Fe hydroxyl adsorbents may be present as coatings on silicate minerals.

Boron adsorption maxima in 15 arid zone soils correlated with specific surface areas, clay contents, and pH values (Goldberg and Glaubig, 1986). For these soils, a Freundlich adsorption model gave a better description than a Langmuir model for B adsorption over the whole range of B concentrations.

The relationship of pH to B adsorption in soils below pH 7 varies, depending upon the nature of the inorganic and organic components with which B associates. The energy with which B is retained when adsorbed by ligand exchange and when held electrostatically by a pH-dependent positively charged site are quite different.

The highly variable occurrence of B in different soils in various fractions is shown in Table 3.2. Fractionation of the B in the 14 diverse soils, all from eastern USA, was accomplished by sequential treatment with various reagents. Adsorbed B accounted for only a very small fraction of the total soil B.

The amounts of soluble and easily solubilized B are most important for meeting plant growth needs. The range between concentrations (0.01 mmol L^{-1}) of soil solution B that are needed for some plants, including corn, soybean and small grains, and concentrations (0.03 mmol L^{-1}) toxic to B-sensitive plants, including citrus and peach (Maas, 1986), is relatively narrow. Separation of the B in 14 soils with diverse properties into various fractions by sequential treatment with

TABLE 3.2   Distribution of B in Various Fractions of 14 Soils Extracted Sequentially with Indicated Reagents

Five different soil orders, and widely different textures, organic matter (4 to 35 g kg^{-1}), and clay (54–489 g kg^{-1}) contents included in soil sampling

Extractant	Amount of B, mg kg^{-1}	Percent of total soil B
H_2O	< 0.01–0.22	nil–0.32
Mannitol*	< 0.01–0.34	0.08–0.53
Acidified $NH_2OH \cdot HCl$†	0.10–1.31	0.46–1.52
NH_4–oxalate‡	8.7–73.4	25.2–88.3
Not extracted (residual)	1.7–76.3	2.4–79.2

*Nonspecifically and specifically adsorbed B.
†Occluded in Mn oxyhydroxides.
‡In other crystalline and noncrystalline oxyhydroxides.
SOURCE: Jin et al., 1987.

various reagents did not indicate any clear relationship of soluble and adsorbed B, nor to organic matter or clay contents (Jin et al., 1987).

Boron occurs in soil solutions mostly as undissociated boric acid, H_3BO_3. The occurrence in most soils predominantly in a molecular form is a distinctive feature not shared by any other plant essential nutrient. Boric acid behaves as a Lewis acid and reacts with OH^- groups, but the pK_h (9.2 at 25°C) indicates that hydrolysis is an important reaction only under highly alkaline conditions. Hydrolytic products are $B(OH)_4^-$ and H_3O^+.

Besides the amount of soluble B present, the rate of release also contributes to the effectiveness with which the supply of B in soil serves plant nutrient needs. The release of B from silicate minerals by weathering is a slow process, and the specific mechanisms involved are not well defined. Several models to describe the kinetics of B desorption from multisites differing in retention energy have been proposed. For soils with relatively high B levels, desorption follows a first-order integrated rate equation and the maximum adsorption values are consistent with a two-site analog of a linear form of the one-site Langmuir adsorption model (Griffin and Burau, 1974).

In arid and semiarid regions, phytotoxic B effects may result from irrigation with waters containing B concentrations in excess of plant tolerance. Continued use of waters with concentrations below those expected to cause phytotoxicity may result in an eventual accumulation in soils to levels that may adversely affect plants, especially the more B-sensitive types (Maas, 1986).

Molybdenum

The amounts of Mo, both in soils and in needs by plants, are the lowest of any of the generally recognized plant essential nutrients. The ratios of Mo to N and to Cu atoms in plants are about $1{:}1 \times 10^6$ and 1:300, respectively. Plant requirements for Mo are probably greater than those for Ni, but there is as yet insufficient data to make this comparison with certainty. The amounts of Mo in soils ($< 10\mu g\ g^{-1}$) generally are less than those of Ni by several orders of magnitude.

Soil minerals containing Mo in combination with either Fe, Pb or Ca are Mo nutrient sources. The most soluble of the three, $CaMoO_4$, accounts for a higher proportion of the total Mo in alkaline than in acid soils. In some soils most of the Mo is present in the organic fraction, and problems of Mo toxicity to livestock usually occur on muck or peat soils.

Much soil Mo is present in a sorbed form. Hydrous oxides of Fe, Al, and Ti are effective adsorbents of molybdate, and the adsorption reaction follows a Freundlich model modified to include a parameter for pH (Reisenauer et al., 1962). Sorption by $Fe_2O_3 \cdot xH_2O$ was accompanied by a stoichiometric release of two OH groups and one H_2O, indicating a ligand exchange mechanism. Phosphate ions also effectively replace sorbed molybdate. In some soils essentially all of the sorbed Mo can be removed by repeated leaching with hot water (Follett and Barber, 1967). Mechanisms of molybdate sorption by soil organic components are not well known, but presumably protonated functional groups serve this purpose.

Soluble soil Mo occurs primarily as MoO_4^{2-} in most soils. Under acidic conditions, a low proportion of $HMoO_4^-$ and even less H_2MoO_4 will be present. Higher levels of soluble Mo occur in soils with pH's at or above 7 than in acidic soils. Either the same adsorbents are present, but the energy of retention is lower, or the adsorbents are of a different kind, at the higher pH. Increasing the pH of a soil generally increases the level of soluble Mo. The increased amount of soluble Mo may result from a change in the energy of retention of molybdate, or possibly from more active ligand exchange in the presence of larger amounts of OH^- and $H_2PO_4^-$ at the higher pH. While in most soils concentrations of soluble soil Mo at equilibrium are related to the amount and kind of sorbed molybdate, little is known about the rates at which Mo levels are restored during or after depletion.

Chlorine

The unique feature of soil Cl, relative to other plant essential nutrients, is the low proportion of the total present in forms other than as the soluble ion. Amounts of Cl^- deposited in soils by precipitation can supply a major portion, and in some areas the entire needs of plants. Chloride is nonspecifically adsorbed in kaolinitic soils, but relative to other common anions except NO_3^-, the amounts adsorbed are small.

Because of the ubiquitous occurrence of Cl^- in the biosphere, in order to show its essentiality for plants, care must be taken to exclude access of the plants to extraneous Cl^- sources. Toxicities of Cl are much more common than deficiencies. Benefits to plant growth, not because of lack of Cl to meet plant metabolic needs per se, but for other reasons such as lessening growth impairment from diseases, were described in Chap. 1.

Appendix

Relationship of *Eh* to p*e*

Reaction $Fe^{3+} + e^- \leftrightarrows Fe^{2+}$ coupled to $\frac{1}{2}H_2(g) \leftrightarrows H^+$ ($E = Eh$):

$$K^\circ = \frac{Fe^{2+}}{(Fe^{3+})(e^-)} \tag{A.1}$$

$$\log \frac{Fe^{2+}}{Fe^{3+}} = \log K^\circ - \log \frac{1}{e^-} \tag{A.2}$$

Eh for the reaction can be calculated from the Nernst equation:

$$Eh = Eh^\circ - \frac{2.303\,RT}{nf} \log \frac{Fe^{2+}}{Fe^{3+}} \tag{A.3}$$

where R = gas constant
n = electron change
T = absolute temperature
f = Faraday constant

For the standard redox potential

$$Eh^\circ = \frac{2.303\,RT}{nf} \log K^\circ \tag{A.4}$$

Substituting Eq. A.4 into Eq. A.3 gives

$$Eh = \frac{2.303\,RT}{nf} \log K^\circ - \frac{2.303\,RT}{nf} \left(\log K^\circ - \log \frac{1}{e^-} \right) \tag{A.5}$$

And since for the reaction $Fe^{3+} = Fe^{2+}$, $n = 1$, at 25°C, then

$$Eh = \frac{2.303\,RT}{f} \text{ p}e = 59.2 \text{ p}e \ mV \tag{A.6}$$

Effects of pH and *Eh* on Fe^{2+}

Assume $Fe(OH)_3$–soils at equilibrium:

$$Fe(OH)_3 + 3H^+ \leftrightarrows Fe^{+3} + 3H_2O \qquad \log K^\circ = 2.70 \tag{A.7}$$

$$Fe^{3+} + e^- \leftrightarrows Fe^{2+} \qquad \log K^\circ = 13.04 \tag{A.8}$$

$$Fe(OH)_3 + 3H^+ + e^- \leftrightarrows Fe^{2+} + 3H_2O \tag{A.9}$$

$$K = \frac{Fe^{2+}}{(H^+)^3(e^-)} = 10^{15.74} \tag{A.10}$$

$$\log K = \log Fe^{2+} - [\log (H^+)^3(e^-)] \tag{A.11}$$

$$= \log Fe^{2+} - (3 \log H^+ + \log e^-) \tag{A.12}$$

$$\log Fe^{2+} = \log K + 3 \log H^+ + \log e^- \tag{A.13}$$

$$= 15.74 + \log H^+ + \log e^- + 2 \log H^+ \tag{A.14}$$

$$\log Fe^{2+} = 15.74 - (pH + pe) - 2 pH \tag{A.15}$$

Water Uptake by Plants

Introduction

Nearly all land plants undergo a reduction in water potential each morning. This reduction occurs because water vapor diffuses outward, mostly through open stomata. At the same time, CO_2 diffuses into the substomatal cavities through the open stomata. Loss of water causes the leaf tissue to dehydrate and the total water potential to be lowered all along the pathway from the rhizosphere soil to the cells of the substomatal area. As the radiant energy load onto the leaves increases during the morning hours, the water potential continues to decrease there. In the afternoon, the energy load decreases, there is less evaporation from the leaves, and the plant tissues dehydrate until they become turgid during the night if sufficient water is supplied by the roots. Uptake rates by the roots lag behind evaporation from the leaves (transpiration) during the morning, but uptake is greater than transpiration during the afternoon hours (Fig. 4.1).

The pathway for water movement is from bulk soil to the rhizosphere, across the rhizosphere and the soil-root interface, across the cortex and the endodermis, and then into the lumen of the xylem. Water then moves along the xylem to the substomatal cavities where it undergoes a phase change to vapor and diffuses through the stomata and the leaf-air boundary layer. Any part of the liquid transport process can be reversed if water potentials are reversed.

Three major factors control the extent to which plant water potential decreases during the daily stress period: (1) the input of energy into the leaves to convert liquid water to vapor; (2) the difficulty with which water vapor can move from internal evaporating surfaces through the stomata and cuticle to the ambient atmosphere; and (3) the supply rate for water from the soil to the substomatal evaporating sites within the leaves. Because this book deals with soil and plant

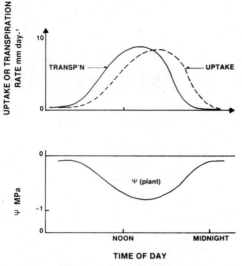

Figure 4.1   Some representative values of transpiration rates, uptake rates, and plant water
potentials as they develop on a clear day.

interrelationships, the third factor, the supply rate of water from soil
to plant parts, is stressed in this chapter.

Transport of Water in Soil

The water potential concept discussed in Chap. 1 provides a basis for
predicting the direction that water will move in a given system but
provides no basis for predicting the rate of transport.

The rate of water transport was put on a quantitative basis by
Henri Darcy, who studied seepage rates through sand filters at Dijon,
France, in 1856. Darcy showed that the volume flow rate was proportional to the gradient in hydraulic head. Generalizations of this principle are called *Darcy's law*. If Darcy's law is expressed in hydraulic
head terms, then

$$J_w = \frac{- K_w \, dH}{dx} \tag{4.1}$$

where J_w = flux of water, $L^3 \, L^{-2} \, t^{-1}$
   K_w = soil hydraulic conductivity, $L \, t^{-1}$
   dH = hydraulic head difference, L
   dx = distance along the flow path, L

Mathematically, Darcy's law is similar to the linear transport equations of classical physics, such as Ohm's law, which states that the flow rate of electricity (current) is proportional to the electrical potential gradient (voltage divided by resistance).

If the soil is saturated with water and structurally stable, hydraulic conductivity is a constant affected only by pore geometry and fluid characteristics such as viscosity. In unsaturated soil, hydraulic conductivity decreases with soil water content because the cross-sectional area available for transport, the mean effective pore radius, and the effective path length all vary with water content. Each of these factors also varies in saturated, but structurally unstable, soil.

The criterion for equilibrium in soil water is uniform total water potential, not uniform soil water content. In unsaturated soils it is possible to have virtually no gradient in water content or in hydraulic conductivity, but considerable flow, such as in the transmission zone behind a wetting front (Fig. 4.2). In this special case, gravity potential is the driving force, but in the usual unsaturated conditions, matric potential differences provide most, but not all, of the potential differences causing flow.

The hydraulic conductivity term K_w varies by several orders of magnitude within the range of soil water potentials encountered by plant roots. This large variation in hydraulic conductivity creates problems

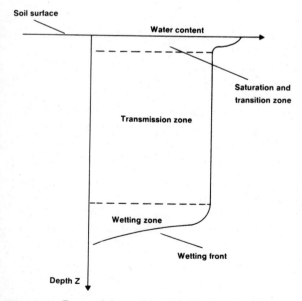

Figure 4.2 Zones of the moisture profile during infiltration. (*Bodman and Coleman, 1943.*)

when attempting exact mathematical solutions to flow equations. If the pressure form of Eq. 4.1 is used and $(d\psi/d\theta)(d\theta/dx)$ is substituted for the dh/dx term, a new term, soil diffusivity D_w, can be defined as $K_w\,(d\psi/d\theta)$. Because both K_w and ψ are functions of water content, Eq. 4.1 is altered to

$$J_w = D_w \frac{\partial\theta}{\partial x} \tag{4.2}$$

The soil water diffusivity equation often can be solved explicitly even though the soil water conductivity form of the same data must be solved by approximation. Although the D_w term is called soil water diffusivity, it pertains to situations involving macroscopic pressure differences, not the random thermal motion of diffusion, but soil water flow problems are linearized and easier to solve, especially in three dimensions.

The major justification for using the soil water diffusivity equation is the situation where water contents differ among soil layers, but not with time (steady-state flow). The much more common situation is that water content differs not only among layers, but also with time. To solve for vertical flow through a thin layer of soil where water content changes with time and distance, we can apply the continuity equation (Richards, 1931):

$$\frac{\partial\theta}{\partial t} = \frac{\partial}{\partial z}\frac{K_w}{\partial z}\frac{\partial H}{\partial z} + \frac{\partial K_w}{\partial z} = \frac{\partial}{\partial z}\frac{D\partial\theta}{\partial z} + \frac{\partial K_w}{\partial z} \tag{4.3}$$

The water content changes with time or depth can be expressed either in the conductivity or the diffusivity form of Eq. 4.3 (Klute, 1973).

Various configurations of Eq. 4.3 have been used to calculate water flow from one soil layer to another one or from bulk soil through the rhizosphere. Some factors that affect water transport are as follows.

Effects of pore size and continuity on transport

Both D_w and K_w depend ultimately on the distribution of the soil pore sizes and their continuity. The magnitude of soil pores depends on soil compaction, structural changes induced by puddling, and the method of soil wetting. At a specific water content, soil water diffusivity (and conductivity) is less on the drying than on the wetting portion of a hysteresis loop (Fig. 4.3).

Infiltration

The maximum flow rate through a profile often is controlled by the rate at which water enters the soil surface. The standard equation

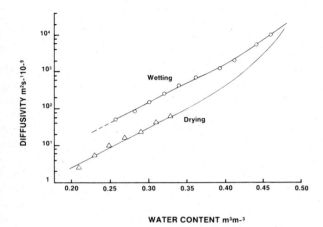

Figure 4.3 Diffusivity as a function of volumetric water content for Grenville silt loam during wetting and drying. (*After Staple, 1965.*)

used involves the square root of time:

$$V = \frac{1}{2} st^{-1/2} + a \qquad (4.4)$$

where V = infiltration rate
  s, a = constants
  t = time

At large times, the infiltration rate equals the hydraulic conductivity of the soil at the particular water content in the transmission zone (Fig. 4.2). This conductivity varies widely from soil to soil.

Water vapor transfer. It has been known for considerable time that water vapor will move through porous materials, but it is very difficult to accurately describe this process for naturally occurring soils. The separation of liquid and vapor fluxes is difficult because liquid water tends to concentrate at points of constriction in continuous pores. This liquid acts as a block to the mass flow of vapor, but vapor condenses on the menisci of the liquid. Vapor phase transport probably becomes negligible at soil water contents where liquid flow to plant roots becomes appreciable. Cowan and Milthorpe (1968), however, calculate that vapor phase transport can supply water to roots at a 7×10^{-7} m^3 m^{-1} day^{-1} rate when a potential difference of 0.5 Mpa exists across a 40-μm gap. A large uncertainty exists about the results of these calculations because a phase change occurs twice during the transport and also because the root cortex likely will have a water po-

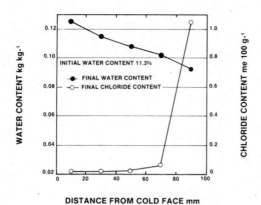

DISTANCE FROM COLD FACE mm

Figure 4.4   Distribution of water and chlorides in a column of loam soil subjected to a temperature gradient for 18 days. Initial water content was 11.3 percent by weight. (*After Gurr et al., 1952, with permission of Williams and Wilkins, Inc.*)

tential that closely tracks that of the rhizosphere soil if no suberized hypodermis is present.

Water movement through soil by temperature and solute gradients

Water also may be transferred by temperature and solute gradients. Diurnal and seasonal temperature changes occur regularly, and these changes may be drastic near the soil surface, especially in bare soils. Temperature changes alter both the vapor pressure and surface tension of water. Gurr et al. (1952) showed that a temperature gradient maintained for 18 days substantially altered the relative distributions of water and chloride in an initially uniform soil (Fig. 4.4). Water content decreased linearly with distance from the cold face, but chloride was highly concentrated within 30 mm of the warm face.

Quantitative theories are available to deal with thermally driven fluxes of heat and water. Cassel et al. (1969) showed that one theory by Philip and De Vries (1957) estimated fluxes reasonably well. The Philip–De Vries theory separates water and thermal driving forces under the assumption that no interaction exists between the two fluxes; therefore

$$V = - D_w \frac{d\theta}{dx} - D_t \frac{dT}{dx} \tag{4.5}$$

where V = total vapor flux

D_w = water diffusivity driven by water content differences

D_t = equivalent value water flux driven by temperature difference

Both D_w and D_T have liquid and vapor components.

A gradient in a solute concentration (therefore osmotic potential) will cause counterfluxes of water and solute. Solutes, however, tend to be excluded from the electrical double layers surrounding soil particles. This exclusion causes the flow of water to be somewhat enhanced and that of solute to be diminished relative to that, if no double layer existed.

This exclusion phenomenon is too complex to cover here but is important when one considers the process of a fertilizer salt diffusing through moist soil. For further information, the reader is referred to Parlange (1973).

Transport of Water across the Rhizosphere, Soil-Root Interface and Radially within the Root

The quantity of water that moves across the rhizosphere, the soil-root interface and the root tissue to the xylem is about equal diurnally to that lost through transpiration. However, root uptake is less than transpiration during morning hours and is greater than transpiration during later afternoon (Fig. 4.1). No technique exists that will accurately and simultaneously measure water potential and flux at the root surface under normally occurring flow rates. Because there is no direct means for resolving the controversy, considerable uncertainty exists about the location of the principal resistances that control water flow from the rhizosphere to the root xylem.

Three major schools of thought have arisen about the location of the principal resistance in this region. The first possibility is that uptake is controlled by a relatively dry soil layer that exists in the rhizosphere under conditions of moderate to high transpiration rates. This dry soil layer with its low hydraulic conductance will allow a steep gradient in water content and water potential to develop around the individual root, if the single-root models of water uptake (Philip, 1957; Gardner, 1960; Cowan, 1965) are correct. Newman (1969a,b) examined the experimental evidence supporting the conclusions that significant rhizosphere resistances exist in the soil near the root-soil interface and concluded that they probably do not occur at field rooting densities and flow rates when the soil is wetter than -0.7 to -4.0 MPa soil matric potential.

Many researchers have attempted to resolve the uncertainty. One attempt was that of Taylor and Klepper (1975), who used cotton grown in the Auburn rhizotron (Taylor, 1969) to examine three assumptions commonly found in root uptake models. Taylor and Klepper (1975) concluded that (1) water uptake was proportional to root length within a soil layer; (2) water uptake was not proportional to soil hydraulic conductivity, but was instead proportional to the hydraulic conductivity of the soil-to-xylem pathway (Fig. 4.5); and (3) water uptake was not proportional to the water potential decrease in the bulk soil, but was proportional to water potential decrease from bulk soil to the root xylem. Taylor and Klepper (1975) also calculated a value for water uptake rate per unit root length per unit potential difference between plant root and bulk soil, q_r'. They found that q_r' linearly increased with soil water content (Fig. 4.6). Taylor and Klepper (1975) were unable to specify whether the principal resistance was at the soil-root interface or in the root tissue, but they concluded that the soil hydraulic conductivity in their experiment did not decrease to the hydraulic conductivity of the soil-root pathway until the soil water potential was about -1.5 MPa. This research has been criticized as being somewhat atypical because the rhizotron compartment was filled with fertile, sieved, sandy topsoil that allowed the greatest possible root exploration. As Hamblin (1985) has pointed out, heterogeneous root distribu-

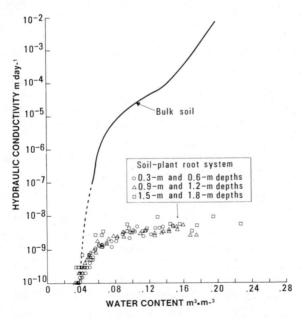

Figure 4.5 A comparison of the hydraulic conductivity of the soil-plant root system at various soil depths and soil water contents with that of a duplicate soil sample. (*Data of Taylor and Klepper, 1975; used with permission.*)

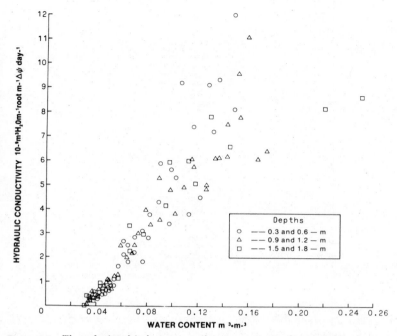

Figure 4.6 The relationship between soil water content of a particular layer and water uptake per centimeter of root per centimeter potential difference per day. (*Data of Taylor and Klepper, 1975; used with permission.*)

tions are more common than homogeneous ones in field soils. These heterogeneous root distributions will tend to cause overlapping rhizospheres, thus increasing the probability that a dry soil zone will occur around the epidermis of some roots.

In addition to the heterogeneous vs. homogeneous rooting argument, the possibility exists that dry soil layers will develop around the particular root lengths that absorb water more rapidly than the average absorption rate. As Sanderson (1983) has shown, the region of barley roots located 40 to 80 mm from the tip absorbs water at three times the rate of water absorption in more mature regions (Fig. 4.7). Most calculations assume uniform absorption rates along the entire length of root. This more rapid absorption rate near the root tip may possibly cause a drier than average soil layer around these rapidly absorbing areas.

The second possibility is that the principal resistance to radial flow of water is at the soil-root interface. In Chap. 2, we discussed the complexities that occur at the soil-root interface in chemical, physical, and microbiological properties. These rhizosphere and rhizoplane properties are so different from the bulk properties of the soil or of the root

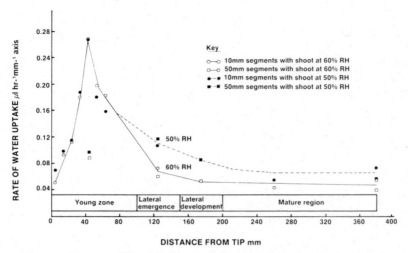

Figure 4.7 The rate of water uptake by intact segments along with the length of the seminal axes of barley, at two humidity regimes, in relation to the development of the endodermis. (*From Sanderson, 1983; used with permission.*)

that it is almost impossible to predict their effects on water transport. However, at high water fluxes, it is entirely possible that a sharp gradient arises across the interface because of these rhizosphere properties, while only a slight gradient is present within the soil itself.

A sharp gradient also might arise at the interface because of soil and root shrinkage as the soil dries. These shrinkages can cause most of the root epidermis to pull away from the soil because roots may shrink to 60 percent of their original diameter as the soil dries to -0.1 MPa (Cole and Alston, 1974; Rowse and Goodman, 1981; Taylor and Willatt, 1983). Faiz and Weatherley (1977) provide some evidence that root shrinkage during drying will alter plant water status. They mechanically shook rapidly transpiring plants and showed that leaf water potential increased if it had decreased below that present at any previous shaking incident. Faiz and Weatherley (1978) compared soil hydraulic resistance from one soil layer to another with soil resistance around the roots and concluded that a gradient of about 0.8 MPa mm^{-1} existed at the interface.

Tinker (1976) examined several mechanisms that might allow sufficient water to cross any shrinkage gap without large drops in water potential. Tinker (1976) stated that (1) mucigel around the roots might act as a cement between one side of a root and the soil, thus maintaining contact; (2) root hairs and mycorrhizae will bridge the gap and might maintain high transport rates; and (3) water vapor might flow to the roots at a sufficient rate to maintain uptake, but with an increased resistance at the air gap. Tinker (1976) concluded that more definitive experiments were necessary before magnitudes of interfacial resistance could be specified for various soil and plant root combinations. The same conclusion is valid today.

The third possibility is that site of the major resistance from bulk soil to root xylem is located within the roots. Plants suffer a diurnal water deficit in their aboveground parts even though their roots are located in wet soil. This deficit is reduced if the plant root system is severed under water so that a major resistance is located somewhere in the soil-root interface to root xylem pathway.

Newman (1976), Läuchli (1976a,b), and Drew (1987) discuss resistances along the pathways shown in Fig. 5.1. These are designated as the apoplastic-endodermis and symplastic pathways. Both apoplastic-endodermis and symplastic pathways potentially are available for water and ion transport. It is widely believed that the two membranes in each cell along a cell-vacuolar pathway provide resistances too great for that pathway to contribute much flux of water or nutrients.

The cell wall portion of the apoplastic-endodermis pathway is a hydrated polysaccharide gel, which consists of water-filled micropores between cellulose microfibrils that are cross-linked with pectin and glycoprotein (Läuchli, 1976a). The apoplast is thought to be freely permeable to water and ions, hence the term *free space* sometimes is used. Weatherley (1982) has calculated that the cell wall conductance of a cortical cell is up to 250 times that of the plasma membrane. Newman (1976) concluded that the apoplastic pathway likely has a greater resistance than the symplastic path. The calculations of Weatherley (1982) and Newman (1976) are very sensitive to the value of hydraulic conductance, which is difficult to measure.

The casparian band of the endodermis is a cell wall feature that blocks the pores between microfibrils. It consists of suberin and possibly lignin. The plasmalemma is tightly bound to the casparian band at this point so water and ions must move through at least one living cell, the endodermis. It seems likely that water and ions move through the symplastic pathway from the endodermis to the xylem.

In many species, the layer of cells immediately below the epidermis produces suberin in the cell walls. This layer of cells is called the hypodermis, or exodermis after suberin is deposited. There is considerable doubt whether the exodermis is as much a block to water and ions as the endodermis. If the exodermis blocks movement, then water and ions enter the symplasm at the exodermis, except for the apical few centimeters of the roots where suberin has not yet been deposited.

In the symplastic pathway, water enters the cytoplasm and then moves from cell to cell through plasmadesmata. It is widely accepted that ions are loaded into the symplasm by a H^+-coupled pump and unloaded by another H^+-coupled pump at the inner plasma membrane of xylem parenchyma cells. However, it is difficult to determine whether ions enter the symplast at the epidermis or whether the cortex acts in some manner as a collection device.

Transport of Water Longitudinally in the Xylem

Water moves along the xylem through a number of xylem vessels with different radii. If these radii are known, an effective radius r_e can be calculated by the following equation:

$$r_e = \left(\sum_1^i r^4 \right)^{1/4} \tag{4.6}$$

This effective radius then is used in the Poiseuille-Hagen equation to calculate longitudinal conductivity of a root. The equation is

$$q_x = \frac{\pi r_e^4 \, \Delta\psi_h}{8\eta \, \Delta L} \tag{4.7}$$

where q_x = rate of water flow, $m^3 \, s^{-1}$
  r = radius of specific xylem element
  $\Delta\psi_h$ = change in hydraulic potential along flow path, m
  L = length of root member, m
  η = viscosity of water, poise
  r_e = theoretical radius of single xylem vessel equivalent to series of vessels in parallel

Longitudinal conductivity also can be measured. Emerson (1954) applied pressure to detached root segments and measured flow rates. Conductivity through timothy roots was 23 times greater than that through orchardgrass. The data of Kozinka and Luxova (1971) indicate that the conductivity of corn roots is about 100 times greater than that of timothy. The real question, however, is whether these differences are significant when compared to other resistances in the flow path. Calculations by Cowan and Milthorpe (1968) indicate that the longitudinal resistance may be important in some crops if distance of travel is greater than about 0.1 m. Calculations by Passioura (1974) showed that a pressure drop as great as 4 MPa m^{-1} of xylem might be required to maintain an average flow rate when only seminal roots are supplying water to wheat tops. Cornish (1981) has shown that longitudinal resistance in the subcrown internode is significant in wheat until the crown root system develops. Data for cotton, however, indicate that longitudinal resistance of cotton roots probably is insignificant, with respect to other resistances in the flow path (Fig. 4.5). Evidence in the literature seems to indicate that longitudinal resistance usually is significant for many grasses when considering the uptake of water from greater than 1 m, but probably is not significant for dicotyledonous crops with secondary xylem.

The probable differences in magnitudes of axial resistance may be the result of secondary xylem being formed in dicots, but the differences also may result from a delayed disappearance of transverse walls in xylem vessels in some grasses.

McCully (1987*a*) has pointed out that many of the ideas prevalent in the literature about root structure have developed from examining the root tips of laboratory-grown seedlings. When she compared corn roots grown in the laboratory with those grown in the field, many of the field-grown roots had a persistent soil sheath while none was present on the laboratory-grown roots. The persistent soil sheaths coincided with the presence of mucilage and curled root hairs while the nonsheathed roots showed no apparent mucilage and the root hairs were straight.

The longitudinal xylem conduits in corn are composed of narrow metaxylem elements which mature early and much wider elements which mature very late (McCully, 1987*b*). These later developing wide elements still have transverse walls 250 and 300 mm from the root tips (Canny, 1987). The disappearance of the soil sheath apparently coincides with the disappearance of the transverse walls in the large metaxylem elements. The longitudinal conductance of soil-sheathed roots was calculated to be on the order of one one-hundredth of that of bare roots (Canny, 1987).

Water Transfer through Roots from Wet to Dry Soil

Water can move from a plant root at high water potential to soil at a lower water potential (Rosene, 1944; Jensen et al., 1961; Thorup, 1969; Baker and Van Bavel, 1986). This fact immediately raises the possibility that a root system can absorb water from a soil zone at a high water potential and deliver the water to a soil zone at a low water potential.

Several reports have demonstrated such a water transport with deep-rooted perennials in arid environments (McWilliam and Kramer, 1968; Mooney et al., 1980; Richards and Caldwell, 1987). Simulation studies have suggested that under certain circumstances, the rates of transfer can be comparable to rates of transpiration (Whisler et al., 1968; Van Bavel et al., 1984).

Baker and Van Bavel (1988) investigated whether plants with partially irrigated root systems could deliver water to unirrigated plants through overlapping root systems. They concluded that water moved through cotton root systems from wet to dry soil.

Baker and Van Bavel (1988) also investigated whether a computer simulation based on a two-dimensional version of WATBAL (Van Bavel et al., 1984), would accurately track the actual water transfer processes. They considered plant hydraulic resistance to be a constant throughout their experiment. The simulation predicted that a point in time should have been reached where water transport through the roots should have been sufficient to replace transpiration losses. Their experimental data showed that water was never transferred at that rate.

At least two reasons exist to explain why the usual simulation model of water uptake does not accurately track experimental data. First, a growing plant does not equilibrate with a very high water potential during an overnight period. This growth-generated potential may be as much as 0.20 and 0.25 MPa (Boyer, 1968; Boyer, 1974). Second, there may be a minimum potential difference that is required for flow into roots as suggested by Passioura and Munns (1984). This would be analogous to the back pressure required to open a float valve. When Baker and Van Bavel (1988) incorporated the concept that a 0.35-MPa minimum potential difference was required for flow in either direction, the WATBAL simulation gave results that were more consistent with their experimental results. There is no morphological or anatomical evidence that suggests such a back pressure mechanism actually exists.

Models of Water Uptake

Many articles have been written describing mathematical models of water uptake. These models usually are classified as "macroscopic" or "microscopic." The macroscopic models consider the vertical transient flow of water in a stable and uniform zone of soil. In the macroscopic models, the root system is a diffuse sink for water that permeates each depth layer uniformly, though not necessarily at the same root length density throughout the root zone. The microscopic models consider the root to be an infinitely long cylinder of uniform radius and water-absorbing properties and water is assumed to move only in the radial direction.

The macroscopic models

The general formula for the one-dimensional flow of water is given in Eq. 4.3. This equation is modified to include a term accounting for extraction by plant roots, for example:

$$\frac{\partial \theta}{\partial t} = \frac{\partial}{\partial z}\left(K_w \frac{\partial H}{\partial z}\right) + A(z, t) \tag{4.8}$$

where $A(z, t)$ is the root extraction term, which is a function of soil depth and time.

Several macroscopic models have been constructed, each varying from the others in specific items, but all include the assumption that $A(z, t)$ is a function of root activity. Often, the models include the explicit assumption that root activity is a function of water potential difference between plant and soil, of distance between the uniformly spaced roots, and of some measure of conductivity in the root-soil system. For example, Nimah and Hanks (1973) defined the root uptake term:

$$A(z, t) = H_{\text{roots}} + [\text{RRES(Z)}] - H(z, t) - S(z, t) \, \text{RDF}(z) \, \frac{K_w}{\Delta x \Delta z} \tag{4.9}$$

where H_{root} = effective water potential in root at $z = 0$

RRES(Z) = root resistance equal to $1 + Rc$ where Rc is a coefficient to account for longitudinal resistance in xylem

$H(z, t)$ = soil matric potential (in weight water potential units)

$S(z, t)$ = soil osmotic potential (in weight water potential units)

RDF(z) = proportion of total active roots in depth increment

K_w = soil hydraulic conductivity at depth Z

Δx = distance between roots at position where $h(z, t)$ and $s(z, t)$ are measured

Δz = depth increment of soil

The macroscopic models disregard flow patterns toward individual roots, thus avoiding the geometrical complications involved in analyzing the distribution of fluxes and potential gradients on a microscale. The major shortcoming of macroscopic models is that they utilize a gross spatial average of matric and osmotic potentials and take no account of the decrease in water potential and of the change in concentration of salts in the soil at the immediate soil-root interface, the rhizosphere.

The microscopic models

The microscopic models usually consider the root to be "an infinitely long cylinder of uniform radius and water-absorbing properties and water is assumed to move only in the radial direction" (Gardner, 1960). These line sinks of uniform properties are uniformly spaced at definable distances in the soil profile and are connected to form a root system.

Under steady conditions, the microscopic models assume that the rate of water uptake per unit length of root $q_r{'}$ from a soil at uniform equilibrium water content can be calculated using a radial flow equation:

$$q_r{'} = -2\pi K_w \frac{H_p - H_s}{\ln (r_{soil}/r_{root})} \tag{4.10}$$

where K_w = soil hydraulic conductivity, a function of water content
$\quad\quad H_p$ = matric head in root epidermis, but by use often is total leaf water potential
$\quad\quad H_s$ = matric head in soil surrounding root
$\quad\quad r_{soil}$ = radius of cylinder of soil surrounding root
$\quad\quad r_{root}$ = radius of root itself

These models contain the assumptions that water uptake per unit length of root is proportional to the soil hydraulic conductivity and to the difference between hydraulic (matric plus gravitational weight water potential) head in the plant and that in the soil. To obtain water uptake by the roots in a specific volume of soil, root length density (meters of roots per cubic meter of soil) is multiplied by q_r. The transpiration rate T, assumed to be equal to uptake rate, is calculated by summing the uptake in all soil layers from the deepest, i, to the soil surface, 1, by using the following equation:

$$T = \sum_i^1 q_{ri}L_{vi} \tag{4.11}$$

Newman (1969a,b) questioned the assumption that the appropriate conductivity term was the soil hydraulic conductivity. Plants undergo a diurnal decrease in leaf water potential even when their roots are placed in aerated nutrient solution. Much of this decrease is alleviated in some plants when the roots are severed. Many experiments have shown that a major impediment to water flow probably occurs at the suberized endodermis. The appropriate hydraulic resistance for the single root models must be a combined resistance determined radially from bulk soil to the xylem elements.

Taylor and Klepper (1975) used the hydraulic conductivity of the combined pathway to determine whether soil water content can be tracked by a modification of the single root model. Using the data shown in Fig. 4.6, they calculated water content by the following equation:

$$\theta_{final} = \theta_{initial} - (q_r')(L_v)(H_p - H_s) \qquad \text{days} \qquad (4.12)$$

where θ_{final} and $\theta_{initial}$ are the volumetric water contents at the end and beginning of a measuring period, and q_r' is the water uptake rate per unit root length per unit head difference per day.

Calculations showed that measured soil water contents were tracked reasonably well by Eq. 4.12 (Fig. 4.8). Taylor and Klepper (1975) claimed that water flow axially must have encountered insignificant resistance in their cotton plants, or soil depth effects would have been apparent in their results.

When the soil solution contains an appreciable concentration of ions, the roots may exclude part of these ions when absorbing water. A detailed study of the simultaneous uptake of water and ions must consider both the hydraulic conductance and the osmotic permeabilities of the various root tissues and flow pathways, especially at the endodermis.

Results from water uptake modeling exercises show that uptake in any particular pot or plot can be tracked fairly successfully using Eq. 4.11 or 4.12. These equations require a value for *specific water uptake rate,* i.e., cubic meters of water extracted from soil by a meter of root length in a second of time. Key questions in modeling water uptake revolve around uncertainties in being able to extrapolate specific water uptake results to other situations.

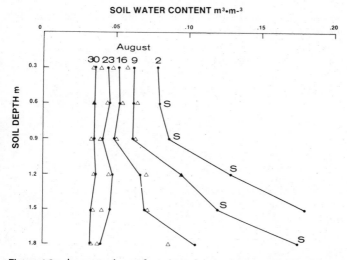

Figure 4.8 A comparison of measured water contents with water contents calculated using Eq. 4.12 (open triangles). The S near a measured water content signifies the starting point for the calculated water content at that depth. (*Data of Taylor and Klepper, 1975; used with permission.*)

One key question is, Can the specific water uptake rate obtained for one species be used to predict with sufficient accuracy the uptake rate for another crop? Some values for uptake rates are listed in Table 4.1. Hamblin (1985) provides specific water uptake rates for lupin and wheat conducted at the same locations and times. Uptake rates from wet soil were 2×10^{-9} and 1×10^{-12} $m^3 m^{-1} s^{-1}$ for lupin and wheat, respectively. Obviously, species differ in their specific water uptake rates when grown under identical conditions.

A second question is, Can specific uptake rates be extrapolated across treatments within the same species? Eavis and Taylor (1979) conducted an experiment where soybeans were subjected to a drying cycle in containers of two sizes. The soybeans had two fertilizer levels and two watering regimes prior to the drying cycle. These treatments created root length to leaf area ratios that ranged from 0.39×10^4 to 1.40×10^4 m of root per square meter of leaf area. Specific water uptake rates were 4.9×10^{-12} and 1.9×10^{-12} $m^3 m^{-1} s^{-1}$, respectively (Fig. 4.9). Intermediate root length to leaf area ratios of the other six treatments also showed decreases in specific uptake rates with increases in the length of roots supplying water to unit leaf areas. These decreases in specific uptake rates occurred without a significant change in leaf water potential. Radin and Eidenbock (1984) showed that the specific water uptake rate of cotton was reduced significantly by either N or P stress (Fig. 4.10). Obviously, specific water uptake

TABLE 4.1 Specific Water Uptake Rates for Some Tropical and Temperate Species as Determined in Various Experiments

Species	References	Water uptake rate, $m^3 m^{-1} s^{-1}$
Cotton	Bar-Yosef and Lambert (1981)	5×10^{-12} to 5×10^{-11}
	Taylor and Klepper (1975)	$< 1 \times 10^{-14}$ to 8×10^{-12}
Field pea	Hamblin (1985)	1×10^{-12} to 2×10^{-11}
Lupin	Hamblin (1985)	3×10^{-12} to 2×10^{-9}
Corn	Allmaras et al. (1975)	3×10^{-12} to 2.4×10^{-10}
	Taylor and Klepper (1973)	1×10^{-12} to 2.4×10^{-11}
Oats	Ehlers et al. (1980)	8×10^{-12} to 1×10^{-10}
Soybean	Allmaras et al. (1975)	2×10^{-11} to 3×10^{-10}
	Willatt and Olsson (1982)	2×10^{-12} to 9×10^{-10}
	Willatt and Taylor (1978)	2.8×10^{-11} to 2.2×10^{-10}
Spring wheat	Greacen and Hignett (1976)	1×10^{-12} to 2×10^{-12}
	Hamblin (1985)	4×10^{-13} to 1×10^{-12}
Temperate grasses	Welbank et al. (1974)	About 1×10^{-12}
Winter wheat	Gregory et al. (1978)	2×10^{-13} to 2×10^{-12}

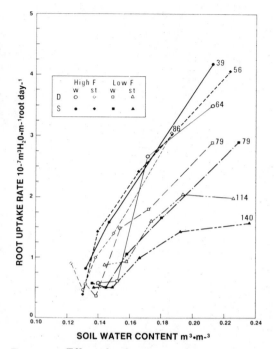

Figure 4.9 Effect of soil water content on the apparent root uptake rate. Numerals near the data trend lines are the root length to leaf area ratios (meters of roots per square meters of leaf area). D and S are deep and shallow containers. W and st are watered and stressed; High F and Low F are high and low fertility pretreatments, respectively.

rates cannot be extrapolated across treatments for a particular cultivar.

A third question is, Does specific root uptake rate vary with the aerial environment of the plant? Bunce (1978) determined the relationship between the specific root uptake rate and leaf water potential for soybean plants 1 and 3 h after uptake became constant when the photon flux was 500 microeinsteins (μE) m^{-2} s^{-1} and after 3 h when the photon flux was 1500 μE m^{-2} s^{-1}. There were large differences in leaf water potential at specific root uptake rates among the three treatments (Fig. 4.11). One hour was not sufficient time for steady-state conditions to be established. In the field, radiation intensity is never constant for long periods so steady-state conditions never prevail during daylight hours. Specific root uptake rates are time-dependent.

Answers to these three key questions indicate that root uptake mod-

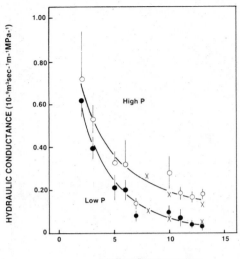

Figure 4.10 Hydraulic conductances of excised root systems. Seedling plants were transferred to nutrient solutions containing 9.5 mM (high) or zero (low) P. Values shown are means ± SE of four replicates. The X symbols indicate estimates of hydraulic conductance from intact transpiring plants. (*After Radin and Eidenbock, 1984; used with permission.*)

els must be calibrated for the specific location, crop species, and time. The great need now is for greater experimental validation of the existing models, not for more sophistication in the models, and for greater simplification, not for greater complexity.

The articles by Gardner (1960, 1964, 1965, 1973), Gardner and Ehlig (1962, 1963), and Gardner and Nieman (1966) have provided the basis for many other articles on modeling water uptake by root systems. However, Gardner (1983) proposed that a simplified model probably was sufficiently accurate to be useful for describing uptake in many field studies. Gardner (1983) observed (1) that transpiration rate seems to be relatively unaffected by soil water content (Fig. 4.12) or soil water potential over a considerable range, and (2) that, starting with a uniformly wet soil profile, water is first extracted from the region nearest the surface with the zone of maximum extraction proceeding downward through the profile with time (Fig. 4.13). Gardner normalized all the curves of water extraction from drying soil by assuming that the maximum amount of extraction occurs in the surface, that 50 percent of surface extraction would occur at 50 percent of the

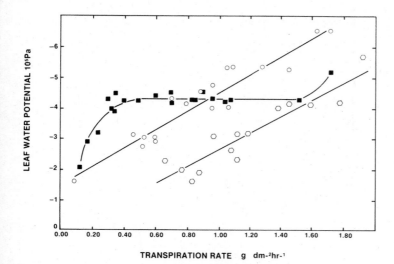

Figure 4.11   Dependence of leaf water potential on transpiration in soybean: ■, leaf water potential measured after transpiration became constant, 500 μE m^{-2} s^{-1}; ○, 3 or more hours after transpiration became constant, 500 μE m^{-2} s^{-1}; ○, or more hours after transpiration became constant, 1500 μE m^{-2} s^{-1}. Transpiration is per unit root surface area; average leaf (one side) to root (total) surface area was 0.8:1.0. (*After Bunce, 1978; used with permission.*)

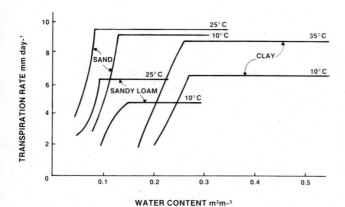

Figure 4.12   Transpiration rate as a function of soil water content for bird's-foot trefoil in three different soils at two different room temperatures. (*From Gardner, 1983; used with permission.*)

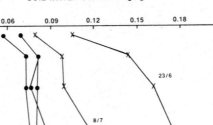

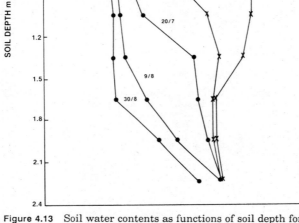

Figure 4.13 Soil water contents as functions of soil depth for soybeans grown at Castana, Iowa, in 0.25-m row widths during the 1976 growing season. (*For experimental details, see Taylor, 1980.*)

rooting depth, and that extraction was negligible at depths greater than 80 percent of the depth to which roots were observed.

Some water is extracted by roots deeper than that predicted by Gardner (1983), especially in soils where roots can ramify thoroughly the subsoil layers. Data from some 40 experiments show that Gardner's (1983) analysis is reasonably correct (Fig. 4.14). In those situations, 40 percent of the extraction occurs in the upper 20 percent of the profile, then 33, 20, and 7 percent from successive layers. As stated before, his model predicts that no extraction occurs below 80 percent of the rooting depth. He acknowledges that some, but not much, extraction occurs below that depth.

Another possibility exists for simplifying water uptake models without sacrificing their utility in predicting extraction among soil layers. Nimah and Hanks (1973) partitioned total rooting into fractions that occurred within each soil layer. Because of the large differences in

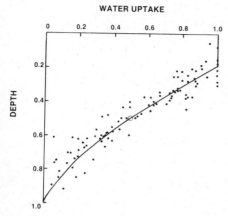

Figure 4.14 Normalized water uptake curves for 40 different experiments. Data for day of first wilt, as estimated. (*From Gardner, 1983.*)

root length that can occur at equal transpiration rates, the relative root length or relative root mass technique seems about as satisfactory as the absolute values for partitioning root uptake. Relative root length can be determined more easily than absolute root lengths, using the core-break (Böhm, 1979) or minirhizotron (Upchurch and Ritchie, 1984) techniques.

A second simplifying technique is to use soil water content directly in the model rather than soil water potential and soil hydraulic conductivity, because both are functions of soil water content.

When these two simplifications are made, water content can be tracked by assuming that uptake from any layer is a function of relative root length (or mass) multiplied by the fraction of available soil water that is present in the rooted profile. This technique should be able to partition water uptake among soil layers across locations, times, and cultivars accurately enough for most purposes.

Uptake of Ions by Plant Roots

Mechanisms of Mineral Nutrient Uptake

Overview of nutrient acquisition

Mineral nutrient elements required by plants enter entirely or predominantly via roots, and generally as ions. Each essential element must be taken up in an amount equal to or above the minimum needed to produce the amount of biomass that the conditions of growth allow. Other elements not now recognized as essential may also enter if present in the vicinity of an active root.

Acquisition of essential mineral nutrients by plants growing in soil depends upon plant and soil factors. Routes for entry of these nutrients into root cells must be available. Plant root uptake mechanisms restrict and select ions taken up to some degree, but this regulation is not absolute. Various reactions and processes in soils determine the accessibility of nutrients for root uptake. Plant nutrient availability as used here refers to nutrients present in the soil solution and those readily dissolved or desorbed from the solid phase. Access to nutrients may be achieved by roots proliferating through the soil, and possibly by "contact exchange" as discussed in Chap. 3, but generally for most nutrient uptake, mechanisms of transport to the roots are involved in meeting growth needs.

Discussed in this chapter are basic concepts of nutrient uptake mechanisms in plant roots, and the parameters needed to develop mathematical expressions for nutrient flux into roots. Nutrient acquisition is assumed to be governed primarily by external nutrient concentrations and processes of nutrient transport in the soil. In Chap. 6, growth will be considered both as a response to soil nutrient supply and as a regulator of nutrient acquisition. Shoot physiological processes and reactions in which mineral nutrients are involved, such as in energy metabolism, protein biosynthesis, and internal transport, may affect plant growth rates, and thus influence nutrient acquisition.

Some mineral nutrients, for example, K, remain in the ionic form in which they are absorbed and as such serve vital functions. Others, including N and S, may undergo chemical changes in roots and shoots and, in part at least, become incorporated into more complex forms such as proteins. These can serve vital physiological functions as in enzymes for example, or become part of storage pools.

Soil physical, chemical, and biological characteristics and processes determining the portion of the nutrient supply present in soluble forms, or converted from insoluble forms, were discussed in Chap. 3. Nutrient acquisition also involves rates of solubilization relative to root growth and mycorrhizal development, interactions between various ion species, and pathways and rates of movement through soil pore spaces.

Renewed interest in ion uptake by plants has been stimulated by the availability of better analytical techniques and by concerns regarding possible food chain and environmental impacts resulting from high rates of additions of chemicals during fertilization or waste disposal. This renewed interest has helped progress toward gaining a better understanding of the mechanisms involved in the soil-plant relationships of mineral nutrition. Many unanswered questions remain, however, particularly regarding the quantitative aspects of nutrient uptake, and the reasons for differences in uptake between and within species.

Nutrient flux and nutrient demand

An expression to describe the relationship between the solution concentration c_l of a given nutrient and its uptake by plant roots in contact with the solution was proposed by Bouldin (1961) and further developed by Nye (1966):

$$J = \alpha c_l \tag{5.1}$$

where J is the rate of uptake (flux) expressed in terms of quantity per unit root area per unit time, and α, the proportionality term, expresses the "root absorbing power." The applicability of Eq. 5.1 as a basis for quantitatively describing uptake of a plant nutrient requires that α does not vary greatly, and that c_l is below the concentration where the flux is at its maximal value.

In terms of uptake per unit root length rather than root area,

$$J = 2\pi \alpha r c_l \tag{5.2}$$

where r is the root radius. The terms α and r combined, $\overline{\alpha r}$, are called the *root demand coefficient* (Nye and Tinker, 1969). For expressing total uptake by an intact plant, a term for the total length L of the entire root system is added to the right-hand side of Eq. 5.2:

$$J = 2\pi\alpha r c_i L \tag{5.3}$$

The J term then has units of quantity per unit of time, and r has units of length per time.

The soil and plant factors affecting $\overline{\alpha r}$ need to be identified and evaluated in order to develop a more testable expression. These factors include (1) the nutrient demands for plant growth, (2) the operation of metabolically driven uptake and transport mechanisms, and (3) the functioning of physical and chemical processes in the root environment. These variables are not independent. Thus, the basis for the essentiality of certain mineral nutrients for growth is to play a role in the operation of uptake and transport mechanisms, as for example to serve as an activator or a structural component of an enzyme catalyzing some physiological reaction. Mechanisms by which mineral nutrients are absorbed by plant roots will be discussed before further consideration of some expressions for quantitatively describing nutrient uptake.

Mineral nutrients, generally as soluble ions but in some cases as molecules, enter plant root cell walls and intercellular spaces through mass flow generated by transpiration. This movement (apoplastic pathway) toward the conducting elements in the interior of the root can proceed until some barrier to nutrient transport is encountered, as shown in Fig. 5.1. One obstruction is the casparian strip, which forms at some variable distance back from the root tip. In corn, for example,

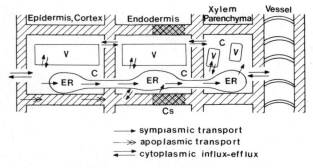

Figure 5.1 Schematic model of ion transport through a plant root: C = cytoplasm; V = vacuole; ER = endoplasmic reticulum; Cs = casparian strip. (*Reproduced from A. Laüchli, "Symplasmic transport and ion release to the xylem," in Transport and Transfer Processes in Plants, edited by I. F. Wardlaw and J. B. Passiora, pages 101–115, by permission of the author and Academic Press.*)

it begins at 13 to 16 mm from the tip (Dupont and Leonard, 1977). At very best, the casparian strip may be only slowly permeable to nutrient ions. Other structures located in the hypodermis and resembling the casparian strip may also interfere with ion movement (Drew, 1987).

Some apoplastic movement of ions via diffusional processes may also occur. Gradients favorable for this kind of transfer could result from the presence of a "sink" for the ion involved. Possibilities include becoming bound in a more complex form with a lowering of chemical activity, a buildup at some barrier selectively preventing passage of certain ions, and assimilation. The operation of mass flow and diffusion in nutrient acquisition will be considered in more detail later when mechanistic models relating ion uptake to plant and soil parameters are discussed.

Besides the apoplastic pathway, another route for the passage of mineral nutrients to the conducting vessels is through the plasmalemma into the cytoplasm, and then cell-to-cell movement through the plasmadesmata (symplastic pathway) (Fig. 5.1). Generally, for plants growing in soil, this kind of movement means overcoming an unfavorable ionic concentration (activity) gradient or creating a favorable electrochemical gradient. Either way, expenditure of metabolic energy (active transport) must occur. Two concepts, not entirely unrelated, have been proposed to explain the operation of metabolically driven ion uptake mechanisms in higher plants. One invokes the operation of a "carrier" (Epstein and Hagen, 1952), the other proposes the presence of "ion pumps" (Higinbotham, 1964).

The carrier uptake hypothesis

According to the carrier theory, ions become complexed with special molecules (carriers) on the plasma membrane surface, and the complex becomes activated by energy from ATP as it moves through the membrane. Inside the cell, the ion is freed from the complex and released into the cytosol, with energy being provided from conversion of ATP to ADP through action of ATPase. No specific membrane components have yet been identified as carriers, but uptake studies indicate that there are different kinds present in plasma membranes and that each kind complexes with only one ion species or chemically very similar ions. Thus, the relationship of K flux for excised barley roots to external K concentration is not affected by the presence of Na (Fig. 5.2). This kind of selectivity, in this case an inability of Na to compete with K in uptake, is an important attribute of plant nutrient uptake mechanisms, and functions only in the presence of an adequate level of Ca. Sodium efflux may contribute to the apparent preference for uptake of K (Läuchli and Pflüger, 1979). Regulation of K/Na ratios has

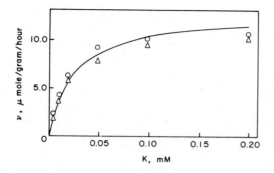

Figure 5.2 Rate v of absorption of K by barley roots from solutions differing in K concentrations, and with no Na added (○), or added as 0.50-mM NaCl (Δ). (*Reproduced from E. Epstein, Mineral Nutrition of Plants, 1972, page 126, by permission of John Wiley and Sons, Inc.*)

been suggested as an important aspect of incorporation of ammoniacal N into protein in young barley plants grown in salinized nutrient solutions (Helal and Mengel, 1979).

Epstein and Hagen visualized carrier-mediated transport as analogous to enzyme-mediated catalysis, with the flux J of the species absorbed described by Michaelis-Menten kinetics:

$$J = \frac{J_{\max}c_l}{K_m + c_l} \tag{5.4}$$

where $J_{\max}$ = maximal influx

c_l = the concentration of the absorbed species in the external solution

K_m = is the Michaelis-Menten constant

For the derivation of Eq. 5.4, see the Appendix at the end of this chapter. As indicated in the derivation, K_m is the concentration at which the reaction proceeds at one-half the maximum uptake rate. Low values of K_m indicate a strong affinity of the carrier for the ion being absorbed.

Evaluating the effects of treatments on the K_m and $J_{\max}$ terms in Eq. 5.4 reveals insights regarding the physiology of nutrient uptake mechanisms. The techniques used in the evaluation must be well-defined and the conditions well-controlled in order to obtain reproducible results. Nutrient uptake characteristics of plant roots and the magnitudes of K_m and $J_{\max}$ change with time, as they are influenced by physiological processes occurring during plant development and by the external environment. Obtaining the kind of data needed to construct the plot shown in Fig. 5.2 and to interpret the response physiologically requires relatively short periods of exposure of plant tissue, in this case excised roots, to the nutrient solution. The use of radioisotopes as tracers makes it possible to distinguish the amounts of nutrient taken up during short time periods. The isotope must be amenable to analysis with the required accuracy and have a decay rate sufficiently slow so that uptake can be determined for a reasonable period of time. For studying uptake of K, use of its isotope ^{42}K is limited because of its short, 12.4-h, half-life. Thus ^{86}Rb, which is absorbed similarly to K, is used as a surrogate for K in uptake studies. During the test period in uptake experiments, nutrient concentrations must be maintained at a constant level.

The results of many experiments showing that ion flux is sensitive to temperature and aeration indicate that the uptake mechanism is active, i.e., dependent upon metabolic energy (Epstein, 1972). Some caution should be exercised, however, in interpreting temperature responses. Although Q_{10} values greater than 1.5 have been interpreted as indicating active metabolic processes, cases in which passive processes having similar higher values have been observed (Clarkson, 1976). A decreased uptake in the presence of respiration inhibitors has also been offered as evidence of the coupling to plant energetics. These chemicals, however, can have other effects, such as adversely affecting the movement of water (Pitman et al.,1981) and influencing membrane permeability (Jackson, 1982).

The mechanism of nutrient uptake that is described by Michaelis-Menten kinetics and that saturates at relatively low nutrient concentrations, as shown in Fig. 5.2, has been referred to as *mechanism I,* to distinguish it from other mechanisms functioning at higher (>1-mM) nutrient concentrations (Epstein, 1972). At the higher concentrations a saturating type of uptake mechanism (*mechanism II*) was also indicated. In studies using excised corn roots, Kochian and Lucas (1982) found a linear relationship between K flux and nutrient solution K concentrations greater than 1 mM. They concluded from their results that this linear type of uptake mechanism also functions at lower concentrations, but the contribution of the saturable component to uptake is greater.

Evaluating the magnitudes of K_m and J_{max} has also been used in the search for plant varieties or strains that are most efficient in nutrient acquisition. Using intact seedlings of 10 Canadian barley cultivars, Glass and Perley (1980) found that their ranking of low to high values of both K_m and J_{max} depended upon the level of K used in the nutrient solution in which the plants were grown. At the lower K level, values of K_m ranged from 10.9 to 24.1 μM, but when the K level was increased by 5 mM, the range was from 56 to 188 μM. The K_m values reported for corn in the studies reviewed by Barber (1984) are comparable to the lower range of values found by Glass and Perley (1980).

Values of K_m comparable to those found by Glass and Perley (1980) for K were found for NO_3–N uptake by three cultivars and two accessions of barley (Bloom, 1985). With NH_4–N, the K_m was slightly greater for one cultivar, but for the others the value was comparable or much lower than with NO_3^- as the N source. A continuous flow culture system with nutrient concentrations and pH maintained by continuous monitoring and adjusting, and with close temperature control was used.

Conditions during uptake may have both qualitative and quantitative effects on nutrient acquisition by plants and thus influence K_m values. Since energy is required for moving nutrients against concentration gradients, rates of nutrient uptake and internal transport mechanisms are influenced by temperature differences (Clarkson and Warner, 1979). These influences may involve more than the generally recognized effects of temperature change on the rates of biological reactions. The structure of membrane components and thus their permeability respond to differences in temperature regimes (Drew, 1987). Results of electron paramagnetic resonance measurements with plasma membrane–enriched microsome preparations from barley roots indicated very abrupt changes in lipid and protein mobilities at 12 to 14°C (Caldwell and Whitman, 1987). Modifications in membrane lipid structures were suggested. At about this same temperature, a marked change in the relationship between the temperature and rate of transport of NH_4^+ by roots of Italian ryegrass has been observed (Clarkson and Warner, 1979).

Values of K_m may be quite different if determined with plants growing in solutions maintained at as near a constant concentration as possible, or in solutions in which the nutrient of interest is not replenished during the test period. For both perennial ryegrass and radish, K uptake K_m values were below 1 μM with the K concentration held constant, but 15 to 20 μM with K depletion (Wild et al., 1979).

The functioning of carrier mechanisms has also been indicated in anion transport. Leggett and Epstein (1956) found that SO_4^{2-} and SeO_4^{2-} are competitive in their uptake by excised barley roots, indicating that they are transported with the same carrier. Lowering of plant Se concentrations associated with yield responses resulting from increases in S supply may be from dilution effects (Westermann and Robbins, 1974).

The behavior of NO_3^- in its uptake by plants, as related to selectivity, respiration, and Michaelis-Menten parameters, also indicates the likelihood of transport as proposed by the carrier model (Huffaker and Rains, 1978). Uptake of NO_3–N by a corn root preparation enriched in tonoplast and/or endoplasmic reticulum membrane vesicles induced synthesis of a 40-kilodalton polypeptide (McClure et al., 1987). The possibility of such cell components serving as ion carriers needs further investigation. Improved techniques for determining compartmentation of NO_3^- in plant cells are needed, so that intracellular transport can be more quantitatively defined (Clarkson, 1985).

In considering uptake mechanisms by roots growing in soils, differences in the functioning of uptake mechanisms in cells at different sites in the root must be taken into account. Differences in both the longitudinal (see review by Lüttge, 1983) and radial (Läuchli et al., 1971) dimensions have been described, so conditions in different zones of the soil profile can influence nutrient acquisition.

Ion pumps

Ion pumps provide another mechanism aiding the transport of ions from the soil solution through plant root cell membranes. Some features of this mechanism are similar to the carrier-type mechanism, but its operation is explained in thermodynamic terms. The difference between the carrier and ion pump concepts can be illustrated by using nutrient uptake from a relatively simple system as an example: A metabolically active root in a solution of K_2SO_4, with the K concentration <1 mM. Visualized as proposed by the carrier hypothesis, K moves into the cytosol of root epidermal or cortical cells in consort with a carrier molecule. Because generally SO_4^{2-} enters more slowly than K, in order for electrical neutrality to be maintained in the external solution, positively charged ions in amounts chemically equivalent to the entry of the excess of K^+ over SO_4^{2-} move out of the cells. These positively charged ions could be protons, and thus the pH of the external solution would tend to decrease.

An alternative view of the uptake mechanism with the single salt system is that proton efflux accounts for the entry of K, rather than being a consequence of a system favoring the entry of K over SO_4. Such an efflux mechanism for accomplishing ion uptake is called an electrogenic pump, since transfer of a net charge across the plasmalemma results in a negative charge inside the cell. For the simple single salt system being considered, the magnitude of the electrochemical potential difference (EPD) between K in the cytosol and in the external solution can be calculated from the Nernst equation:

$$E_K = \frac{RT}{zF} \ln \frac{a_K}{a_K'} \tag{5.5}$$

where E_K = EPD of K in cytoplasm and in external solution
R, F = gas and Faraday constants, respectively
z = valence of K
a_K and a_K' = activities of K outside and inside cytoplasm, respectively

If the entry of K into the cell is metabolically driven (active transport), then the measured membrane potential E_m will be more negative than the value of E_K calculated from Eq. 5.5. In common with ion uptake via carriers, proton pumps also are visualized as being powered by energy from ATP (Leonard, 1984).

How energy is transduced to power uptake mechanisms is not clear, however. In in vitro studies, K^+ stimulates plasma membrane ATPase activity, but the relevance of this observation to uptake mechanisms in vivo is uncertain because of the magnitude of the response and the levels of K^+ required (Briskin, 1986). The stimulating action of K^+ may be specific for H^+–transporting ATPase, and involve K^+–H^+ exchange. A more detailed knowledge of the mechanism would help to understand the effects of pH and the role of Ca on nutrient acquisition.

Roots of plants growing in soil are in contact with a solution containing a wide array of different ions, not a single salt like K_2SO_4. Expressions much more complex than the Nernst equation would thus be necessary to calculate EPD values. Parameters taking account of differences in the propensities of ions to permeate membranes would have to be included in designing a model as a basis for calculating uptake. A modified Goldman equation has been proposed (Lüttge and Higinbotham, 1979; Pitman, 1982).

Two modes of anion entry might function in conjunction with the ion pump mechanism. Anions could accompany protons being pumped across a membrane (symport), or anions in one cell or compartment could exchange for anions of another species in an adjacent cell or compartment, passing through the membrane separating them.

The relationships between the concentration of nutrients and their uptake by plant roots in the presence of a solid phase may be quite different than uptake from solution alone. Potassium concentrations needed in sand culture solutions to obtain maximum growth by four plant species were found to be more than 100 times greater than those needed with a flowing solution culture system (Wild et al., 1974). In the sand culture system and in soil, nutrient flux is more likely to be limited by diffusional processes.

Effects of Nutrient Uptake on the Rhizosphere Environment

The uptake of ions influences the environment of the root-soil interface. Protons exiting the cytoplasm, either in exchange for entering cations or through the operation of an ion pump, decrease the external pH; the magnitude of the decrease depends upon the soil buffering capacity and the presence of neutralizing ions. Similarly, anion influx in conjunction with OH^- or HCO_3^- efflux tends to increase the pH. Since both of these events are occurring when plants are growing, the direction and magnitude of pH changes at sites of uptake depend upon the relative rates at which cations and anions are being absorbed and the ions H^+, OH^-, and HCO_3^- are being excreted.

Differences between nitrate and ammoniacal fertilizers in their effects on soil pH have been recognized for many years (Pierre, 1928). For example, after growing a crop of oats in containers with a sandy loam soil, the pH of the unfertilized soil was 5.35, while that fertilized with ammonium sulfate or calcium nitrate was 4.45 and 5.60, respectively. The acidity produced with the ammoniacal N was attributed to chemical reactions and nitrification. The higher pH with the nitrate source was attributed to a more rapid uptake of the anion than its associated cation and to the exchange with bicarbonate from the roots. In interpreting the results of more recent similar studies, greater emphasis was placed on the role of ion uptake in producing acidity in the external environment (Pierre et al., 1970). The amounts of $CaCO_3$ needed to neutralize the acidity in soils which were fertilized with ammonium nitrate and cropped were related to greater absorption of inorganic cations than inorganic anions (excluding nitrate). The magnitude of HCO_3^- accumulation and pH increase at the surface of soybean roots was related to the concentration of NO_3^- in the soil solution (Riley and Barber, 1969).

Results from studies using solution cultures have shown that the uptake of ammoniacal N results in acidification, even if the amount of nitrification is nil. For example, the growth of two tomato plants in 7 L of a solution with an initial level of 5 mmol of NH_4–N^{-1} and a pH of 5.5, decreased the pH by about 1 unit (mean of six replicate treatments) in about 3 days (Kirkby and Mengel, 1967). Using flowing culture techniques, Reisenauer et al. (1982) found that the proton release I_H from the roots of perennial ryegrass (cv. 'S23') was closely related to the uptake of NH_4^+ (I_{NH_4}) as indicated in the expression

$$I_H = -38 - 1.1(I_{NH_4}) \tag{5.6}$$

Rates of uptake of N ranged from 200 to 300 μmol (g dry matter)$^{-1}$ day^{-1}. Assuming an NH_4–N uptake of 0.56 g m^{-2} day^{-1}, the estimated proton release rate is slightly greater than 0.1 mmol of H^+ per kilogram per day.

Changes in soil pH associated with differential cation-anion uptake rates are of course greater at the soil-plant root interface than in the bulk soil of the root zone. Differences of up to 2.2 pH units were found between soils in the rhizospheres of 3-week-old wheat plants grown in the greenhouse in soils to which ammonium sulfate plus N-Serve or calcium nitrate were applied (Smiley, 1974). Differences in effects of the two N sources on rhizosphere soil pH were also found in field studies, but the magnitudes were less. The rhizosphere pH of conifer seedlings grown in containers to which 400 mg of NH_4–N per kilogram was added decreased 0.7 units during a 24-week period of growth, while the pH values for seedlings provided NO_3–N increased 1.2 units (Rollwagen and Zasoski, 1988). Similar trends in the effects of N on the pH of rhizosphere soil were also found in a 40-year-old stand of Douglas fir to which the two N sources had been applied. Concentrations of soluble soil Ca will influence the severity of adverse growth effects associated with the acidity resulting from the predominant uptake of NH_4–N (Taylor et al., 1985).

Rhizosphere pH measurements are made by analyzing the soil held by the roots after their careful removal from the growing medium. More direct measurements of the nature of the rhizosphere can now be made in situ with miniature electrodes. Using this technique, Blanchar and Lipton (1986) found differences of more than 2.5 units in the pH of main and lateral roots on the same alfalfa seedling.

Nye (1981) has proposed the following expression for predicting the time-course and magnitude of pH changes around plant roots in relation to various soil parameters, and assuming H_3O^+–H_2O and H_2CO_3–HCO_3^- are the dominant mobile acid-base components in the soil system:

$$\frac{\partial pH}{\partial t} = \frac{\partial}{\partial x}\left(D_{HS}\frac{dpH}{dx}\right) \tag{5.7}$$

where D_{HS} is the soil acidity diffusion coefficient, calculated as follows:

$$D_{HS} = \frac{2.303\phi f}{b_{HS}}(D_{LH}[H_3O^+] + D_{LC}[HCO_3^-]) \tag{5.8}$$

where
ϕ = volumetric water content
f = diffusion impedance factor
D_{LH}, D_{LC} = diffusion coefficients of H_3O^+ and HCO_3^-, respectively, in free solution
b_{HS} = soil pH buffer power $[-\ d(HS)/dpH]$
HS = soil acid

Calculations based on these equations show that the extent of change in rhizosphere soil pH resulting from proton flux from plant roots depends upon the initial pH at the soil-root interface (Fig. 5.3).

Some dicotyledonous plants growing under conditions of Fe stress have mechanisms that make it possible to alter their rhizosphere pH and hence create conditions which may be more favorable for Fe uptake. Marked differences are shown within as well as between species

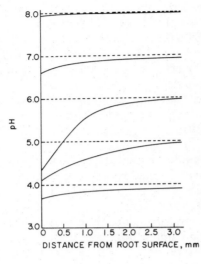

Figure 5.3 Effect of initial soil pH on pH profiles following release of H^+ from a root ($r = 0.02$ cm) surface for 10^6 s, and with $P_{CO_2} = 0.01$ atm [$\phi = 0.2$, $f = 0.1$, $b_{HS} = 11$ μmol mL^{-1} (pH unit)$^{-1}$]. (*Reproduced from P. H. Nye, "pH changes and phosphate solubilization near roots—an example of coupled diffusion processes," in Roots, Nutrient and Water Influx, and Plant Growth, ASA Special Publication no. 49, 1984, edited by S. A. Barber and D. R. Bouldin, pages 89–100, by permission of the Soil Science Society of America, Inc.*)

in this regard. In a comparison of several genotypes, including both monocots and dicots, only one, a tomato genotype (T3238 FER), considered Fe-efficient because it did not become chlorotic when grown in soil, released significant amounts of H^+ into the solution in which it was grown (Olsen and Brown, 1980). An Fe-inefficient tomato genotype did not alter the solution pH, nor did either Fe-efficient or Fe-inefficient genotypes of soybeans, oats, or corn. Plant responses to Fe stress may also involve internal changes that influence Fe translocation (Clarkson, 1981).

Römheld et al. (1984) showed that the acidity of the nutrient solution in which sunflower plants were grown was increased at low levels of Fe in the nutrient solution. Effects of ATPase inhibitors indicated that the pH decrease was related to proton efflux. The degree of acidification associated with Fe deficiency exceeded that induced by the preferential cation uptake from K_2SO_4, or by the presence of fusicoccin. Proton efflux was greatest (28 μmol per gram of fresh water per hour) from the apical zones of the roots. Assuming that the density of fresh roots is unity and that their average radius is 0.02 cm, H^+ efflux from the root apex would equal 1.6×10^{-6} μmol cm^{-2} s^{-1}. This value is comparable to that used in calculating the data for plotting Fig. 5.3. Proton extrusion by bean (var. 'Prelude') plants is aided by an increased production of organic acids induced by Fe deficiency (DeVos, 1986).

The effects of nutrient uptake on the pH of the rhizosphere have important implications in plant nutrition. Lowering soil pH may adversely affect P absorption by enhancing the activity of the soil components which influence P solubility (Chap. 3). More direct effects of acidity on P nutrition have been shown using solution culture. The response in the growth of wheat seedlings to changes in solution pH were different if the level of P was in the range of concentrations (1 to 10 μM) generally found in soils, or at 100- to 1000-μM levels (Webb and Loneragan, 1985). Greater acidification around clustered densely branched (proteoid) roots of P-deficient than P-adequate white lupin plants has been noted (Römheld and Marschner, 1986). Secretion of citrate is involved in this response (Gardner et al., 1983).

Plant root activity other than proton extrusion may also result in changes in the rhizosphere and influence nutrient uptake. An increased activity of a NADPH-dependent reductase and the release of chelating substances (phytosiderophores) from plant roots have been demonstrated under conditions of Fe stress (Römheld and Marschner, 1986). Functioning of this kind of chelation mechanism is more common in monocots than dicots. Sections of barley roots 1 to 4 cm from the tip are more active in absorbing and translocating Fe than other parts of the root system (Clarkson and Sanderson, 1978). Soils in which corn or wheat were grown were much more effective in complexing Co and Zn than soils from fallowed areas (Merckx et al., 1986). Less Mn was complexed than Co or Zn. The presence of mycorrhizae may have a very significant influence on the acquisition of nutrients by plants (Raju et al., 1987).

Nutrient Uptake Models

Basic concepts for modeling nutrient uptake from soils

Various soil and plant factors need to be evaluated in order to describe nutrient uptake quantitatively. Besides the need for accurate measurements of these factors is the need to consider how they interact with each other. The capability of evaluating the interactions involved has been enhanced considerably with the use of computers and improved analytical techniques. These technological advances make it possible to more readily test models describing nutrient acquisition, and thus to help identify and quantify appropriate parameters needed to express the relationships involved mathematically.

Much attention has been recently focused on the processes involved in the movement of nutrients in soil systems, with regards both to soil-plant relationships and possible impacts on the environment. The view that nutrient transfer processes deserved greater consideration in mineral nutrition studies was expressed by Roger Bray (1954): "The mobility of nutrients in soils is one of the most important single factors in soil fertility relationships. The term 'mobility', as used here, means the overall process whereby nutrient ions reach sorbing root surfaces, thereby making possible their sorption into the plant. Thus the term involves the solution or exchange of the nutrient as well as its movement to the root surfaces. A correlative process, just as important, is the growth of the roots and the extension of the root surfaces into areas where the nutrients occur. These two processes, complementing each other, largely determine the soil fertility requirements of a plant."

A mathematical statement relating nutrient acquisition to specific soil physical processes and root activity was proposed by Barber (1962). Included in the expression were terms for concentration gradients (relative to the linear distance from the root surface), diffusion coefficients of ions in solution and on particle surfaces, and the concentrations and rates of mass flow of ions in the soil solution moving toward the root. Also included was a fraction designated as a "replenishment factor." The results of many studies providing the basis for designing models that could be tested experimentally, and aid in identifying important plant and soil characteristics influencing nutrient acquisition, are described by Barber (1984).

From published data, comparisons were made between the amounts of various mineral elements in crops with the sum of the amounts that might be brought to the roots by a mass flow of water (with contained solutes) needed for crop transpirational needs, plus the nutrients present in that portion of the soil solution directly contacted by roots as they grew through the soil (root interception). The large fraction of the needs of crops for some mineral nutrients, in particular P and K, not accounted for by mass flow and root interception, was attributed to diffusional processes. A similar conclusion with regard to P uptake had been drawn earlier by Bouldin (1961).

For some ions, e.g., Ca, the levels commonly occurring in the soil solution were such that more than enough to meet plant needs would be delivered by mass flow, and the concentrations near the root surface could exceed those in the bulk soil solution. That these kinds of responses actually occurred was verified by the use of radioactive tracer techniques. Accumulation or depletion of isotopically labeled nutrient elements around the roots was visualized by exposing the root zone to x-ray film after a period of uptake. In interpreting such observations, however, consideration should be given to the possibility of other contributing factors. For example, changes in pH at the soil-plant root interface might account for at least some of the accumulation of Ca attributed to mass flow.

One model proposed to express the effects of soil processes on nutrient acquisition by plants relates external nutrient concentrations to nutrient uptake rates using Michaelis-Menten kinetics (Nye and Marriott, 1969).

The Nye-Marriott model

To construct this model it was assumed that nutrients are transported to plant roots by diffusive and convective (mass flow) processes. A section of root with a uniform diameter, and serving as a water and nutrient sink, was visualized as being encased by an imaginary coaxial cylinder containing water and nutrients. Assuming conservation of water and solutes in the system, changes in their rates of transport (flux) out of the cylinder and into the root, and the resulting change in nutrient concentration around it, could be expressed in mathematical terms. Contributions to the total flux were assumed to be from mass flow (the product of the nutrient concentration in the soil solution and the quantity of water absorbed to meet plant transpirational needs), and from diffusion, calculated from Fick's law. The modified diffusion coefficient D' was used to take into account the geometry, water content, and solid phase characteristics of the soil. The labile fraction of the nutrient supply was assumed to be diffusible. Generally, the rate of flow of the soil solution toward the root is too slow to have appreciable dispersive effects on diffusion and thus was ignored.

Expressed in appropriate parameters, the soil characteristic variables were related to changes in nutrient concentration with time t as shown in Eq. 5.9 (see the Appendix at the end of this chapter for the derivation):

$$\frac{\partial c_l}{\partial t} = \frac{1}{r}\frac{\partial}{\partial r}\left(rD'\frac{\partial c_l}{\partial r} + \frac{r_o v_o c_l}{b}\right) \tag{5.9}$$

where c_l = ion concentration in solution
  r = radius of imaginary coaxial cylinder encasing root
  r_o = radius of root
  D' = apparent diffusion coefficient
  v_o = velocity of flow of soil solution to root
  b = buffer capacity = $(\partial c/\partial r)/(\partial c_l/\partial r)$

The amounts of nutrient supplied by diffusion and mass flow were assumed to equal nutrient flux as described by a modified Michaelis-Menten equation:

$$D'b\frac{\partial c_l}{\partial r} + v_o c_l = \frac{J_{\max}(c_l - c_{\min})}{K_m + (c_l - c_{\min})} \tag{5.10}$$

The external nutrient concentration c_l is corrected for the concentration c_{min} at which influx and efflux are equal. This correction is important for nutrients such as P which are present, relative to plant needs, at very low levels in soil solutions. For various crops, c_{min} ranges from 0.04 to 0.24 μM P (Barber, 1984). Using ^{32}P and solution concentrations (< 2 μM) similar to those commonly occurring in soil solutions, Elliott et al. (1984) concluded that P efflux is a substantial component of net P accumulation. Corn seedlings depleted solution P levels to 0.15 μM in 24 h, and to 0.05 μM in 60 h. The ratio of ^{32}P efflux to ^{32}P influx was about 0.68 at 0.2 μM and 0.08 at 2.0 μM.

Under conditions where the value of c_l is low relative to K_m, the constant can be replaced by J_{max}/α, where α is the root absorbing power, the proportionality constant relating flux to nutrient concentration at the root surface (Eq. 5.1). Equation 5.10 then can be written as

$$D'b \frac{\partial c_l}{\partial r} + v_o c_l = \frac{\alpha(c_l - c_{min})}{1 + \alpha(c_l - c_{min})/J_{max}} \tag{5.11}$$

The Claassen-Barber model

The relationships expressed in these equations provided the basis for developing models to predict nutrient uptake (Barber, 1984). The assumptions made in constructing the Claassen-Barber model (Claassen and Barber, 1976), in addition to those already stated in deriving Eq. 5.9, included the following:

1. The soil is homogeneous and isotropic.

2. Soil water conditions in the root zone are maintained at or near field capacity and are considered constant. Mean values of water content were calculated in some cases.

3. Nutrient uptake occurs only from nutrients in solution at the root surface, and there is no appreciable influence of exudates or microbial activity on the flux.

4. D' and b are independent of the concentration of the nutrient being studied, but in some tests mean values were calculated for the range over which the concentration changed.

5. Influx characteristics do not change with age of roots or plants.

6. The convective component of flux is not affected by nutrient concentration.

The following parameters are needed in order to compare nutrient uptakes calculated from the Claassen-Barber model with those determined from plant growth experiments:

1. Concentration of the nutrient in the soil solution at the start of the plant growth period.
2. Apparent diffusion coefficient D' of the nutrient.
3. Differential soil buffer capacity b for the nutrient.
4. Initial root length.
5. Rate of root growth.
6. Average root radius.
7. Maximum influx J_{max} of the nutrient.
8. External nutrient concentration K_m to obtain one-half J_{max}.
9. External nutrient concentration c_{min} where net nutrient uptake is nil.
10. Water influx.

To evaluate these parameters, plants of the kind to be studied are grown with two culture systems. One set of plants is grown, usually in a greenhouse or growth chamber but in some cases in field plots, in soil with various nutrient levels added, and all of the above parameters, except 7, 8, and 9, along with the total nutrient uptake are determined. Values for J_{max}, K_m, and c_{min} are determined from data obtained using solution culture techniques. The kinds of plants grown and conditions of growth are as similar as possible to those present at the sites in the growth chamber, greenhouse, or field where data for growth in soil are obtained. Growth conditions can have large effects on the parameters used in the model. For example, the J_{max} of K with corn plants was only about one-half as great at 15°C as at 29°C, and root growth was eight times as great at the higher temperature (Ching and Barber, 1979).

Nutrient uptake by the roots of soil-grown plants at successive time steps is calculated by solving Eq. 5.9 with finite-difference and Crank-Nicholson mathematics; these quantities are integrated to determine total uptake. Predicted nutrient uptake values are compared with actual uptakes. Boundary conditions specified for $t = 0$ are $r > r_o$ and for $t > 0$, $r = r_o$.

The predicted uptake of K by corn grown in several soils in the greenhouse was about 50 percent greater than that determined by plant analysis (Claassen and Barber, 1976). The discrepancy was attributed to a failure to take into account interroot competition, which would be a more important factor in the case of K than of P because of a much lower contribution from diffusional flux. Much better agreement ($r \geq 0.9$) between observed and predicted uptake values was obtained for uptake of P by several corn varieties both in greenhouse and field studies (Schenk and Barber, 1979, 1980).

The Cushman-Barber model

A mechanistic model similar to that of Claassen and Barber but modified to take into account interroot competition was developed by Cushman (1979). This parameter was calculated (Silberbrush and Barber, 1983a) as: 2 (soil volume/π root length)$^{1/2}$. Uptake of P by several soybean cultivars, as predicted by the model, agreed closely with uptake determined by analysis. For one of two soils used, uptake of K was also predicted well, but for the other predicted uptake was greater than that measured. In field studies, the Cushman model accurately predicted K uptake by five soybean cultivars grown at two sites with different soil types (Silberbrush and Barber, 1984). At one of the sites with the higher soil solution P concentration (52 μM), the model accurately predicted P uptake, but at the other site (17.8 μM P) it overpredicted P uptake.

In using these models to predict nutrient uptake by some plant species, parameters must be added to include the contribution of root hairs. In a study by Itoh and Barber (1983) it was found that the estimated uptakes of P by tomato and lettuce were about 50 percent, and for Russian thistle only 30 percent, of that determined by biomass analysis. Including root hair parameters had little effect when using the model as a basis of predicting uptake by onions, carrots, or wheat.

When nutrient uptake determined by biomass analysis agrees with the uptake predicted by a model, estimates can be made of the magnitude of changes in uptake that would occur if values of one parameter of the model are changed while the others are held constant. This kind of sensitivity analysis is helpful in identifying the relative importance of the parameters in influencing uptake. A plot of results from such a study is shown in Fig. 5.4. In this study, the root parameters, growth rate, area, and radius were of particular importance for predicting K uptake. It should be noted that interactions with other parameters must be considered in interpreting the response. Thus when uptake is estimated with varying root growth rates, and with the interroot distance held constant, soil volume occupied by roots must also increase. Under circumstances where interroot distance changes, but because of some restriction the accessible soil volume does not change, other root parameters may also change, altering the predicted flux. For example, as interroot distance decreases, root growth rate could increase and radius decrease in such a way that both root and soil volume would remain constant (Fig. 5.5). This example of interdependence of growth factors illustrates how models ex-

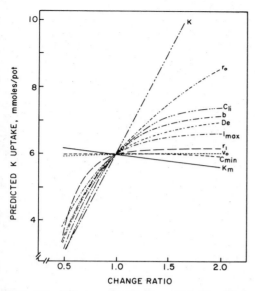

Figure 5.4 Effects on K uptake predicted by solving the Cushman model as each parameter was increased above or decreased below its measured value, while the other parameters were held constant at each of their measured values. Interactions between parameters assumed to be nil. (*Reproduced from M. Silberbrush and S. A. Barber, "Sensitivity analysis of parameters used in simulating K uptake," Agronomy Journal, volume 75, 1983b, pages 851–854, by permission of the American Society of Agronomy.*)

pressing quantitative relationships between growth parameters and nutrient uptake can aid genetic approaches by identifying plant attributes that influence mineral nutrient acquisition. In natural systems, the ability of plants to change morphologically and physiologically in order to adapt to different conditions of growth (phenotypic plasticity) enhances competitiveness and survivability, as well as development. Thus species with the capability of extending growth of roots to deeper soil depths or producing finer roots may be more effective in obtaining plant needs for nutrients as well as water.

As shown in Fig. 5.4, external K concentration c_l is next to root growth characteristics in sensitivity as a determinant of nutrient flux. In other studies, it was shown that simulated changes in external P concentrations were also among the most sensitive factors in P uptake (Silberbrush and Barber, 1983c).

An educational version of the Cushman-Barber model written in Pascal and compiled for the IBM PC and compatibles, using DOS 2.0

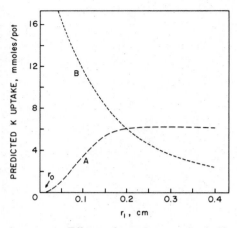

Figure 5.5 Effects of varying r_1, the half-distance between roots, on K uptake predicted by solving the Cushman model when (a) the remaining parameters are held constant, and (b) root growth rate and radius are varied as r_1 varies, so that both soil volume per plant and root volume per plant are constants. (*Reproduced from M. Silberbrush and S. A. Barber, "Sensitivity analysis of parameters used in simulating K uptake," Agronomy Journal, volume 75, 1983, pages 851–854, by permission of the American Society of Agronomy.*)

and MS-DOS 3.1, is available (Oates and Barber, 1987). Using experimental values obtained for soil and plant parameters, the program provides a means of predicting nutrient uptake for a specified period of growth, and nutrient concentration profiles in the vicinity of roots. This provides a valuable research and instructional aid for helping to estimate the quantitative effects that differences in soil and plant characteristics can have on nutrient uptake, and for identifying parameters that might be incorporated into better predictive models.

For making a good test of the predictability of the models described here or any other model, accuracy in determining nutrient concentrations at the root-soil interface is certainly one of the most severe limitations. This is particularly so for nutrients such as P for which diffusion is of great importance as a mechanism moving an ion or complex toward and into the soil-plant root interface. Nutrient movement in strict accordance with Fick's law of diffusion indicates that the steeper the gradient of concentration (activity), the greater the flux.

Ion-specific electrodes are making it possible to measure ion activities at soil-plant root interfaces. This improved technology should help advance research on soil fertility aspects of soil-plant relationships, as well as in problems related to environmental concerns, such as in waste management. A Cu-ion-selective electrode has been used to determine the activity of Cu in a sewage sludge treated soil and to relate this activity to Cu uptake by plants (Minnich et al., 1987). From comparison of the functional relationships between activity and uptake using the ion-sensitive electrode with that using a perm-selective membrane, it was concluded that nutrient replenishing factors (buffering capacity) and chelation have important effects on ion uptake and thus must be taken into account. The influences of these factors in regulating response are particularly evident with heavy metals, such as Cu, which have a propensity to form stable organic complexes, as discussed in Chap. 3. In models describing the uptake of Fe, Cu, and Zn, parameters need to be included to take into account soluble complexes of the metals with organic acid and amino acids (Inskeep and Comfort, 1986).

The Tillotson-Wagenet model

A simulation model containing expressions to relate transport and plant uptake both of soil water and of N from applied fertilizer has been proposed (Tillotson and Wagenet, 1982). Inputs required for the simulation include several parameters describing the amounts and distribution of water in the soil profile, rate and partitioning coefficients of N transformations as related to soil temperatures, and plant growth and N uptake factors. An equation similar to Eq. 5.2 was used to estimate N flux into the roots. The method of calculating α (root absorbing power) was that of Warncke and Barber (1973).

Data from a field corn experiment were used to test how well the model predicted changes in soil water content and soil solution NO_3^- during the growing season. Predicted and measured changes in soil water content agreed quite well, but the predicted concentrations of NO_3^- in the soil solution generally exceeded the measured values. Also, more N was taken up by the plants than was predicted. Several reasons for these discrepancies between predicted and measured values were suggested. For calculating N uptake, estimates of α were based on data from studies using young seedlings grown in nutrient solutions where mass flow is the dominant mechanism involved in moving soluble N to the plant roots. Results of longer term field studies have shown that contributions from diffusive mechanisms increase during later stages of growth when available soil N concentrations are generally lower (Strebel et al., 1980). The inability of the proposed model to effectively predict the changes and movement of soil N were attributed to the lack of parameters to take proper account of spatial variability and insufficient knowledge regarding the dynamics of soil N transformations via biological activities and physical processes (Tillotson and Wagenet, 1982).

Appendix

Derivation of Michaelis-Menten equation

Beginning with the reaction

$$R + I_o \underset{k_2}{\overset{k_1}{\rightleftharpoons}} RI \underset{k_4}{\overset{k_3}{\rightleftharpoons}} R + I_p \tag{A5.1}$$

where R = carrier
$\quad RI$ = carrier-ion complex
$\quad I_o$ = ion outside root
$\quad I_p$ = ion inside root cell
$\quad k$ = rate constants

Then, designating the concentrations of I_o and I_p as c and c_p, respectively, and the concentrations of R and RI as c_R and c_{RI}, respectively,

$$k_1 c_R c - k_2 c_{RI} = k_3 c_{RI} - k_4 c_R c_p \tag{A5.2}$$

Rearranging,

$$k_4 c_R c_p + k_1 c_R c = k_2 c_{RI} + k_3 c_{RI} \tag{A5.3}$$

$$\frac{c_{RI}}{c_R} = \frac{k_4 c_p + k_1 c}{k_2 + k_3} \tag{A5.4}$$

Assuming that k_4 is negligibly small, and substituting K_m (Michaelis constant) for $(k_2 + k_3)/k_1$,

$$\frac{c_{RI}}{c_R} = \frac{c}{K_m} \tag{A5.5}$$

and

$$\frac{c_R}{c_{RI}} = \frac{c_{Rt} - c_{RI}}{c_{RI}} = \frac{c_{Rt}}{c_{RI}} - 1 = \frac{K_m}{c}$$

where c_{Rt} = total carrier concentration, and $c_{Rt} - c_{RI}$ = concentration of "free" carrier. Assuming that the overall reaction rate (flux) J is controlled by $k_3 c_{RI}$, and J_{max} is the maximum reaction rate, or $J_{max} = k_3 c_{Rt}$, then

$$\frac{J_{max}}{J} = \frac{K_m}{c} + 1 \quad \text{and} \quad J = \frac{J_{max} c}{K_m + c} \tag{A5.6}$$

The meaning of K_m can be shown by considering the uptake at one-half of the maximum uptake rate, i.e., $J = J_{max}/2$:

$$\frac{J_{max}}{2} = \frac{J_{max}c}{K_m + c} \tag{A5.7}$$

and

$$J_{max}K_m + J_{max}c = 2J_{max}c \tag{A5.8}$$

$$K_m = c \tag{A5.9}$$

Thus, K_m is the ion concentration at which the uptake rate (influx) is one-half of the maximum rate.

Derivation of Nye-Marriott expression

The Nye-Marriott (1969) expression can be used for describing the relationship between changes in nutrient concentrations at the surface of an imaginary coaxial cylinder encasing a plant root, uniform in diameter and surface, extending through the center of the cylinder, and acting as a nutrient "sink." The nutrient flux can be expressed as

$$J_r \text{ mmol cm}^{-2} \text{ s}^{-1} = D\,\frac{\partial c}{\partial r} + v_w c_l \tag{A5.10}$$

where D = diffusion coefficient, $\text{cm}^2 \text{ s}^{-1}$

c, c_l = concentration of ion in labile form and in solution, respectively, mmol cm^{-3}

r = radial distance from root axis, cm

v_w = water flux, $\text{cm}^3 \text{ cm}^{-2} \text{ s}^{-1}$ or cm s^{-1} at r

For conservation of solute in the cylinder over time t,

$$\frac{\partial 2\pi r J_r}{\partial r} = 2\pi r\,\frac{\partial c}{\partial t} \tag{A5.11}$$

Combining Eqs. A5.10 and A5.11,

$$\frac{\partial 2\pi r}{\partial r}\left(D\,\frac{\partial c}{\partial r} + v_w c_l\right) = 2\pi r\,\frac{\partial c}{\partial t} \tag{A5.12}$$

and

$$\frac{\partial}{\partial r}\left(D\,\frac{\partial c}{\partial r}\right) + v_w c_l) = \frac{\partial c}{\partial t} \tag{A5.13}$$

For conservation of water with a flux of v_o at the surface of the root with radius r_o,

$$2\pi r v_w = 2\pi r_o v_o \tag{A5.14}$$

or

$$v_w = \frac{r_o v_o}{r} \tag{A5.15}$$

Combining Eqs. A5.13 and A5.15,

$$\frac{\partial}{\partial r}\left(D\frac{\partial c}{\partial r} + \frac{r_o v_o c_l}{r}\right) = \frac{\partial c}{\partial t} \tag{A5.16}$$

Multiplying Eq. A5.16 by r,

$$\frac{\partial}{\partial r}\left(rD\frac{\partial c}{\partial r} + r_o v_o c_l\right) = r\frac{\partial c}{\partial t} \tag{A5.17}$$

Rearranging,

$$\frac{1}{r}\frac{\partial}{\partial r}\left(rD\frac{\partial c}{\partial r} + r_o v_o c_l\right) = \frac{\partial c}{\partial t} \tag{A5.18}$$

For application to soils, a porous matrix with only a fraction of most nutrients present in a soluble state, the model needs to be modified in two respects. Account must be taken of the fact that the movement of nutrients from and through the soil is unlike movement through a continuous liquid medium. Some ions not in a soluble state will contribute to the total quantity moving toward the root by diffusion, and the path of travel will be more tortuous because the liquid phase will be interspersed with air spaces. Also surface charges on solid particles may impede movement in soil solution films. Thus an apparent diffusion coefficient, commonly designated D', should be used rather than the liquid diffusion coefficient designated above as D.

The second modification is needed to take into account the supply of any given nutrient associated with the solid phase, but in a labile state and readily released when the nutrient level in the solution phase is diminished. The parameter, commonly designated b (buffer capacity or buffer power), is calculated as the ratio of the concentration of the total amount of diffusible nutrient to the soluble fraction c_l. By expressing b in the differential form, $\partial c/\partial c_l$, and invoking the chain rule, b can be incorporated into Eq. A5.18:

$$\frac{\partial c}{\partial r} = \frac{\partial c}{\partial c_l}\frac{\partial c_l}{\partial r} \tag{A5.19}$$

$$\frac{\partial c}{\partial t} = \frac{\partial c}{\partial c_l} \frac{\partial c_l}{\partial t}$$

(A5.20)

From the definition of b indicated above,

$$\frac{\partial c}{\partial r} = b \frac{\partial c_l}{\partial r}$$

(A5.21)

$$\frac{\partial c}{\partial t} = b \frac{\partial c_l}{\partial t}$$

(A5.22)

Substituting Eqs. A5.21 and A5.22 into Eq. A5.18, and D' for D,

$$\frac{1}{r} \frac{\partial}{\partial r} \left(r D' b \frac{\partial c_l}{\partial r} + r_o v_o c_l \right) = b \frac{\partial c_l}{\partial t}$$

(A5.23)

Finally, dividing through by b gives:

$$\frac{1}{r} \frac{\partial}{\partial r} \left(r D' \frac{\partial c_l}{\partial r} + \frac{r_o v_o c_l}{b} \right) = \frac{\partial c_l}{\partial t}$$

(A5.24)

Relationships of Mineral Nutrition to Plant Growth and Composition

Introduction

In the contexts of crop production and of plant competitiveness in natural systems, relationships of nutrient supply to quantitative growth responses are commonly of more concern than relationships of supply to nutrient uptake, the focus of the discussion in Chap. 5. Nutrient supply is related to both uptake and growth, but the response functions over the range of supply levels from much below to much above plant needs for growth differ. Shapes of plots constructed from actual data vary depending upon the controlling factors involved in uptake and growth, and how these are interrelated. In one situation, uptake rate may be regulated by processes of nutrient transport; in another, influences of external supply on the functioning of plant uptake mechanisms may be of more importance. Interrelationships between uptake mechanisms, growth, and external nutrient concentrations and transport mechanisms in influencing flux of N, P, and K into plant roots are discussed by Robinson (1986).

Expressing Quantitative Relationships of Growth Responses to Nutrient Supply

The search for mathematical expressions to relate plant growth directly to soil nutrient supply and to applied nutrients has a long history, and it continues today. Models proposed by von Liebig (1840), commonly referred to as Liebig's law of the minimum, and by Mitscherlich (1909) are still used as a basis for relating crop responses to fertilizer application. Modifications of these models have included the contributions toward plant needs from the nutrient supply in the soil along with that added as fertilizers. Some of the changes suggested by various researchers will be discussed here.

The root demand coefficient, $\overline{ar}$, a term introduced earlier (see Eq. 5.2) to relate nutrient flux to external nutrient concentration, is also considered further here. An expression indicating the parameters needed to relate $\overline{ar}$ to plant growth and composition is derived.

Liebig's law of the minimum

The basic premise of this model is that, as the deficiency of the mineral nutrient limiting growth is corrected by adding increments of that nutrient, plant growth increases linearly until another nutrient becomes limiting. The maximum yield possible when the deficiency of each nutrient is completely corrected can be represented as a plateau on an added nutrient x versus yield y plot, or by a response surface as shown in Fig. 6.1. For the latter, Waggoner and Norvell (1979) derived the following expression to relate yield to the supply of two min-

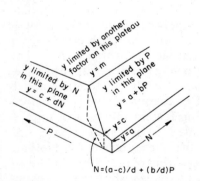

Figure 6.1   Depiction of Liebig's law of the minimum. Yield y is in the plane $y = a + bP$ when limited by P, in y, $l = c + dN$ when limited by N, and on the maximum yield plateau, $y = m$ when limited by another factor. The a, b, c, and d are parameters of the law, Eq. 6.1. (*Reproduced from P. E. Waggoner and W. A. Norvell, "Fitting the Law of the Minimum to fertilizer applications," in Agronomy Journal, volume 7, 1979, pages 352–354, by permission of the American Society of Agronomy, Inc.*)

eral nutrients, z_1 and z_2:

$$y = \text{MIN}(a + bz_1, c + dz_2, m) \tag{6.1}$$

where MIN( ) indicates successive y increments as deficiences of z_1 and z_2 are corrected, and m is the limit of y imposed by deficiency of a third nutrient. The terms a and c are the intercepts of the response surfaces on the ordinate for z_1 and z_2, respectively, and b and d are the respective slopes relating y to changes in amounts of the two nutrients.

A test of the model as expressed in Eq. 6.1 was made using published data from fertilizer trials in which N and P were applied to corn, and P and K applied to alfalfa and red clover (Heady, 1955). Estimates of parameter values were based on calculations of minimum residual sums of squares for the yield responses to fertilization. Using the Liebig model, values of R^2 for the corn data were equal to or better than those obtained when quadratic, logarithmic, or square root regression models were applied to the same data. The square root regression model described the responses of additions of P and K to alfalfa and red clover somewhat better than the Liebig model. This was attributed to possible interactions at the lower rates of fertilizer application.

A modification of the Liebig model, which includes the contribution to plant growth of nutrients present in the soil prior to fertilizer additions, as estimated from soil tests, has been proposed (Ackello-Ogutu et al., 1985). This modified Liebig model described corn yield responses to additions of P and K better than the square root or quadratic regression models applied to the same data. Results from 7 years of a 30-year study of fertilization responses in a corn-soybean-wheat-hay rotation were selected for making the comparison of the three models. The use of this response plateau type of model as a basis for fertilization recommendations, rather than with more commonly used polynomial models, was proposed as a means of lessening the likelihood of additions of nutrients in excess of crop needs.

The Mitscherlich model

The relationship of plant growth responses to increasing levels of nutrient supply as proposed by Mitscherlich (1909, 1947) differs from the Liebig model in two respects. According to the Mitscherlich hypothesis, (1) plant growth may be increased by the addition of a mineral nutrient even though that nutrient is not the most limiting; and (2) increases in growth are proportional, not to the amount of limiting nutrient added as proposed by Liebig, but to differences between the yield prior to nutrient addition and the maximum yield. Plots of yield responses to increasing nutrient levels are curvilinear, since each successive increment of nutrient increases growth less than the prior addition.

The relationship between yield increments dy resulting from increments dx of an added nutrient can be stated in mathematical terms:

$$\frac{dy}{dx} = k(A - y) \qquad (6.2)$$

where A = maximum yield
$\quad\quad y$ = actual yield at given level x of nutrient addition
$\quad\quad k$ = proportionality term

An expression to use in testing the applicability of the model to experimental data can be derived as follows:

$$\int \frac{dy}{A - y} = \int C\, dx \qquad (6.3)$$

$$y = A(1 - 10^{-Cx}) \qquad (6.4)$$

Whether or not the integration constant C represents an "efficiency factor," as has been suggested (Balba and Bray, 1956), is debatable. Its meaning will be considered later in this discussion.

Because of the nature of the integrated form of Eq. 6.4, mathematical expressions based on the Mitscherlich concept are commonly referred to as negative exponential models. In the log form, Eq. 6.4 is

$$\log (A - y) = \log A - Cx \qquad (6.5)$$

If yields are expressed on a relative basis, Eq. 6.5 can be written as

$$\log (100 - y) = \log 100 - Cx \qquad (6.6)$$

If a unit of x is defined as the amount required to obtain 50 percent of the maximum yield, then

$$\log (100 - 50) = 2 - C(1) \qquad (6.7)$$

and

$$C = 0.301$$

Application of a second unit of the nutrient will increase by 50 percent the difference (referred to as the *decrement from the maximum*) between the maximum yield and the yield obtained from addition of the first unit. Successive additions of this same amount of the nutrient would each result in another yield increase of 50 percent of the decrement from the maximum. The amounts of nutrient to produce these incremental responses were called *Baule,* named for the mathematician who collaborated with Mitscherlich (Baule, 1918).

Three questions need to be answered in attempting to check the applicability of the model to experimental data: (1) What are the amounts of nutrient in generally used units, e.g., kg ha^{-1}, equivalent to a Baule? (2) How is the amount of a nutrient already present in the soil, prior to further additions, taken into account? (3) Is the meaning of C changed under the conditions indicated by the two previous questions?

From the very large number of fertilization tests conducted by Mitscherlich, mean values of 250, 22, and 70 kg ha^{-1} for N, P, and K, respectively, were estimated as equivalents of Baule units. These estimates were largely from experiments with grain crops grown in Germany. Equivalence values for each nutrient would be more variable if a broader range of different kinds of plants and greater differences in growth conditions were included.

The derivation of the expression (Eq. 6.5) for the Mitscherlich model takes into account only nutrient additions as fertilizers. For the contribution to plant needs from the nutrient supply in the soil prior to fertilizer additions, a term for this amount (*b*) of the nutrient was added. It was assumed that the coefficient C was the same for the nutrient obtained from the soil supply and from that added as fertilizer:

$$\log (A - y) = \log A - C(x + b) \tag{6.8}$$

This equation was used both to predict yield responses using estimates of *b* from soil analysis and to estimate *b* in different soils.

The meaning of the C term, its assumed constancy, and how to evaluate it are probably the most controversial aspects of the Mitscherlich model. As a coefficient relating the relative yield response to increases in nutrient amounts, viewing its function as an efficiency factor (Balba and Bray, 1956) seems appropriate, at least in a qualitative sense. Its quantitative meaning in mechanistic terms is not as apparent, however, even if the responses are expressed on a relative basis and nutrient additions are expressed in Baule units. If C is a constant, then C*x* for each equal increment of nutrient added is also constant. But since yield responses to increases in nutrient supply are curvilinear, less efficiency of some part of the soil-plant system as the nutrient level increases is indicated. Less efficient use of nutrient at higher levels of supply could be because of both plant and soil factors.

Various modifications of the expressions based on the Mitscherlich diminishing returns concept have been tested for their applicability for describing relationships of yield responses to increasing nutrient supply. Different values of C have been used for the nutrient added and the portion of nutrient uptake contributed from the soil supply b, i.e.,

$$\log (A - y) = \log A - Cx - C'b \qquad (6.9)$$

To relate corn grain yields to K nutrition, Bray (1944) expressed nutrient supply in terms of the amount of exchangeable soil K, which was assumed to be linearly related to the amount of plant available K. With yields expressed in terms of bushels of grain per acre and exchangeable K as milliequivalents (meq) per 100 g of soil, mean values of C of 0.0077 and 0.012 were found for soybeans and wheat, respectively.

The Mitscherlich concept has also been used to relate tuber yields Y of potatoes to a P soil test value T, as indicated in the following expression (Mombiela et al., 1981):

$$Y = A(1 - e^{-C[x + f(T)]}) \qquad (6.10)$$

where $f(T) = \gamma + \gamma_o T$, with γ and γ_o representing linear coefficients, and A and C as defined previously. Yield data obtained from studies in Maine correlated equally well with yields estimated using Eq. 6.10 as with yield estimates using expressions derived from square root or quadratic regression models. To apply Eq. 6.10 to potato yield data from North Carolina, it was necessary to use an A value lower than that used for the data from Maine where potato yields are greater.

A review of other models that have been proposed to relate nutrient supply to plant response, including various modifications of the Mitscherlich model, has been published by Nelson et al. (1985).

Diagnosis of nutrient status by plant analysis

The relationships indicated in Fig. 6.2 serve as a basis for using plant tissue testing techniques to help diagnose the nutrient status of soils, and to develop effective fertilizer management practices. *Critical nutrient concentrations* in plants, or more often in particular plant parts, are defined as those necessary to obtain 90 percent of the maximum yield (Ulrich and Hills, 1967). Generally, there is some arbitrariness in identification of critical levels, since plotted data points typically show some scatter (Fig. 6.3). Because of this variability, a critical nutrient range (CNR), rather than a single critical value, is often specified. Application of the critical nutrient concept as a fertilization guide for a great number of different crops is discussed in publications

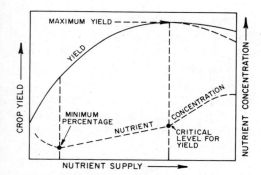

Figure 6.2 Idealized relationship of nutrient supply to crop yields and plant nutrient concentrations.

by Reisenauer (1983), Tisdale et al. (1985), and Walsh and Beaton (1973).

Another technique of plant analysis for diagnosing soils with respect to meeting nutrient needs of crops is the Diagnosis and Recommendation Integrated System (DRIS) proposed by Beaufils (1973). Originally proposed for several tropical crops, including sugar cane and rubber trees (reviewed by Beaufils and Sumner, 1977), it has since been tested for use in fertilizer management of other crops in-

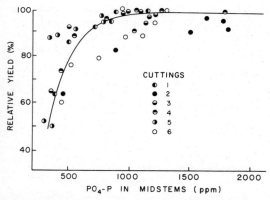

Figure 6.3 Relationship between yields and nutrient concentrations of PO_4–P in midstems of different cuttings of alfalfa. (*Reproduced from R. D. Meyer and W. E. Martin, "Plant analysis as a guide for fertilization of alfalfa," in Soil and Plant Tissue Testing in California, Bulletin 1879 (rev.), 1983, pages 32–33, edited by H. M. Reisenauer, Division of Agricultural Science, University of California.*)

cluding N, P, and K for soybeans (Sumner, 1977*a*), corn, and wheat (Sumner, 1977*b*); S for corn and wheat (Sumner, 1981); N, P, K, Ca, Mg, Zn, Cu, and B for alfalfa (Walworth et al., 1986), and N, P, S, K, Ca, and Mg for subclover (Jones et al., 1986). The procedure is designed to identify which nutrient or nutrients limit the growth of a crop of interest in a selected soil area. The premise upon which the diagnosis is based is that the suitability of a soil as a mineral nutrient source for plant growth can be best evaluated from ratios of concentrations of nutrients in the plants. Ratios of each pair of nutrients that may be influencing plant growth in a selected soil area are compared with mean values of the ratios (diagnostic norms) for each of the same nutrient pairs found in plants grown under conditions in which maximum yields are obtained. Large-scale surveys are needed to establish a meaningful data base for calculating the norm values.

Applying DRIS as proposed by Jones (1981), index values for each nutrient are calculated from equations expressing the differences between nutrient ratios found in crop plant samples from a test area and the diagnostic norms for that same kind of crop. As an example, assuming that N, P, K, Ca, S, Mg, and B are possible growth limiters, an N index is related to ratio functions of these nutrients as indicated in the following expression:

$$\text{N Index} = \frac{f(\text{N/P}) + f(\text{N/K}) + f(\text{N/Ca}) - f(\text{S/N}) - f(\text{Mg/N}) - f(\text{B/N})}{X} \quad (6.11)$$

where X is the number of functions in the numerator, and each of the nutrient ratio functions is calculated as shown in the following for $f(\text{N/P})$:

$$f\left(\frac{\text{N}}{\text{P}}\right) = \left(\frac{\text{N}}{\text{P}} - \frac{n}{p}\right)\frac{10}{S_d} \quad (6.12)$$

where N/P = ratio of mean concentrations of N to P in plant samples collected from test area
n/p = diagnostic norm value
S_d = standard deviation of the norm's population
10   converts $f(\text{N/P})$ to a whole number

The other $f(\ )$ values in Eq. 6.11 are calculated similarly to that for $f(\text{N/P})$ as shown in Eq. 6.12, using the appropriate ratios determined for samples from the test area and for diagnostic norms.

The nutrient for which the calculated index value is most negative is predicted as the nutrient most limiting growth of the crop in the selected area. If that deficiency were corrected, the nutrient with the next most negative index would become limiting, and so on. Including a dry matter index value for diagnosing alfalfa growth needs has been proposed (Walworth et al., 1986). The prediction of nutrient needs of soybeans was improved if the norm values used had been obtained from samples collected at the same stage of growth as the samples being evaluated for nutrient status (Hallmark et al., 1988).

A very complete review of the development and use of DRIS as a diagnostic tool, with many examples of its application, has been published (Walworth and Sumner, 1987). Equation 6.11 is only one of several expressions that have been used as a basis for applying DRIS to predict nutrient responses.

Quantitatively relating plant nutrient needs to nutrient supply in ways that may be more meaningful physiologically is becoming possible through the development of analytical techniques by which nutrient concentrations can be measured at specific sites, such as in organelles. For example, vacuolar K contributes to cytoplasmic K homeostasis and thus may be a better indicator of K insufficiency, because adverse effects on growth may not occur until the level in the vacuole decreases to some minimum concentration (Leigh and Wyn-Jones, 1984).

Growth, Internal Concentration, and the Root Demand Coefficient

A concept seemingly the opposite of that indicated by the Liebig and Mitscherlich models is that growth, along with internal concentration, be considered as regulating rather than responding to nutrient uptake. Potassium accumulation by four varieties of tomato was found to be related to relative shoot dry weight increase (Fig. 6.4). Williams (1948) found that large differences in P uptake between oat plants grown in sand culture with nutrient solutions containing relatively high and low concentrations of P were not apparent when uptakes were calculated on the basis of plant dry weight increments. Using radioactive tracer techniques, Drew et al. (1969) found that much greater amounts of K were absorbed per unit surface area when its entry was confined to 1-cm segments of roots of both leeks and onions than when entry could also occur through other parts of the root system. Nutrient transport is also involved in the relationship between growth rate and nutrient acquisition (Fig. 6.5). Shoot feedback effects on nutrient uptake were indicated (Pitman, 1972).

Regulatory influences of shoots on mineral nutrient acquisition are also indicated from rapid effects of detopping on the electrical conductance (EC) of xylem exudate (Neumann and Stein, 1986). The ECs of exudate of bean plants, one day after being detopped, were about 30

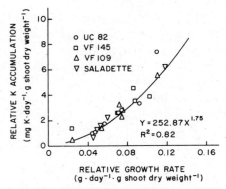

Figure 6.4 Regression of K accumulation rate relative to the vegetative shoot dry weight on growth rate relative to the vegetative shoot dry weight. (*Reproduced from I. E. Widders and O. A. Lorenz from "Potassium nutrition during tomato plant development," in Journal of the American Society for Horticultural Science, volume 107, 1982, pages 960–964, by permission of the authors.*)

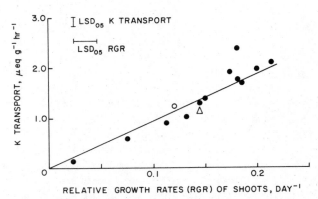

Figure 6.5 Relationship between K and Na transport into shoots and relative growth rates (RGR) of barley seedlings grown in nutrient solutions, K only (•), soil, K + Na (o); or sand, K + Na (△) cultures. (*Reproduced from M. G. Pitman, "Uptake and transport of ions in barley seedlings. III. Correlation between transport to the shoot and relative growth rate," in Australian Journal of Biological Science, volume 25, 1972, pages 243–257, by permission of CSIRO.*)

percent lower than those of intact plants. Over longer periods, other factors, such as the supply of photosynthate and hormonal influences, contribute to the response.

Internal concentrations as well as growth rates influence nutrient demands. Siddiqi and Glass (1982) found that the influx of K (^{86}Rb labeling) by barley from a 60-μM K solution decreased exponentially from about 14 to less than 1 μmol $\cdot$ g^{-1}. Both J_{max} and K_m were affected by internal concentration. A modified Michaelis-Menten expression was proposed (authors' symbols altered):

$$J = \frac{(\text{Max } J_{max})(e^{-\pounds s})c}{(\text{Min } K_m)(e^{\pounds' s}) + c} \tag{6.13}$$

where Max J_{max} = maximum value of J_{max} when determined at internal nutrient concentrations

$\pounds$ and $\pounds'$ = slopes relating J_{max} and K_m, respectively, to the root nutrient concentrations s

c = external nutrient concentration

Min K_m = minimum value of K_m when determined at internal concentrations

Measured K uptake rates J for barley seedlings agreed well with those calculated using Eq. 6.11, and with external solution K and root K concentrations ranging from 0.01 to 0.20 mM and 7.30 to 39.70 μmol g^{-1}, respectively.

An expression incorporating the effects of growth and internal concentrations was proposed by Nye and Tinker (1969). Mineral nutrient flux J as the product of plant weight W and internal concentration c_p was stated mathematically as follows:

$$J = \frac{d(c_p W)}{dt} = \frac{c_p \, dW}{dt} + \frac{W \, dc_p}{dt} \tag{6.14}$$

Combining this expression for flux with Eq. 5.3 gives

$$2\pi \alpha r L c_l = \frac{c_p \, dW + W \, dc_p}{dt} \tag{6.15}$$

where α = root absorbing power

r = root radius

L = total root length

c_l = concentration of nutrient in solution

If αr is the root demand coefficient (Chap. 5), then,

$$2\pi\overline{\alpha r} = \frac{c_p \, dW + W \, dc_p}{Lc_l \, dt} \tag{6.16}$$

$$= \frac{c_p \, dW}{Lc_l \, dt} + \frac{W \, dc_p}{Lc_l \, dt} \tag{6.17}$$

Increases in biomass and internal nutrient amounts can be converted from absolute to relative terms as follows:

$$2\pi\overline{\alpha r} = \frac{W c_p \, dW}{W \, Lc_l \, dt} + \frac{c_p \, W \, dc_p}{c_p \, Lc_l \, dt} \tag{6.18}$$

$$= \frac{W c_p}{L c_l}\left(\frac{1}{W}\frac{dW}{dt} + \frac{1}{c_p}\frac{dc_p}{dt}\right) \tag{6.19}$$

For calculating the root demand coefficient from experimental data, use

$$\overline{\alpha r} = \frac{W}{2\pi L}\frac{c_p}{c_l}\left(\frac{\ln W_2 - \ln W_1}{t_2 - t_1} + \frac{\ln c_{p2} - \ln c_{p1}}{t_2 - t_1}\right) \tag{6.20}$$

With the other parameters in Eq. 6.18 expressed as follows: W, g; c_p, g g^{-1}; L, cm; and t, s, $\overline{\alpha r}$ has the dimensions of $cm^2 \, s^{-1}$, units in which D, the diffusion coefficient, is also expressed. A value of $\overline{\alpha r}$ lower than the diffusion coefficient for the nutrient being absorbed indicates that uptake is rate-limiting, assuming diffusive processes are involved.

Evaluating root demand coefficients by Eq. 6.18 requires relatively long periods of growth in order to satisfactorily measure relative growth and relative concentration rates. Wild et al. (1974) determined the values of $\overline{\alpha r}$ for four plant species—orchardgrass, spring grass, red clover, and yellow trefoil—grown for 42 days at four different levels of K using a flowing culture technique. At K concentration levels below those needed for maximum growth, $\overline{\alpha r}$ ranged from 7.2 to 30.1×10^{-6} $cm^2 \, s^{-1}$, while at the highest level the values ranged from 0.4 to 2.3×10^{-6} for the four species. The order of ranking of $\overline{\alpha r}$ values for the four species was similar at the different solution K concentration levels.

Because of incomplete data for all parameters required in Eq. 6.20, estimates of $\overline{\alpha r}$ for other mineral nutrients growing in different environments cannot be calculated with certainty. Using data published for other purposes, and making certain assumptions to obtain needed parameters which were not provided by the published data, Nye and Tinker (1969) estimated $\overline{\alpha r}$ for P uptake was about 20 times greater

$(4 \times 10^{-5}$ vs. 2×10^{-6} cm^{2}s$^{-1})$ with the P concentration in the external solution 0.04 μM rather than 25 μM.

Equation 6.20 as a model describing nutrient demand provides a means of testing the hypothesis that effectiveness of uptake of nutrients is a function of their concentrations in the plant, plant growth, and root extension. A regulatory function in the uptake of a plant nutrient is indicated if their combined effects, as revealed by estimation of $\overline{\alpha r}$, are less than the diffusion coefficient of that nutrient. Data needed to verify the applicability of the concept to soil-plant systems are not easily obtained, but as the necessary technology develops, results of such testing will aid in the understanding of dynamic aspects of nutrient acquisition from soils. Crucial for verification is accurately determining the available nutrient concentrations at the interface between soil and the actively absorbing regions of the root system. Growth rates might be more closely monitored by use of non-destructive measurements such as rates of CO_2 exchange rather than dry matter accumulation. A clearer understanding of the relationships of growth to nutrient acquisition requires that measurements taken recognize the dynamics of the soil-plant system. Improved technology should help identify the important parameters needed for designing and testing more accurate and complete predictive models.

Mineral Nutrition, Plant Composition, and Crop Quality

Luxury consumption of mineral nutrients

Plant uptake mechanisms provide some control and selectivity in the absorption of nutrients and other solutes present in soil solutions, but such regulation is not absolute. Absorption of nutrients in excess of growth needs has been referred to as "luxury consumption" (Macy, 1936). Judged only with regard to perceived growth needs, the term "luxury" may be appropriate, but other aspects need to be considered. As levels of nutrient supply are increased above those needed for growth, commonly the rate of change of internal concentration relative to the supply increases, and this may be accompanied by adverse growth effects (Fig. 6.2). Elevated amounts of nutrients may also serve other purposes or alter metabolic pathways in plants, and thus affect, either positively or negatively, such factors as quality, survivability, and competitiveness.

N uptake in excess of growth needs

Because of its great mobility in soils, nitrate is generally readily accessible for uptake by plant roots. Reduction mechanisms catalyzed by reductase enzymes convert this N to nitrite and to ammonical N, and in the -3 redox state, N becomes assimilated into organic forms. In most plants nitrate and nitrite reductases are present in both roots and shoots, but the levels of their activities in these two organs differ between species. Under conditions where uptake greatly exceeds plant growth needs nitrate will accumulate. For example, accumulation will occur where the source of energy for enzyme synthesis and other metabolic needs is limited (Oaks and Hirel, 1985), or where soil moisture or mineral nutrient levels are low. Molybdenum and Mn serve physiological functions in N reduction systems, and thus nitrate may accumulate in plants grown in soils where these elements are present at low levels (Wright and Davidson, 1964).

The extent to which nitrate accumulates in plants differs greatly between different species and cultivars, and between different parts of the same plant. Published data for cultivated plants, summarized by Nelson (1984), show levels in excess of 1 percent nitrate-N of dry weights being found in grasses, including sudangrass and reed canarygrass, and in the vegetables radish, collards, and celery. Comparable high levels are found in certain wild plants, including milk thistle and lamb's-quarters (Tucker et al., 1961). Commonly, the greatest accumulation occurs in petioles and in the older, outer leaves of plants such as head lettuce, but the relative distribution depends upon species and variety, as well as on other conditions of growth. Through plant breeding and genetic manipulation, cultivars with a tendency to accumulate less nitrate are possible.

Numerous cases of disorders of livestock associated with intake of high nitrate levels, manifested mainly as abortion and impaired O_2 transport in blood (methemoglobinemia), have been reported. A critical level at which plant nitrate may be a livestock health hazard cannot be specified with certainty because of other contributing factors, but generally forages containing less than 1 percent nitrate are safe for most domestic animals (Herrick, 1980). When properly ensiled, nitrate in forages is completely degraded (Spoelstra, 1985).

When nitrate levels are high, either in the soil or plants, the more toxic nitrite may also be present at above normal levels. A greater abundance of nitrite is most often noted under conditions in which plants have been stressed, for example, by drought or by freezing, or when induced by methods used in handling and processing. The possibility of carcinogenic nitrosamines being formed in plants in the presence of nitrites has been suggested, but no cases of health problems as a result of this reaction have been clearly established.

Uptake of N in excess of growth needs may also be shown by accumulation of nonprotein N other than as nitrate. This commonly occurs when mineral nutrients other than N are insufficient for optimum plant growth. Dramatic increases in nonprotein N concentrations occur in plants severely deficient in S. For example, in young corn plants growing under conditions of severe S deficiency, as much as one-third of the total N may be present as amide, largely as asparagine (Rendig et al., 1976). Sulfur is required for effective functioning of nitrate reductase (Oputa, 1971; Friedrich and Schrader, 1978), but the accumulation of soluble organic N in S-deficient plants indicates that there is a more demanding need for S for other metabolic functions.

The amount of nitrate N reduced in roots varies with species (Pate, 1973). The amounts present at any given time are the net result of uptake, translocation and incorporation in macromolecules. Of the nitrate $-^{15}N$ taken up and reduced in roots of decapitated corn seedlings, the proportions accumulated as soluble N and that translocated (measured in exuded xylem fluid) are inversely related (Morgan et al., 1986). This indicates a close linkage between reduction of the nitrate-N and incorporation of reduced N into macromolecules. In intact plants, however, N distribution may be different since decapitation removes a sink and source for N reduced in roots (Cooper et al., 1986).

Arginine is an important form of N storage in trees and vines. In roots of solution culture grown grape ('Thompson seedless') plants, tissue concentrations of arginine at bloom stage increased almost linearly as solution N concentrations were increased beyond the levels producing maximum growth (Kliewer and Cook, 1971). An ability to store N not required for immediate growth needs is an important survival feature in wild plants (Chapin, 1980).

Adequate but not excessive soil N levels are important if one is to grow sugar beets with high yields and good quality roots. If plant N is maintained at too high a level at the time of harvest, leaf-root ratios may be undesirably high, and the roots will contain a lower percentage of sugar. Good recovery of pure sugar from root extracts is impaired because greater amounts of nonsugar components, such as soluble reduced N, have to be separated from the sucrose. Other soil conditions, for example, the water regime during the growing season, influence the relationship of soil N supply to beet yields and quality.

Another example of a change in plant composition and quality that can result from an uptake of N in excess of growth needs is shown in the relationship between the N nutrition of some cereal plants and both the amounts and proportions of different forms of protein in their grain. The impact of a positive response to N nutrition in terms of quality depends upon the kind of plant and the manner in which the plant serves as a food source. For example, increasing the concentration of protein in wheat grain by N fertilization may improve both baking and nutritional qualities. With the higher levels of N supply, however, a greater proportion of the N taken up is used for biosynthesis of proteins of the prolamine (soluble in aqueous alcohol) type, not only by wheat, but by other cereals as well, including barley, rye, and corn. For example, the prolamine (zein) concentration in the grain of a corn hybrid increased twofold as the level of fertilizer N applied was increased, but other grain protein fractions showed little or no response (Tsai et al., 1980). Relative increases in prolamine proteins result in decreases in overall concentrations of two essential amino acids, lysine and tryptophan, since prolamines contain no amounts of these amino acids. Quality assays using rats as test animals indicated positive growth responses to increased wheat grain protein contents, but animal weight gains per unit of grain protein decreased as the concentration increased (Syltie et al., 1982).

Biochemical changes brought about by gene substitutions can lessen the dominance of prolamines as a N sink. In corn this change in genetic makeup can be accomplished by introducing the *opaque*-2 (*O*-2) gene (Mertz et al., 1964). In the grain of rice and oats, the prolamine fraction is a weaker N sink, and thus in these cereals shows less response to higher soil N levels.

In developing fertilizer management practices by which N is most effectively used for growth and for achieving desired protein levels in cereal grains, account needs to taken of (1) timing of application, (2) other soil characteristics related to N nutrition, and (3) species and cultivar differences. Nitrate N taken up in excess of growth needs and stored in vacuoles may not be efficiently assimilated, since this ion does not readily pass through the plasmalemma (MacKown et al., 1981) and is phloem-immobile. Mobility of nitrate also is influenced by internal levels of K, since the latter is generally the most abundant counterion (Pan et al., 1986). More information is needed about species and cultivar differences as related to N nutrition and the partitioning of N absorbed prior to and after anthesis. Results of a greenhouse study with a corn hybrid ('Pioneer 3369') and its *O*-2 counterpart showed that N taken up prior to and after anthesis is distributed similarly in grain protein of the two genotypes (Rendig and Crawford, 1985). Other species and cultivars grown under field conditions may respond differently.

An extensive review of the results from research relating effects of gene modification and N fertilization to the makeup of corn grain protein has been published by Glover and Mertz (1987).

Plant responses to soil P supply

Assuring an adequate supply of P to meet needs of plants throughout their life cycles poses some unique problems, because of the nature and behavior of P compounds in soils. Soil solution P commonly is present at concentrations of less than 1 μM, the lowest for any of the major plant essential elements. As plants grow and develop, the needs of P may exceed the capacity of the soil to maintain an adequate available P level. Changes in other soil conditions may also contribute to an accentuation of plant P deficiencies. For example, if soil water levels decrease, delivery of P to plant roots by diffusional processes may be slowed because of the lengthened pathway of ion movement. Such a change could be wholly or partially offset if there is a concurrent rise in soil temperature with drying. Even with an unlikely rise of 10°C, the increase in diffusional movement of P ions would at most double, however, assuming a Q_{10} value in the 1 to 2 range. Under some conditions, changes in soil temperature could have the opposite effect. While incubation studies have indicated that soluble P concentrations associated with native soil P may be insensitive to temperature differences over a 7 to 27°C range (Power et al., 1964), concentrations in soils to which fertilizer salts are applied may decrease more rapidly at higher temperatures (Beaton et al., 1965). In soils to which K, NH_4, or Ca phosphate salts were added, much lower percentages of the added P remained soluble when the soils were incubated at 35°C than at 20 or 5°C.

Whether a given available soil P level is adequate to meet plant growth needs is also a function of phenotypic plasticity, i.e., the capability of a species or genotype to adjust morphologically and physiologically to changes in environmental conditions, including mineral nutrition. Favorable responses to conditions limiting available soil P supply include the ability to increase the root-shoot ratio, and to encourage mycorrhizal infection. These responses could account for instances in which symptoms of P deficiency appear in the early stages of seedling growth, but subsequently disappear.

Another favorable plant trait lessening the likelihood of stress because of inadequate P, is the ability to absorb luxury amounts of the element early in the growth period, or at times when a change in conditions creates a temporary flush in available P. This capability not only may help sustain growth and assure survivability, but may be the factor determining which species or genotype prevails in mixed culture systems. Phosphorus fertilizer management practices can have important effects on the relative proportions of grasses and legumes in mixed species pastures, but short- and long-term effects may vary (Rossiter, 1964). After an initial positive response to P application, a decrease in the proportion of legumes could result from a depletion of other nutrients such as S or Mo, creating an environment relatively more favorable for nonlegumes.

Differences in adaptability to conditions in which P stress may occur during growth are important in the establishment, survival, and competitiveness of wild plant species (Rorison, 1968). Adaptation of such species to limitations of nutrient supply, as well as to other stresses, includes slowing of relative growth rates and thus lessening nutrient demands (Chapin, 1980).

Physiological mechanisms associated with the uptake of P in amounts exceeding current growth needs include enhanced storage in vacuoles and greater synthesis of polyphosphates. Few data are available for the quantities of vacuolar storage in plants growing in soils, but results from studies using nutrient solutions show that the capacity for such storage is large (Bieleski, 1973). Over 70 percent of the inorganic P in spinach leaves is present in vacuoles. While all chemical forms of P, both organic and inorganic, serve as storage pools, inorganic P is the major contributor (Chapin and Bieleski, 1982). The vacuolar pool helps buffer the P level in the cytosol.

Polyphosphates have been identified in several lower plant species and in a few angiosperms (Bieleski, 1973). This form of P is present in very low amounts in plant tissues, and its contributions to metabolic reactions and nutrient storage have not been defined. Polyphosphate granules are transported by cytoplasmic streaming in mycorrhizal fungi hyphae (Cox et al., 1980). The activity of ATPase provides the energy needed to power the transfer of P at the fungus-host interface (Marx, 1982). Mycorrhizal activity is of greatest importance when soil P levels are low, since at high levels little or no infection occurs.

Phosphorus nutrition is a regulatory factor in seed development during grainfill. Phosphates are phloem-mobile, and much of the grain P needs are met by remobilization from leaves and stems (Hill, 1980). In soybeans, metabolic reactions that influence the number of seed pods formed and those affecting weight per seed have different P concentration optima (Grabau et al., 1986). Other P nutrition-related plant physiological processes involved in this kind of response include leaf senescence and carbohydrate metabolism. These processes affect both the rate and extent of grain biomass accumulation.

In seeds and in potato tubers, phytates, salts of the hexaphosphate ester of inositol (phytic acid), account for most of the P present (Bieleski, 1973). Phytates interact with proteins and mineral elements with the result that their effectiveness as nutrient sources in foods may be impaired (Reddy et al., 1982). Hydrolysis of phytates during germination or breaking of dormancy provides P for resumption of growth.

High soil P levels are implicated in plant Zn deficiencies. When originally observed, this relationship was interpreted as a consequence of a soil reaction resulting in Zn immobilization. Another interpretation is that the correlation of leaf symptoms with tissue P/Zn ratios indicates a possible inactivation of some plant Zn by elevated P levels. Results obtained by Loneragan et al. (1982) showed that, if soil Zn levels are low, P can be more readily absorbed by plant roots and transported to the shoots; thus leaf toxicity symptoms are enhanced, even though there is no change in leaf Zn concentration. In barley seedlings grown under low-Zn conditions, a greater uptake of P occurred at 20°C than at 10°C (Schwartz et al., 1987). Welch et al. (1982) found direct evidence for the involvement of Zn in the maintenance of root cell membrane integrity.

To maximize feeding quality of forage crops, available soil P levels may need to exceed those required for maximum yields (Ozanne, 1980). Forages absorbing luxury amounts of P produced greater weight gains of livestock than similar forages grown with lower soil P levels. The beneficial effects on feeding quality are attributed to factors besides higher crop P concentrations, including effects of elevated P on feed palatability and digestibility, and on other plant components.

Magnesium for plant growth and quality

Forages grown in soils in which Mg levels are high enough to produce maximum growth may contain insufficient Mg to meet the needs of livestock consuming the forage. The disorder that results, hypomagnesemic tetany, most often affects grazing cows in the period following parturition, and if not promptly treated is commonly fatal. Serious losses of livestock have occurred from this deficiency.

Factors other than simply the level of Mg in the feed consumed are involved in the occurrence of hypomagnesemic tetany. A critical Mg level cannot be specified with certainty, but forage with Mg concentrations below 0.2 percent are considered tetany-prone (Grunes et al., 1970). Since it occurs more frequently when grasses are the dominant species consumed, the disorder is often referred to as grass tetany. The Mg in young grasses appears to be particularly poorly utilized by livestock, but no particular plant component to account for this low availability has been clearly identified. Negative effects of high-forage K levels has been shown, but influences of this factor have not been consistently observed. Kemp and 't Hart (1956) proposed that the ratio of K to Ca and Mg was the important factor and related an increasing incidence of the disorder to forage in which the value of K/(Ca + Mg) (expressed on a milliequivalent basis) exceeds 2.2.

High rates of the uptake of K interfere with Mg uptake. Concentrations of K and Mg in the shoots and roots of a tall fescue hybrid (*Lolium multiflorum* Lam. × *Festuca arundinacea* Schreb.) indicated competition of K with Mg at xylem unloading sites (Hannaway et al,

1984). Nitrogen nutrition has been implicated in tetany because of effects on K uptake and assimilation in plants. Applications of N either as NO_3^- or NH_4^+ to bromegrass had relatively little effect on shoot Mg concentrations, but they resulted in increased concentrations of total N, K, and organic acids, particularly aconitate, along with higher $K/(Ca + Mg)$ ratios (Follett et al., 1977). Binding of Mg by organic acids such as aconitate has been suggested as a contributing factor in hypomagnesemia. Evidence for the involvement of organic acids and other plant factors in contributing to the disorder have been reviewed by Mayland and Grunes (1979).

Some increase in plant Mg concentrations can be achieved by genetic modification, but a forage free of a potential tetany hazard has not yet been developed (Sleper, 1989). To assure adequate Mg intake by animals consuming low-Mg forages, direct supplementation generally is more effective than additions of Mg salts to soils. Where limestone applications are made to correct soil acidity, dolomitic types may provide additional benefits by correcting Mg insufficiencies.

Compared to dietary standards specified by the National Research Council, Mg intakes by a high proportion of the U.S. population are too low (Morgan et al., 1985). Clear evidence for the common occurrence of human Mg deficiencies has not been forthcoming, but the possibility of the need for higher intakes under conditions of physical stress has been suggested (Franz et al., 1985).

Water and Mineral Nutrient Uptake, and Plant Growth, under Special Conditions

Highly Acidic Soils

Soil acidification

Chemical, physical, and biological reactions contribute to soil acidity. Acidification can result from the concurrent exit of protons and uptake of cations during nutrient acquisition (Chap. 5). Acidification can also result from the oxidation of ammoniacal N, either produced by biological activity or added to the soil as ammonium salts, particularly as sulfate added as fertilizer over a period of years.

While H^+-cation exchange uptake by plants and nitrification can lower the pH, especially at the soil-plant root interface in poorly buffered soils, other processes account for most highly acidic (< pH 5) soils. Such soils usually are the result of centuries of severe weathering in areas where the parent materials are low in basic minerals. In areas of heavy rainfall, particularly in climates having relatively high temperatures, basic salts are dissolved and leached, and cations are displaced by protons formed when CO_2 is dissolved in water (Rowell and Wild, 1985). Pure water in equilibrium with atmospheric CO_2 has a pH of 5.6. Acidic components produced from burning of fuels, discharged into the atmosphere, and deposited on soils during precipitation contribute to the acidification of poorly buffered soils.

Soluble Al and Fe ions increase as soil pH decreases, and these ions are subject to hydrolysis. The hydrolytic products, particularly of Al ions and to a lesser extent of Fe ions, also effectively displace exchangeable cations. Acidification is relatively more rapid in the poorly buffered Oxisol and Ultisol soils that are formed from parent materials low in basic cations, and that form kaolinite-type clays as weathering products. The proportion of the total exchange acidity accounted for by exchangeable Al is related to the conditions contributing to acidification. From data reported in the literature, exchangeable Al is relatively more abundant species in geologically acidified soils than in agriculturally acidified soils (Jackson and Reisenauer, 1984).

Exchangeable Al may be estimated indirectly by using various soil properties, including pH, clay content, exchangeable bases, and cation exchange capacity (Jones, 1984). During the extraction of soil samples, H^+ and H_3O^+ may be produced by hydrolysis of Al^{3+} (Kissel et al., 1971).

Amounts and kinds of organic matter influence rates of acidification. Biological activity enhances displacement of bases because CO_2 produced from respiration in roots and organisms provides protons when dissolved in water. The effects of organic matter additions on soil pH depend upon the nature of the organic matter added. Differences in the decomposition process and the products formed will affect the extent to which soil Ca is rendered more leachable.

In some local areas, soil profiles may contain large amounts of sulfides. Oxidation of these sulfides to sulfates results in highly acidic soils. Thus in strip-mined areas, the following reaction may occur and produce soil with a pH as low as 2 (Thomas and Hargrove, 1984):

$$2FeS_2 + 7H_2O + 7^1/_2O_2 \rightleftharpoons 4SO_4^{2-} + 8H^+ + 2Fe(OH)_3 \qquad (7.1)$$

Plant tolerance of acidic soil conditions

Conditions present in highly acidic soils have marked effects on the kinds of plants that can grow and develop. Certain species of plants, particularly of the Ericaceae family, such as rhododendron and blueberry, both the low-bush and high-bush types, grow better in highly acidic than in neutral soils. Seedlings of some conifers, notably western hemlock, grow very well in nutrient solutions at pH 3 (Ryan et al., 1986). In a soil at that pH, factors other than acidity are involved, as discussed later. Species differ widely in their capability to grow under acidic conditions. Reasons for some plants to prefer acidic conditions are not fully understood. Likely factors include more favorable mineral nutrition, especially to meet needs for Fe and Mn, and better resistance to attack by acid tolerant microorganisms.

Legumes are generally considered to be acidity-intolerant, and in many areas large quantities of limestone have been applied to provide more favorable soil environments to grow these crops. There are, however, wide differences between legumes in soil acidity tolerance (Munns, 1986). Generally the acidity tolerance of rhizobial symbionts is similar to the host species with which they enter into a symbiotic relationship.

Plant growth restrictions in highly acidic soils may be due to physical rather than chemical factors. The severe and extended weathering that favors soil acidification may also result in the formation of pedogenic hardpans that limit growth, particularly of deep-rooted plants. The present discussion will focus on the chemical aspects of soil acidity. Excellent comprehensive reviews of soil-plant relationships in acid soils and the use of lime to correct soil acidity are available (Adams, 1984; Kamprath and Foy, 1985).

Soil-plant relationships of Al

Soil acidity and Al in plant establishment and growth. Under very acidic solution culture conditions, H ions may compete directly for uptake with other cations (Rains et al., 1964) and also produce root injury (Islam et al., 1980). In highly to moderately acidic soils with pHs (paste) in the 4 to 5.5 range, secondary effects, rather than direct effects, of abundant H ions more often account for both positive and negative plant responses. Deficient levels of some mineral nutrients, and more favorable levels of others, may occur as a result of acidic soil conditions, but levels of other nutrients and solutes may be toxic to plant growth. The most frequent growth inhibition under acidic conditions is due to soluble Al present in various chemical forms. The pK of the reaction $Al^{3+} \rightarrow Al(OH)^{2+}$ indicates that the predominant species of Al in aqueous solutions below pH 5 is Al^{3+}, but this indicator is subject to the variability of soil conditions and methods of measurement. With increases in pH, Al^{3+} hydrolysis increases, and an increasingly greater proportion of monomeric and polymeric oxyhydroxide complexes is present. The monomeric forms may remain in solution, be held as exchangeable ions on soil colloids, or react with other soil constituents such as phosphate, sulfate, and fluoride anions.

Trivalent Fe ions also hydrolyze, but the pK of the reaction

$$Fe(H_2O)_6^{3+} + H_2O \leftrightharpoons Fe(OH)(H_2O)_5^{2+} + H_3O^+ \qquad (7.2)$$

is much less than for the analagous Al reaction, and thus iron hydrolysis has much less effect on controlling soil pH (Bohn et al., 1985).

Exchangeable Al has been proposed as a basis for establishing a "critical" value, i.e., the maximum Al percentage of cation exchange sites at which plant growth is not inhibited (Adams, 1984). Values for the percentage of Al saturation ranged from 5 to 25 percent for different cultivars of soybeans grown on different soils. The effectiveness with which exchangeable Al serves as a basis for critical values depends upon the influences of root activity on Al concentrations at the soil-plant root interface and the readiness with which soluble and exchangeable forms equilibrate.

Since soil solution is in direct contact with plant roots, soluble Al analysis should provide a better basis than exchangeable Al for defining a "critical" value. Plant growth should be more clearly related to the activity of Al than its concentration in the soil solution, but activity values are not readily quantified. All four inorganic monomeric forms, Al^{3+}, $Al(OH)^{2+}$, $Al(OH)_2^+$, and $Al(OH)_4^-$, and at least some organically bound Al are toxic and must be considered in relating acidic soil conditions to phytotoxic effects (Hodges, 1987). Accurate determinations of Al activity in soil solutions are complicated by the readiness with which the various inorganic forms interconvert and the influences of other soil constituents on their chemical behavior.

An activity of less than about 2 μM Al, both in nutrient solutions and in soil solutions, was estimated as generally being critical to avoid adverse effects on growth of roots of cotton roots (Adams, 1974). However, in particular soils, the restriction of cotton root growth may occur at much lower levels (0.4 μM) (Adams and Hathcock, 1984), and much higher soil solution levels (134 μM) may not have adverse effects (Adams and Moore, 1983). The latter circumstance was attributed to the presence of Al-complexing components. Increasing the Ca concentration from 0.5 to 15 mM approximately doubled the level of monomeric Al required to reduce root elongation by 50 percent (Alva et al., 1986).

Small changes in pH and in exchangeable Al may have large effects on Al activity. After growing three corn hybrids in an acid subsoil for about 2 weeks using a specially designed culture system, Kirlew and Bouldin (1987) found a highly significant difference between the means of the pH of the rhizosphere (pH 4.80) and of the bulk soil (pH 4.91). There was also a small but consistent difference in KCl-extractable Al(3.86 vs. 4.02 cmol kg soil^{-1} in bulk soil vs. rhizosphere soil, respectively). Based on the results from previous studies using a similar soil, Kirlew and Bouldin estimated that soluble Al activity in the rhizosphere and bulk soil could differ two- to threefold.

Next to adverse effects of acidity per se and toxic levels of Al, excess Mn most often inhibits plant growth in highly acidic soils. Calcium concentrations in such soils are relatively low, but generally sufficient to meet plant nutritional needs. Peanuts are an important exception (Cox et al., 1982). Since developing fruits obtain needed Ca by direct absorption, soil solution Ca concentrations need to be relatively high. Blossom-end rot in tomatoes is caused by insufficient soil Ca, but interference in Ca uptake by other cations may be a contributing factor

(Adams, 1984). Secondary effects of a lack of Ca on root growth may occur (Chap. 2).

Entry, distribution, and influences of Al in plants. The first plant manifestation of the presence of high levels of soluble soil Al is a restriction on root growth, and both cell division and cell elongation are adversely affected (Chap. 2). The effects of Al on shoots and roots are interrelated, however, and evidence of adverse effects on shoot growth may be the result of secondary effects from root damage. The interrelationship varies widely within and between species. Three kinds of plant responses in the uptake and distribution of Al in roots and shoots are described by Foy (1984): (1) excluding Al from root uptake; (2) entrapment of Al in roots; and (3) accumulation of Al in shoots but without phytotoxic effects. Both responses 1 and 2 may be involved in the Al tolerance of species such as some cereals. Mechanisms associated with response 3 may account for the noted tolerance of tea to highly acidic soils.

Concentrations of Al in shoots generally are about an order of magnitude lower in shoots than in roots. Shoot Al concentrations at which growth inhibition occurs range widely among different species and varieties. Published data from studies using solution culture techniques show that critical concentrations (amounts associated with a 10 percent decrease in growth) ranged from 20 to over 200 mg Al per kilogram of dry matter (Macnicol and Beckett, 1985). Most of the data were for various cereals, but values for soybean, cotton, alfalfa, and spinach were included. Part of the variation in critical tissue levels probably reflects difficulties in the quantitative determination of Al. At leaf Al concentrations of 100 mg kg^{-1}, shoot growth of coffee plants was reduced (Pavan et al., 1982).

The chemical characteristics that account for the readiness with which Al and P react in soils, as noted previously (Chap. 3), also influence the behavior of these two elements in plants. Many reports in the literature describe their close association at various sites in plant tissues (Foy et al., 1978). At the pHs generally present in plant cells, soluble P decreases by reacting with both monomeric and polymeric Al oxyhydroxides (White, 1976). Whether the immobilization of P that results from any of these reactions is the primary cause of the phytotoxicity of Al has not been clearly established; differences between plants in their effects are likely. Electron microscopy and x-ray emission detector techniques have shown higher Al/P ratios in the nucleus than in cell walls or cytoplasm for roots of two bean cultivars and for cotton (Table 7.1). Other studies by Naidoo et al. (1978) had shown that cv. 'Romano' is more Al sensitive than 'Dade'; sensitivity of cv. 'Hancock' cotton was not indicated. Higher Al/P ratios in the nu-

TABLE 7.1   Ratios of Al/P in Cell Parts of Root Meristems of Snapbeans and Cotton

Plant	Nucleus	Cytoplasm	Cell wall
Snapbean, cv. 'Dade'	0.80	0.25	0.26
Snapbean, cv. 'Romano'	0.40	0.25	0.26
Cotton, cv. 'Hancock'	0.37	0.22	0.20

SOURCE: Naidoo et al., 1978.

cleus than at other cell sites may indicate a preferential binding of Al to esteric P in nucleic acids, and this could have serious consequences in intermediary metabolism involving nucleotides. However, there is no consistent evidence showing that elevated Al levels impair the activities of ATPases and acid phosphatases in plant roots.

Phosphorus immobilizing mechanisms are less damaging to those kinds of plants that have a low P requirement, and to those capable of producing metabolites, such as organic acids, that form stable complexes with hydroxylated Al ions. Citric acid reacts very readily with Al to form a complex that is very stable over a wide pH range (Muchovej et al., 1986). Failures to relate Al levels in soils to phytotoxic effects are attributed to an inability to determine quantitatively the plant-unavailable fraction of Al present in organic complexes. An extensive review of the literature on the occurrence of Al and its influences on plant metabolism has been published by Haug (1983).

Evidence of the beneficial effects of Al on the growth of some plants has been reported, but these responses may be indirect, as will be discussed later. The possibility that Al is an essential nutrient has been suggested, but the experimental evidence is inconclusive (Ballard, 1983).

Effects of Al on legume establishment and growth.   Aluminum is a major cause of adverse effects of soil acidity on establishment and growth of legumes at pHs < 5 (Munns, 1986). In addition to effects of Al on host plants, there are effects on the ability of symbionts to infect the roots and to function effectively. Critical levels have not been well defined, however, because differences in the effects on Al activity of pH, Ca level, and ionic strength, and interactions between them, make it difficult to establish quantitative relationships.

Most of the knowledge regarding rhizobia and their symbiosis with host legume plants has come from studies using solution culture. With these techniques, plant roots and organisms are exposed to media that can be better controlled and thus have fewer variables than when soil is used. Until appropriate comparisons are made of the responses found under the different culture conditions, however, some caution must be observed in interpreting the applicability of results obtained in laboratory studies to field conditions. The sensitivity of rhizobia to differences in soil pH is not readily identified by their responses to differences in acidity of culture media. A liquid media culture technique, developed from determining effects of pH and added Al on various free-living rhizobia, identified about 65 percent of the strains that proved sensitive to these differences in symbiosis with plants grown in containers with an Ultisol subsoil (Keyser et al., 1979). In field studies, the screening test identified 54 percent of 33 strains of *R. trifolii* that proved symbiotically acid sensitive (Thornton and Davey, 1983).

Nodulation of soybeans (cv. 'Fitzroy') inoculated with *Bradyrhizobium japonicum* and grown in solution culture was completely inhibited at 27.8 μM Al, but a much lower concentration (0.40 μM) decreased the numbers of nodules and plant dry weights (Alva et al., 1987). While the relative sensitivity of the two aspects of the N-fixing mechanisms is probably also valid for soil-grown plants, it is doubtful that these same values would apply to soil solution concentrations. Various soil constituents can influence the chemistry and uptake of Al. A soil solution Al concentration of 4 μM inhibited the root development of soybeans grown in subsoil, but adverse growth effects in topsoils were observed only at higher (9- to 134-μM) levels (Adams and Moore, 1983). The difference in response was attributed to a greater complexing of Al by organic constituents in the topsoil.

Other effects of acidity on mineral nutrition

The nutrients most likely to be insufficient for good plant growth in highly acidic soils are N, P, Ca, and Mo. In most soils, however, and particularly at very low pH, the lack of one or more of these four elements may be obscured by the phytotoxic effects of Al, or perhaps of Mn.

The production, uptake, and utilization of mineral N are influenced by acidic conditions. The pH at which rates of mineralization of organic N and of nitrification decrease varies from 6.0 to 6.5 and 6.6 to 8.0, respectively, and below pH 4.5 the latter virtually ceases (Adams, 1984). Under acidic conditions, most plants take up NO_3^- much more readily than NH_4^+, but at least some Ericaceae, including cranberry (Griedanus et al., 1972), and low-bush blueberry (Townsend, 1966), are exceptions.

Utilization of mineral N may be adversely affected under acidic conditions because of soluble Al influences on nitrate reductase (NR) activity, but there are intraspecific and interspecific differences. For example, both growth and in vitro NR activity in shoots of Anza wheat plants grown in nutrient solutions were adversely affected by the additions of Al to the solutions, but UC 44-111 was insensitive to Al at the level used (Table 7.2). The root growth of Anza plants was also adversely affected by Al; however, NR activity, expressed on a root fresh weight basis, was actually higher in plants receiving the Al treatments.

The uptake of Ca into both the roots and tops of clover was more adversely affected than several other nutrients as Al activity in the solution in which plants were grown was increased. (Fig. 7.1). The lower amounts found in the tops with increasing solution Al may be the result of interference in transport from the roots to the shoots, a lowering of the demand for Ca because of its substitution by Al at some binding site, e.g., in membranes, or of some disturbance in Ca metabolism. In line with the latter possibility, interference of Al in calmodulin metabolism has been suggested (Kinraide and Parker, 1987).

With increasing soil acidity, the availability of Mo for plant growth decreases. An increasing proportion of Mo occurs as H_2MoO_4, rather than as MoO_4^{2-} or as $HMoO_4^-$. Formation of polyanions is also favored as the pH decreases. Other conditions favoring low levels of soil Mo are low amounts of organic matter and high levels of Fe oxides.

Excess Mn in highly acidic soils

Oxisols and Ultisols are the soils most likely to have pHs near or below 5 and to contain high concentrations of soluble and exchangeable Mn. Because of severe leaching during the weathering period over which these soils formed, however, their total soil Mn concentrations

TABLE 7.2   Growth and Nitrate Reductase Activities of Two Wheat Genotypes Grown in Nutrient Solutions with Additions of Al

Genotype	Al added, ppm	Tops* Dry weight, g/pot	Tops* NR†	Roots* Dry weight, g/pot	Roots* NR†
Anza	0	2.86[a]	20.1[a]	0.82[ab]	1.3[b]
	0.5	3.02[a]	18.8[a]	1.02[ab]	0.9[b]
	1.5	2.92[a]	18.5[a]	1.14[ab]	1.0[b]
	3.0	2.98[a]	17.2[ab]	1.33[a]	0.9[b]
UC 44-111	0	3.02[a]	16.2[ab]	1.10[a]	0.8[b]
	0.5	1.95[b]	9.4[c]	0.60[bc]	1.0[b]
	1.5	1.91[b]	13.4[bc]	0.47[bc]	2.2[b]
	3.0	1.71[b]	9.7[c]	0.21[c]	6.3[a]

*Within a column, any two means having a letter in common are not significantly different at the 5 percent level by the Duncan multiple range test.
†NR = nitrate reductase; expressed as μm NO_2 h[1] g[1] (fresh weight).
SOURCE: Foy and Fleming, 1982.

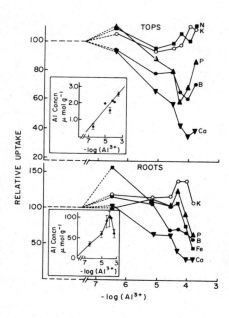

Figure 7.1 Effects of solution Al^{3+} activity on uptake of Al (insert) and the relative uptakes (ratios of the concentrations at a given Al treatment level to concentration in the control) of N, P, K, Ca, B, and Fe by *Trifolium repens* L. cv. 'Grasslands Huia.' (*Reproduced in modified form from Lee and Pritchard, Plant and Soil 82:101–116, 1984, by permission of Martinus Nijhoff.*)

may be relatively low. Elevated soluble and exchangeable Mn concentrations are most pronounced in soils in which there are reducing conditions and a good supply of readily reducible Mn minerals. A commonly occurring Mn mineral that can undergo reduction is MnO_2 (pyrolusite):

$$MnO_2 + 4H^+ + 2e^- \leftrightarrows Mn^{2+} + 2H_2O \tag{7.3}$$

The detrimental effects of excess Mn on shoots are generally more severe than on roots, unlike the case for excess Al effects. Leaf symptoms of injury from excess Mn vary with different species, but chlorosis and necrotic spots are common. Concentrations of soluble Mn at which plant toxicity symptoms appear are commonly in the range 10 to 20 mg L^{-1}, both in nutrient solutions and in soil solutions (Adams, 1984).

The distribution of Mn in various forms in soils is markedly affected by pH. Some results from a study in which different rates of $Ca(OH)_2$ were added to vary the pH of four Coastal Plain (Delaware) soils are shown in Table 7.3. Inorganic and organic (poultry manure) Mn was also added to the soils, and the data shown are mean values from the various treatments. Plant responses indicated that exchangeable Mn generally was the best indicator of soil Mn-supplying capacity, but other fractions were also good indicators for some individual soils.

TABLE 7.3   The Influence of Soil pH on Mn Distribution in Four Soils

Soil	pH*	Percent of extracted Mn		
		EX†	OM‡	Oxide-bound¶
Pocomoke loamy sand	4.1	84	11	7
(Typic Umbraquults)	5.0	48	39	12
	5.8	6	71	22
Rumford loamy sand	4.8	50	17	32
(Typic Hapludults)	5.1	34	28	38
	5.8	22	34	44
Metapeake silt loam	4.7	12	47	42
(Typic Hapludults)	5.2	5	48	47
	5.6	3	56	39
Sassafras silt loam	4.8	19	43	38
(Typic Hapludults)	5.4	4	50	46
	5.9	3	49	48

*In deionized water, 1:1 (w/v) soil-water ratio.
†Exchangeable in $Mg(NO_3)_2$ solution.
‡Organically complexed, by NaOCl extraction.
¶By Mn and Fe oxides.
SOURCE: Sims, 1986.

The plant Mn concentration at which growth impairment occurs is highly variable for different species. A compilation of "critical levels," defined as the minimum tissue concentrations producing a 10 percent yield reduction of soil-grown plants, showed values ranging from 200 to over 1000 mg kg^{-1} (Macnicol and Beckett, 1985). Much higher critical levels in other plants grown in solution cultures were reported. Possibly, in the cases in which soil-grown plants with low Mn concentrations had symptoms identified as Mn toxicity, other factors such as abnormal levels of Al also may have been involved. Interactions with other plant and soil components, especially Ca and Fe, could have an effect on Mn soil-plant relationships.

Uptake of Mn from a medium in which the concentration is maintained decreases as the pH decreases (Islam et al., 1980). Using a flowing culture system, Mn concentrations in corn tops were 44, 14, and 12 mg kg^{-1} in plants grown at pHs of 5.5, 4.0, and 3.3, respectively. Over this same pH range, Fe concentrations in corn were 182, 299, and 258 mg kg^{-1}; wheat showed a similar response. Concentrations of Mn in ginger, tomato, cassava (cv. 'Nina'), and french bean (cv. 'Redland Pioneer') were also lower at the lower pH. There was no consistent response of Fe concentrations to pH in these four species. Soluble Mn is much less inhibitory to growth of rhizobia than Al. Levels of 200-μM Mn had no or little effect on growth of 23 strains of cowpea rhizobia in a pH 4.5 medium, compared to the severe growth inhibition of 25- to 50-μM Al (Keyser and Munns, 1979). These rhizobia had been previously selected for an ability to grow at pH 4.5. Growth differences on exposure to Mn and Al similar to those for the cowpea rhizobia were also found with *Rhizobium japonicum*. As noted previously, results using the liquid culture media techniques also used in these studies were quite accurate in predicting effects of pH and of added Al on the symbiotic effectiveness of plants grown in a greenhouse in Ultisol subsoils (Keyser et al., 1979).

Improvement of plant growth in highly acidic soils

Additions of pulverized limestone are commonly used to raise the pH of highly acidic soils. Effective application generally results in (1) decreasing the amounts of soluble and exchangeable H, Al, and Mn ions; (2) increasing the amounts of soluble and exchangeable Ca; (3) increasing the solubility of Mo; and (4) increasing the soluble and exchangeable Mg, if dolomitic limestone is used.

Generally, the benefit from decreasing the soluble H, Al, and Mn ions is greater than that from increasing soluble Ca. Plant requirements for Ca relative to amounts present even in most acidic soils are low enough that yields usually are not limited by available Ca. For example, leaves of corn grown on an Oxisol with a pH of 4.5, and Al and Ca exchange saturations of 68 and 27 percent, respectively, contained 3.5 percent Ca (Gonzalez-Erico, 1979). When lime was added to bring the pH to 5.0, the exchange saturation of Al and Ca was changed to 43 and 49 percent, respectively, and the yield increased substantially, but the leaf Ca concentration remained the same. In defining Ca needs, the ratio of Ca to the levels of other cations also needs to be considered.

Various methods have been proposed for predicting whether liming will benefit plant growth and for determining the amounts of lime needed, but effectiveness depends upon the kind of soil and cropping conditions. Methods for making such predictions involve determination of pH, most often the best single indicator of the suitability of soils as media for plant growth. To be used as an effective indicator of lime needs, the procedures must include an evaluation of the capacity of the soil for retention of acidity. One commonly used method involves determining the amount of base needed to titrate the test soil to a desired pH. Various buffer methods also have been proposed. These involve determination of the change in pH resulting from adding one or more of a number of buffer chemicals to the test soil.

The amount of lime needed to correct acidity has also been calculated from the amount of exchangeable Al in the soil from the following expression (Kamprath, 1984):

$$CaCO_3 \text{ (t ha}^{-1}) \text{ needed = efficiency factor} \times \text{cmol } (^1/_3 \, Al^{3+}) \, kg^{-1} \quad (7.4)$$

Values of the efficiency factor ranging from 1.5 to 3.3 were indicated from reports of nine studies in which pH responses to lime applications were measured in areas of Oxisol and Ultisol soils.

In some situations, additions of nutrients may be the most effective means of overcoming adverse growth effects in very acidic soils. In highly weathered Oxisols and Ultisols, the lack of sufficient N may be the primary factor limiting plant growth, and fertilizer application may be, at least in the short term, the most appropriate management practice to increase crop yields (Sanchez and Salinas, 1981). Use of nitrate rather than ammoniacal N is preferable since the latter form is not readily absorbed by most plants at low pH, and as described earlier, further acidification can result from the use of the ammoniacal form. Phytotoxic effects of high rates of application of ammoniacal N are less likely in highly acidic than in more neutral soils, since the NH_3/NH_4 ratio is generally lower. Toxic effects are more evident in solution-grown plants. Growth of nonnodulated soybean plants ceased within 10 days when the source of N (1 mM) in the nutrient solution (pH 4.1) was changed from NO_3 to NH_4 (Tolley-Henry and Raper, 1986). Growth in the latter solution was 40 percent less at a pH of 5.1 than at pH 6.1.

Additions of soluble P may aid in the survival and growth of plants in a high-Al environment. The benefit from P applications may be the result of Al immobilization, both outside and inside plants. While the aluminophosphate complexes formed in soils are very insoluble, they still may provide adequate P for those kinds of plants having efficient P uptake mechanisms. In most cases, with regard to cost, the addition of limestone is a better choice than P fertilization for improving plant growth on acid soils.

A genetic approach is another possible means of improving plant growth on acid soils, since there are wide intraspecific and interspecific differences in soil acidity tolerance in the plant kingdom. Some cautions in regards to use of this approach to improve legume plant tolerance, however, have been described by Munns (1986). Acidification may be accelerated by biological N fixation, depending upon soil factors and management practices.

In evaluating tolerance of acidity the conditions under which different species, cultivars, and selections are compared must be clearly defined if the results are to be used effectively as a guide in growing plants in areas of acid soils. A genotype that is tolerant to relatively high levels of Al in a controlled environment solution culture test may or may not grow well in a soil at the same pH (Duncan et al., 1983). Effects of high soil Mn levels can account for some differences in response.

Wetland Soils

Introduction

Poorly drained and inadequately aerated soils occur in many areas of the world, but their exact extent is poorly defined. Dudal (1976) has estimated that 12 percent of the world's land area has excess water at some time during the year. These lands, which include tidal marshes, contain some of the most productive ecosystems found anywhere.

The main associations of soils that are poorly drained, as grouped under the Food and Agriculture Organization (1974) International Legend are gleysols, fluvisols, vertisols, histisols, and planosols. Collectively, they occupy about 1.61×10^9 ha (Dudal, 1976). These soils mostly are classified as Aqualfs, Aquents, Aquepts, Aquolls, Aquox, Aquods, Aquults, Vertisols, Fluvents, and Histosols in soil taxonomy (Soil Survey Staff, 1975).

Much of the wetlands located in the major industrialized nations has been drained artificially. Some of this drained land is located in low rainfall areas where the drainage of irrigated lands helps control soil salinity. However, most drains have been installed to reduce waterlogging. Nosenko and Zonn (1976) have estimated that about 1.55×10^6 ha have been drained. About 0.65×10^6 ha of that are located in North and Central America.

Areas that require drainage

One of the major areas that often requires drainage to produce good crops is the low, flat coastal plain of the United States. This coastal plain extends almost the entire length of the eastern U.S. coastline and, except for the delta of the Mississippi River, across the Gulf of Mexico coastline to Texas. Precipitation ranges from 1000 to 1500 mm year^{-1}. A wide range of temperatures and evaporative conditions exists because the area runs from the subtropical parts of Texas and Florida to the less favorable temperatures of the New England coastline.

The extreme outer fringes of the coastal plains are a series of tidal marshes, which range in elevation from zero to about 3 m above mean sea level. These fringes are subject to frequent overflows either by direct action of the tides or by tidal obstruction of river outflows. During periods of high tides, flood flows from rivers that cross the coastal plains or high-intensity on-shore winds can cause long-term flooding unless the areas are protected by dikes or levees.

Areas of the coastal plain inland from the tidal marshes are less affected by tidal action but still are subjected to inundation when the natural outflow of streams is blocked by tidal action. These areas often have clay subsoils that are nearly impermeable, thus restricting internal drainage. The nearly flat topography has a number of depressional areas that range in size from a few hectares to several hundred thousand hectares, represented by the Dismal Swamp of Virginia and North Carolina and the Okefenokee Swamp of Georgia and Florida. The productive capacity of the coastal plains for upland crops largely depends on a sound land drainage program.

Broad, flat lowlands border the rivers that dissect the upper coastal plains. The best-known example is the Mississippi River delta. These areas are subject to overflow and sometimes to runoff from adjacent higher lands that surround them.

The glaciated areas of the north central states are still another major drainage problem. These areas have flat plains, depressions, and lakebeds that require drainage for improved yields of upland crops. The major problem is providing adequate outlets to carry off excess precipitation collected by surface and subsurface drainage systems.

Effects of flooding an aerated soil

Many experiments have been conducted to evaluate the consequences of flooding soils to grow paddy rice. These results show the major differences in soil characteristics that are important in plant growth.

When an aerated soil is covered by a layer of water, the supply of O to the soil is severely reduced. Oxygen diffuses 10^4 times slower through water than through air space, but some O is carried to the soil surface through convection in turbulent water. The total supply of O, however, will be much less than that consumed by roots and organisms in the soil profile. A thin layer of aerobic soil will persist at the soil surface, but deeper soil layers will undergo progressively more severe reducing conditions (Fig. 7.2). The thickness of the aerated soil layers will depend on the thickness and turbulence of the water layer above the soil, on temperature, and on soil organic matter content.

Roots and soil organisms obtain their energy from the oxidation of organic substrates in a series of enzymatically mediated reactions. In aerobic respiration, molecular O is the usual terminal acceptor of electrons. This O is combined with H to form water. The other end product is CO_2. This process releases about 300 kcal of biologically useful energy per mole of glucose (Russell, 1977).

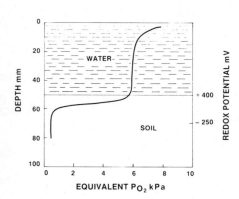

Figure 7.2 Oxygen partial pressures and redox potentials as affected by soil depth. (*Modified from Patrick et al., 1985, used with permission.*)

When molecular O is exhausted, many microorganisms use other substances from their surroundings as electron acceptors. Roots probably cannot use these other acceptors, but the root environment becomes progressively more reduced biochemically as anaerobic microorganisms sequentially deplete the soil system of terminal acceptors. These reactions are governed by redox potentials, with those materials having the highest redox potentials—the highest affinity for electrons—being reduced before those with lower redox potentials. Anaerobic respiration of glucose releases about 16 kcal of biologically useful energy, only 5.3 percent of the aerated soil value (Russell, 1977).

Redox potential. A decrease in redox potential is the most striking electrochemical change associated with flooding a soil. The redox potential falls sharply upon flooding, reaches a minimum within a few days, rises to a peak, and then decreases asymptotically with time (Fig. 7.3). The amount and chemical composition of organic matter affects the rate of decline in redox potential (Fig. 7.4), as does the percent of active iron and manganese (Fig. 7.5). When nitrate fertilizer is added to a reduced soil, the redox potential temporarily rises (Fig. 7.6).

The basic reduction process can be considered as the transfer of an electron to a hydrogen ion. The redox potential therefore depends on hydrogen ion concentration. A well-aerated solution's redox potential falls linearly with pH from $+630$ mV at pH 5.0 to $+510$ mV at pH 7.0.

The various reduction reactions that can take place as a solution becomes more anaerobic depend on the redox potential at which they are most poised. The *poise* of a solution is defined as the amount of electrons, as a reducing substance, that must be added to give a unit reduction in the redox potential. Thus, a solution that accepts a large amount of a reducing substance for a small change in redox potential

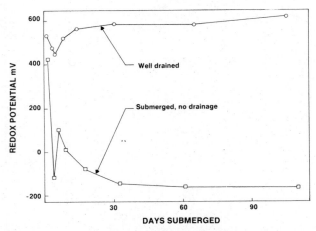

Figure 7.3 Changes in redox potential with time of a well-drained and submerged soil. (*Data of Ponnamperuma, 1981; used with permission.*)

is well-poised. The reactions that are poised at a high redox potential go almost to completion before those poised at an appreciably lower potential become important. Redox potentials of some typical soil systems are given in Table 7.4.

Some of the reactions listed in Table 7.4 are reversible, such as those of iron and manganese; however, some are not. For example, NO_2^- is reduced more easily than NO_3^-, so any NO_2^- formed from NO_3^- is reduced to gaseous N_2O or molecular N; both are readily lost to the atmosphere. When Fe^{2+} is not present, SO_4^{2-} combines with H to form H_2S, which is also lost to the atmosphere.

Soil pH. The pH of an acid soil increases upon flooding, while that of a basic soil decreases (Fig. 7.7). For most soils, a stable pH of between

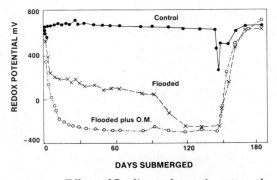

Figure 7.4 Effects of flooding and organic matter addition on redox potential. (*Data of I. R. Willett, 1978; used with permission.*)

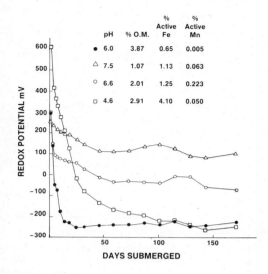

	pH	% O.M.	% Active Fe	% Active Mn
●	6.0	3.87	0.65	0.005
△	7.5	1.07	1.13	0.063
○	6.6	2.01	1.25	0.223
□	4.6	2.91	4.10	0.050

Figure 7.5 Changes in redox potential with time for four soils kept submerged. (*Data of Ponnamperuma, 1981; used with permission.*)

6.3 and 7.5 is reached after several weeks of flooding. Some peat soils and acid sulfate soils may have pH values of 5 even in the flooded state. The pH changes are small in iron-deficient soils.

The increases in pH of acid soils usually are brought about by the reduction of Fe^{+3} to Fe^{+2}, but this reaction is stabilized after a few weeks by the partial pressure of CO_2. The reductions in pH of calcareous and sodic soils are brought about by the accumulations of CO_2.

The pH changes that occur after waterlogging profoundly affect the equilibria of hydroxides, sulfides, phosphates, carbonates, and silicates. These equilibria affect the precipitation and dissolution of solids, the sorption and desorption of ions, and the soil solution concentrations of such nutritionally significant elements as P, Cu, Zn, Mn, and Fe. Toxic concentrations of Al, Mn, Fe, and organic acids may be modified by the pH changes associated with waterlogging.

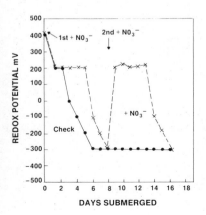

Figure 7.6 Changes in redox potential of the plow layer of a silty clay loam soil with and without nitrate additions. (*Data of Bailey and Beauchamp, 1971; used with permission.*)

TABLE 7.4   Redox Potentials of Typical Soil Systems at 25°C

Soil system	Redox potentials, mV	
	At pH 5	At pH 7
$O_2 + 4H^+ + 4e^- = 2H_2O$	930	820
$NO_3 + 2H^+ + 2e^- = NO_2 + H_2O$	530	420
$MnO_2 + 4H^+ + 2e^- = Mn^{+2} + 2H_2O$	640	410
$Fe(OH)_3 + 3H^+ + e^- = Fe^{+2} + 3H_2O$	170	-180
$(SO_4)^{-2} + 10H^+ + 8e^- = H_2S + 4H_2O$	-70	-220
$CO_2 + 8H^+ + 8e^- = CH_4 + 2H_2O$	-120	-240
$2H^+ + 2e^- = H_2$	-295	-413

SOURCE: Russell, 1973.

Electrical conductance. The electrical conductance of the soil solution increases after submergence then reaches a maximum and declines to a reasonably stable value, which varies with the soil. The changes reflect the balance between reactions that release ions and those that inactivate them. In normal paddy rice soils, electrical conductances occur in the order of 0.2 to 0.4 dS m^{-1} at 25°C. In sandy soils high in organic matter and in acid sulfate soils, electrical conductances may exceed 0.4 dS m^{-1}, which is the harmful limit for rice. Ionic strength patterns follow specific conductance patterns (Ponnamperuma, 1981).

Organic acids. Generally, decomposition of organic matter in soil is slowed by the absence of molecular O. A specific feature of anaerobic decomposition of organic matter is the accumulation of organic acids, such as acetic, butyric, formic, propionic, lactic, and valeric acids. Due

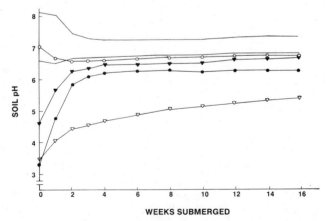

Figure 7.7 Kinetics of the pH values for six submerged soils. (*Data of Ponnamperuma, 1981; used with permission.*)

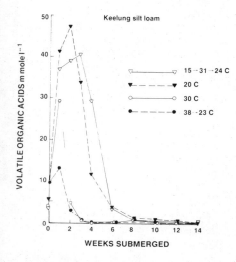

Figure 7.8 Influence of temperature on the kinetics of volatile organic acids of Keelung silt loam soil. (*Data of Ponnamperuma, 1981; used with permission.*)

to retardation of decomposition processes, these accumulations are especially abundant at low temperatures.

The production of organic soils is curvilinear with a peak value to 10 to 50 mmol L^{-1} of soil solution (Fig. 7.8). This peak occurs several days to weeks after submergence. The amounts and peak concentrations of acids depend on soil, temperature, and organic matter. Some of these organic acids can be quite phytotoxic (Lynch, 1983).

Anaerobic microorganisms. Submergence brings about an initial increase in the numbers of aerobic bacteria as organic acids increase, followed by a decline. Obligatory anaerobic bacteria increase to a maximum much later than aerobes, and then their numbers also decline (Fig. 7.9). Enzymatic activity also is changed as the microbial populations fluctuate.

Nitrogen in waterlogged soils. Throughout the waterlogged soils of the world, N is the nutrient most likely to be deficient. The same conditions that favor high plant productivity also favor a rapid turnover and loss of N from the soil. The N supply for plants growing on flooded soils comes from (1) nitrates present at the time of flooding an intermittently flooded soil, (2) N mineralized from organic matter and plant residue under waterlogged conditions, and (3) N applied as fertilizer.

Nitrogen mineralization under anaerobic soil conditions does not proceed past the ammonium stage. The anaerobic microorganisms responsible for mineralization require less N than aerobic microorganisms so the anaerobes can mineralize N at greater C/N ratios than aerobes. The low N requirement by anaerobes results in a more rapid

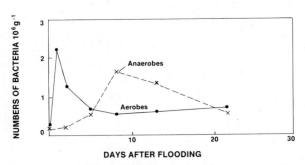

Figure 7.9 Changes in microbial population with time after flooding a paddy soil incubated at 35°C. (*Data of Takai and Kamura, 1966; used with permission.*)

release of ammonia than would be indicated from the C/N ratios prevalent in release of N during aerobic decomposition.

Under waterlogged field conditions, denitrification of applied N fertilizer can be severe unless special precautions are taken. Nitrogen fertilizers applied to the water layer or the uppermost soil layers, which is oxidized, will be converted to NO_3 by nitrification. This nitrate will be leached downward into the reduced soil where the nitrate will be denitrified and then lost as N_2 or N_2O gases. Frequent fluctuations in soil water content present an ideal environment for losses of fertilizer N. For example, experiments have shown that yields of rice grown on N-deficient soils are decreased considerably by draining and reflooding a soil while on soils with excess N, rice yields are increased by draining and reflooding the soil (Patrick et al., 1967a). Placement of urea or ammonium fertilizer deep enough to be located in the soil reducing zone increases rice yield (Mikkelson and Finfrock, 1957; Patrick et al., 1967b) because no further reduction of N will occur.

Sulfur nutrition in waterlogged soils. The sulfate ion readily leaches downward, similarly to nitrate. When the redox potential reaches a low enough value (around -150 mV at pH 7.0) the sulfate is reduced to sulfide. If ferrous iron is present, the very insoluble ferrous sulfide is formed. Presumably, plants, such as rice, growing in flooded soils obtain their sulfur from oxidation of the ferrous sulfide to the more soluble ferric sulfides in the aerated zone of the rhizosphere.

Phosphorus in waterlogged soils. In oxidized soils, much of the P is precipitated in relatively insoluble calcium, ferric, and aluminum phosphates. When the soil becomes anaerobic, the ferric iron becomes reduced to ferrous iron and the ferric phosphate becomes solubilized. Thus, P availability markedly increases upon prolonged flooding of the soil. Phosphorus solubility is also increased in alkaline soils because soil pH is lowered upon flooding. Available P in flooded soils bears almost no resemblance to that predicted by standard soil tests for P conducted on oxidized soils.

Reactions of other elements in waterlogged soils. Nitrogen, Mn, Fe, and S undergo direct transformations of valence in waterlogged soils. The solubility of many other elements will change due to secondary effects, but their concentrations are much less understood. Their concentrations are affected by changes in solubility, precipitation, sorption, chelation, and pH changes. The solubility of silicon, important to rice nutrition, generally increases while that of boron decreases with submergence.

Surface drainage

Surface drainage problems arise from the inability of excess water to move freely over the land surface to a surface outlet or into and through the soil profile to a satisfactory underground outlet. These surface drainage problems usually are found on (1) areas of extremely flat topography where the soils are shallow or underlain by an impermeable soil stratum; (2) areas that have shallow natural or artificially developed depressions that hold water; (3) areas of relatively level bottom lands or terraces that are subject to runoff from surrounding areas; (4) areas subject to overflow from streams or rivers; and (5) areas subject to submergence by either direct tide action or effects of tides on river outflow.

Effective surface drainage must remove the factor that contributes the excess water problem and establish a satisfactory outlet system to prevent future flooding.

Land smoothing. The simplest form of surface drainage is land smoothing. Dead furrows, headlands, other implement scars, ditch bank spoils, and natural depressions or ridges that tend to impound or restrict water flow are leveled off or filled in through the use of earth-moving equipment.

Land smoothing may be the only operation needed for surface drainage if the ground surface has sufficient slope toward an outlet. In extremely flat areas, a natural gradient may not exist, and one must be created by grading to give a positive slope toward an outlet.

Bedding. Bedding is one of the earliest drainage practices. It consists of turning furrows toward the middle to form a ridge flanked on either side by furrows or ditches to carry the water from the field. Some of the early bedding systems in England consisted of broad high ridges 10 to 20 m wide with a crown about 1 m higher than the drainage furrows. Rows are parallel to the beds.

Cross-slope ditch systems.   The cross-slope ditch system sometimes is called a drainage-type terrace. This system collects and conveys excess water to a safe surface outlet. From 80 to 100 percent of the water storage capacity is below ground level, in comparison to about 50 percent for the standard terrace. A gradient of about 0.5 percent along the ditch is desirable but may vary from 0.1 to 1.0 percent, depending upon conditions. Alignment should be as parallel as possible.

Field ditches.   There are two broad categories of field ditch systems: random ditch systems and uniform, or parallel, systems. The random system is used where fields have depressions too deep or too extensive to fill by land smoothing. These ditches connect each depression and lead the excess water to a suitable outlet. They are of sufficient capacity to drain the depression rapidly.

The uniform, or parallel, ditch systems are commonly used on flat, poorly drained soils that are too uneven to permit drainage by land leveling alone. Crop rows are laid out at right angles to the ditches. Spacing of the ditches depends on the length of row that can safely carry runoff without excess soil erosion.

Water table control ditches.   In moderately to highly permeable soils, it may be important to remove surface water rapidly and also to lower the water table to facilitate crop production. In these cases, deeper field ditches with steep sides can be used effectively. When water control structures are installed, the system can be used to control the water table depth during dry periods.

Tidal marsh drainage.   Practices to drain tidal marshes generally follow those developed for the Fens of England or the Lowlands of the Netherlands. Dikes or levees are constructed to prevent tidal overflow. A system of field ditches is then constructed to control water table depth and to carry excess water to an outlet. The outlets are protected with gravity-operated tide gates that allow water outflow at low tides, but not water inflow during high tides. Pump drainage is used when tides are excessive, when upland floods occur, or when peat lands have subsided below water level at low tide.

Subsurface drainage

Pipe drains and mole drains are used as subsurface drains. Concrete tile, burned clay tile, corrugated plastic tubing, or other perforated tubing is used for pipe drains.

Pipe drains. Concrete or burned clay tiles that are used for laterals are laid end to end in the bottom of a trench that is then backfilled. Some tiles also are perforated. Water enters the lateral tile line through perforations and cracks between the ends of adjoining tile. Water then flows by gravity to main lines that carry the excess water to the outlet of the system.

Corrugated plastic tubing largely has replaced concrete or burned clay tiles in recent years. High-density polyethylene and polyvinyl chloride tubing are used. Corrugated tubing weighs about 4 percent of concrete tile, is resistant to soil chemicals, can be extruded in long sections, is easy to join, and is easy to handle in the field. It is suitable to install using a mole plow. The corrugated plastic tubing, however, is subject to rodent damage and has a greater hydraulic roughness. It can be made with a porous fabric covering to prevent inflow of soil particles.

Mole drains. Mole drains are cylindrical channels artificially produced in subsoil without digging a trench from the surface. They are similar to pipe drains except that they are not lined with a stabilizing material.

Moles are temporary drains. Where soil conditions are adequate, mole drains function effectively for a few years, and then their carrying capacity deteriorates. Their maximum life is 10 to 30 years. Mole drains fail principally because the unlined soil is not sufficiently stable to maintain the channel. In general, the greater the clay content of the soil surrounding the mole drain, the greater the stability, but clay content alone cannot be used as a good index for suitability for mole drainage. Small-sized moles are more stable than large-sized ones.

Mole drains, where suitable, are laid across and over pipe drains. Moles can be connected directly to the pipe drains or may empty in a gravel envelope around the pipe drain. Spacings will vary from 1 to 10 m and length usually is less than 500 m. Depth depends upon depth to a stable soil layer.

Soil consequences of drainage

When compared to the same soils before artificial drainage has been installed, the drained soils have the following characteristics:

1. Soil strengths are increased.
2. Oxygen concentrations are greater.
3. Carbon dioxide concentrations are lower.
4. Ethylene concentrations are lower.
5. Diurnal temperature fluctuations are increased.
6. pH of an alkaline soil is increased and that of an acid soil is decreased.
7. Specific ion conductance is decreased.
8. Nitrification rates have increased and denitrification rates have decreased.
9. Ammonium ion concentrations are lower.
10. Manganese has been oxidized from Mn^{+2} to Mn^{+4}.
11. Iron has been oxidized from Fe^{+2} to Fe^{+3}.
12. Any sulfur in the S^{-2} state tends to be oxidized to the S^{+6} state.
13. Organic acid concentrations are lower.
14. Concentrations of Fe, Mn, P, Si, Cu, B, Zn, and Mo are altered in the soil solution.

Saline Soils

Salinization

Plants cannot grow in soils containing high concentrations of soluble salts, and at soil salinity levels less than lethal, plant growth may be impaired. These conditions may be temporary or permanent, depending upon the water status of the soil. Poor drainage conditions enhance the likelihood of salinization. Areas of the world where salinity prevents or limits plant growth are increasing. Much of this increase results from irrigation of crops with waters containing relatively high concentrations of soluble salts. Under such conditions, the rate of uptake of water exceeds the rate of uptake of salts. Of the 230×10^6 ha irrigated worldwide, one-third are salt-affected (Epstein et al., 1980).

In areas of uneven topography, soil salinization may result from deposition of salt-bearing leachates from areas of higher elevation on the soils at lower elevation. Increases in salinity from this kind of seepage may be the result of long-term changes in climate that influence salt retention, or changes in land use and management that increase the quantity of percolating water. The processes involved in the formation of various types of saline seeps are discussed by Brown et al. (1982). The total area affected by such seepage in the northern Great Plains has been estimated at 8×10^5 ha (Black et al., 1981).

In areas subject to soil salinization, provisions for drainage are crucial for maintaining crop production (Kelley, 1949; Raloff, 1984). Where irrigation agriculture is practiced in enclosed basins, increasingly larger areas and production costs must be committed to provide suitable ponds for containing the drain water. Obviously, with these limitations, containment of drain water in ponds is not a long-term solution to salinization. Impoundment of drainage waters can also lead to other problems seriously impacting production agriculture, as shown by the accumulation of Se to toxic levels in parts of the San Joaquin Valley of California (Letey et al., 1986).

Measurement of soluble salts

Soluble salts in soils can be determined simply as the weight of total dissolved solids (TDS) per unit volume of solution extracted by suction or pressure. However, measurements which more accurately reflect effects of salts on properties of soil water are more meaningful for predicting influences on soil-plant relationships.

Solutions containing soluble salts more readily conduct an electrical current than does pure water. Electrical conductance (EC) is linearly related to the amount of salts present, and this relationship provides another means of determining salt concentration. To determine EC, current flow is measured when a known potential is applied across two electrodes immersed in the water sample or extracted soil solution being analyzed. Account is taken of the size of the electrodes and the distance between them. The measured current is calibrated for flow between two electrodes of unit area spaced 1-cm apart. Conductance is the reciprocal of resistance, and thus is expressed as mhos (ohms^{-1}) or mmhos/cm^{-1}. In SI units, conductance is expressed as decisiemens (dS) m^{-1} (1 dS m^{-1} = 1 mmho cm^{-1}).

Generally, soils are considered saline if the EC of the extracted soil solution is greater than 4 dS m^{-1}. As described in Chap. 1, solutes decrease the water potential ψ_w, i.e., their concentration per molar volume decreases the capacity of the liquid phase to do work. The contribution of soluble salts toward decreasing the ψ_w, the osmotic potential ψ_o, and EC are directly related:

$$\psi_o = EC \, (-0.036 \text{ MPa}) \qquad (7.5)$$

Total soil water potential ψ_s includes the matric potential ψ_m and ψ_o. Volumetric ψ_w is expressed in SI units as pascals (Pa), kilopascals (kPa), or megapascals (MPa). These are related to the older unit, 1 bar = 100 kPa = 0.1 MPa.

The effectiveness of soluble ions in chemical reactions depends upon their activity a (see Chap. 3), and a is, in part, a function of ionic strength I. Using data from 151 river waters and soil solutions, Griffin and Jurinak (1973) developed the following regression to relate I (mol L$^-$) and EC (dS m^{-1}):

$$I = 0.0127 \, EC \tag{7.6}$$

To calculate I, account was taken of ion pairing, a significant factor in solutions containing relatively high levels of sulfates and carbonates. The proportionality constant value indicated in Eq. 7.6 is not universal for describing I/EC relationships, as shown by the difference in the regression lines for NaCl and MgSO$_4$ (Fig. 7.10). No correction was made for ion pairing in calculating these regressions.

Because of adverse effects on soil aggregation, Na ions can have very important effects on the physical properties of soils, depending upon the nature of the colloids present and the abundance of other ions. The latter effect is expressed in the sodium adsorption ratio SAR, a parameter commonly used to characterize irrigation waters and liquid phases of saline soils. The SAR is calculated as $(Na)/[(Ca + Mg)/2]^{-1/2}$ where the concentrations of the three cations are expressed as moles of charge (gram equivalents) per liter. By definition, sodic soils are those with SAR values exceeding 15. Reported values of EC and SAR for waters and soil solutions are shown in Table 7.5.

Except under the circumstance where soil Cl$^-$ is abundant, Ca^{2+} is not a major contributor to saline conditions since its salts are relatively insoluble. A saturated solution of gypsum has an EC of about 2 dS m^{-1}, and CaCO$_3$ is much less soluble.

Effects of salinity on plant growth and water relationships

Salinity tolerance of plants. The plant kingdom is divided into two broad groups as regards differences in salt tolerance. Halophytes, those plants native to saline environments, are the most tolerant.

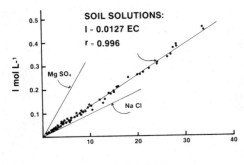

Figure 7.10 Relationship between ionic strength I and electrical conductivity EC in soil solutions and single salt solutions. For soil solutions regression, composition corrected for complexation. (*Reproduced from J. J. Jurinak, "Soil Salinity under Irrigation," Ecol. Studies 51:15–31, 1984, by permission of Springer-Verlag New York, Inc.*)

TABLE 7.5 Salinity in Waters and in Saturation Extracts from Soils

Sources	EC, dS m^{-1}	SAR
Waters*:		
Colorado River, Yuma, AZ	1.38	3.2
Feather River, Nicolaus, CA	0.09	0.2
Mississippi River, Luling Ferry, LA	0.42	0.9
Pacific Ocean†	46	26
Pecos River, Artesia, NM	3.37	3.6
Sacramento River, Sacramento, CA	0.18	0.7
James River, Huron, SD	1.23	3.1
Soil solutions‡:		
Normal soils	0.6–1.8	0.8–7.5
Saline soils	8.8–13.9	10.5–17.4
Nonsaline-alkali soils	1.74–3.16	13.9–35.0
Saline-alkali soils	5.6–16.7	27.6–67.6

*From Ayers and Westcot (1985) except that marked †.
†From Epstein (1983) and Kingsbury and Epstein (1986).
‡From Richards (ed.) (1954) USDA Agric. Handbook, no. 60.

Glycophytes are relatively less tolerant, but have wide intraspecific and interspecific differences in sensitivity to saline conditions; this group includes most crop species. Plant differences in tolerance are modified to varying degrees by other conditions of growth. Phytotoxic effects depend upon both amounts and kinds of salts responsible for saline soil conditions. Only glycophytic plants will be discussed here. Plants of this group that take up and transport Na and/or Cl into shoots least readily, when grown at moderate (below about 100-mM) salt concentrations, are called "excluders."

Effects of saline conditions on the growth and nutrient uptake of many crops have been reviewed (Bernstein, 1975; Kafkafi, 1984; Levitt, 1972). The compilation by Maas (1986) shows wide differences among plants, even among glycophytes, in salinity tolerance. Sensitive plants, those for which growth is approximately halved when grown at soil solution salinities less than 4 dS m^{-1}, include many tree crops, beans, rice, and some ornamentals. Other conditions of growth influence soil-plant relationships under saline conditions. For example, the effects of soil salinity on the growth of beans, a salt-intolerant species, were related to aboveground humidity, but this relationship was not noted in studies with cotton, which is more salt-tolerant (Hoffman et al., 1971). Account must be taken of differences in amounts of salt in different parts of the rooting zone in applying salinity criteria to predict possible impairment of plant growth (Papadopoulos and Rendig, 1983). Drip irrigation can result in very unequal distribution of salts in the soil profile.

Changes in sensitivity to saline conditions also occur during ontogenesis and these changes may be either positive or negative, depending upon species, cultivar, and conditions of growth. Corn showed more sensitivity to salinity during vegetative growth than during grain-fill (Maas et al., 1983). For most of the 16 cultivars tested, the threshold values (salinity level above which yields were reduced) were 1.0 dS m^{-1} (time-averaged) for the dry matter produced during the first 21 days of growth. Threshold values of 4.5 to 5.0 dS m^{-1} were estimated for grain yields. Salinities did not interfere with germination unless they were in the 10-dS m^{-1} range.

In field plot studies with barley, cv. 'Briggs' was more sensitive than cv. 'Arivat' to saline conditions during the seedling stage, but was less sensitive at maturity (Lynch et al., 1982). During later stages of growth, tomato plants became more tolerant of salinity (Papadopoulos et al., 1985). Saline conditions had a greater adverse effect on fresh fruit weights than on shoot weights, as also noted by others (Shalhevet and Yaron, 1973). Fruits from plants grown under the more saline conditions had higher percentages of solids.

Effects of salinity on leaf and root growth.   Leaf expansion rates are relatively lower under saline than under nonsaline conditions for various plants, including cotton (Shalhevet and Hsiao, 1987), and sugar beets (Fig. 7.11). This slowing of growth has been attributed to effects of salts in lowering the water potential ψ_w and thus influencing turgor forces that produce cell expansion, as described in the discussion of plant-water relationships in Chap. 1. Slower leaf expansion rates may be only a temporary response and not the explanation for the adverse effects of salinity on growth over longer periods. Applied pressure (0.48 MPa) produced by growth in a pressure chamber to simulate salinity-generated turgor forces, also increased expansion rates of

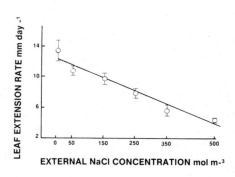

Figure 7.11   Effects of salinity on extension rates of sugar beet leaves. (*Reproduced from Papp et al., Plant, Cell and Environment 6:675–677, 1983, by permission of Blackwell Scientific Publications.*)

leaves of wheat and barley, but this response was only temporary (Termaat et al., 1985).

More precise measurements of intercellular and intracellular salt distribution will be necessary for a better understanding of the mechanisms that influence leaf expansion rates. In order to lower the ψ gradient and thus decrease the tendency for water to enter the cell, thereby decreasing turgor, salts would need to have relatively greater effects on the solution in the apoplast than on cytosolic fluids. The external-internal ψ difference needed to overcome the resistance encountered by water moving to growing tissue, and thus for cell growth to occur, has been estimated as -0.3 MPa (Cosgrove, 1986). Plant and environmental differences that influence plant growth affect this estimate.

Root growth is often less sensitive to salinity than shoot growth. Results from a number of studies showing this difference for barley, bermudagrass, and sorghum have been reviewed by Munns and Termaat (1986). For these three plant species, low to moderate salinity improved root growth. To prevent impairment of root development of cotton plants grown in saline solution culture, Ca levels in the solution had to be maintained above those needed for optimum plant growth under nonsaline conditions (Cramer et al., 1986). The amelioration of salt stress effects by Ca are also related to the abundance and proportions of other ions, and in soils these can be highly variable.

If the amount of Na in the soil relative to Ca is high, root development also may be impaired because of soil physical factors. Exchangeable Na ions on clays can weaken soil structure and increase soil density (Emerson, 1984).

Osmotic adjustment.   Plants have mechanisms providing some ability to retain existing internal U gradients when solute concentrations of the external solution in contact with the roots undergoes a change. This adaptation is called *osmotic adjustment* (Bernstein, 1961). One mechanism by which this is accomplished is through the transfer of salts into vacuoles, thus lessening the likelihood of adverse effects on organelles and enzymes in the cytoplasm (Coughlan and Wyn Jones, 1980). A second means of adjustment is by increased production of compatible organic solutes in the cytoplasm. This results in lowering the ψ and in producing a gradient more favorable for the movement of water into cells. An inverse relationship between concentrations of Cl and of organic anions was indicated in tomato plants grown in sand cultures irrigated with solutions salinized to different levels (Papadopoulos et al., 1985). The relationships of osmotic adjustment to other responses of plants to salinity stress are shown schematically in Fig. 7.12.

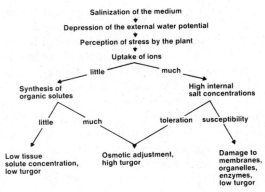

Figure 7.12   The cardinal responses of plants, their organs, tissues, and cells to salinity. (*Reproduced from E. Epstein, Better Crops for Food, CIBA Foundation Symposium 97, pp. 61–82, 1983, by permission of CIBA and the author.*)

Whether adjustment to salinity stress is accomplished by solute redistribution or biosynthesis, expenditure of metabolic energy is required , and thus the response is related to the processes by which energy is produced. A low soil water potential ψ_s in a nonsaline soil may have a more adverse effect on plant growth than at the same ψ_s in a saline soil. An example from a study with cotton plants is shown in Fig. 7.13. Leaf growth rates and biomass accumulations decrease less rapidly as the ψ_s decreases because of saline conditions than because

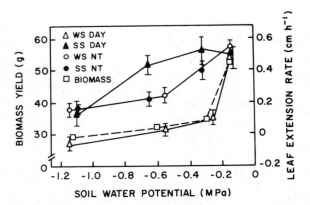

Figure 7.13   Relationship of cotton leaf extension rates during light (DAY) and dark (NT) periods, and final biomass yields (fresh weight), to soil water potentials, with plants under water stress (WS) and salt stress (SS). Vertical bars indicate standard error. (*Reproduced from J. Shalhevet and T. C. Hsiao, Irrigation Science 7:249–264, 1986, by permission of Springer-Verlag, Heidelberg.*)

of a water deficit. Osmotic adjustment is less energy demanding when accomplished by regulating salt distribution than by increased biosynthesis of organic metabolites.

The detrimental effects of salinity on plant growth, protein formation, and CO_2 assimilation of broad beans (cv.'Ackerperle') were greater when grown under shade than when grown at a higher light intensity (Helal and Mengel, 1981). This lesser capacity of the shade-grown plants to produce metabolic products for coping with salinity stress might be interpreted as the basis for poorer plant growth under saline conditions, but other evidence needs to be considered. Leaves of barley plants grown in nutrient solutions containing NaCl had higher concentrations of both soluble and insoluble carbohydrates than leaves of plants grown in similar solutions without added NaCl (Munns et al., 1982). These seemingly discrepant results from the two studies may be because of plant species differences, but more detailed knowledge about the functioning of regulatory mechanisms is needed to better interpret physiological responses to salinity stress.

Physiological effects of salinity. Whether or not higher salt levels in tissue have a direct effect on growth through influences on water potentials and cell turgor forces, physiological reasons for adverse effects of salinity on leaf growth have not been well-defined. Impaired functioning of photosynthetic mechanisms and of photosynthate metabolism have been related to saline conditions, but the level of salinity and the time required for impairment raise doubts as to whether these adverse effects are a primary cause of slowed growth. In sugar beet plants, for example, such effects appeared only at high (> 350 mol NaCl m^{-3}) salinity levels (Papp et al., 1983). At low to moderate salinity, C accumulation was related more closely to reduction in photosynthetic surface area than to photosynthetic rate per unit leaf area. A similar conclusion was drawn from studies with spinach grown in solution culture with NaCl added to give a ψ_o of -0.83 MPa. Plants grown with the added NaCl had smaller, slightly chlorotic leaves. With cotton (cv. 'Acala SJ-1'), net assimilation of CO_2 was 46 and 29 mg dm^{-2} day^{-1} for plants grown in solutions having a ψ_o of -0.04 and -0.64 MPa, respectively (Hofmann and Phene, 1971).

The adverse effects of salinity on photosynthetic rates in some instances are associated with decreases in chlorophyll content. In the sugar beet studies referred to above (Papp et al., 1983), leaf chlorophyll content per unit leaf area showed some increase as salinity levels increased.

Leaves of plants grown under saline conditions are commonly thicker and more succulent than those of nonsaline plants. The thicker leaves have higher ratios of mesophyll surface area to total leaf surface area (Longsteth and Nobel, 1979). The potential for greater photosynthesis resulting from the larger amount of area for CO_2 absorption is negated by an even greater resistance to the entry of CO_2 into mesophyll cells.

The trigger for physiological responses to saline conditions is not certain. Messages transmitted from root to shoot via hormones may be involved, but good evidence about their role has not been obtained (Munns and Termaat, 1986). Increases in abscisic acid concentrations in roots under highly saline conditions have been reported. In soils, the buildup of salinity is generally a gradual process, and the physiological mechanisms involved in longer term osmotic adjustment may differ from those observed when abrupt changes are made using solution culture techniques.

Specific ion effects

Sodium, Cl^-, and SO_4^{2-} are generally the most abundant ions in saline soils and thus are major contributors to the osmotic properties of soil solutions. In addition to their effects on water potential and ionic strength of the soil solution, however, these ions, particularly Na^+ and Cl^-, have specific effects on structural integrity and metabolism of cells.

Sodium ions can displace Ca^{2+} from the root-hair-cell membranes of cotton plants (Cramer et al., 1985). These plants were grown with Ca levels (0.4 mM) and Ca/total cation ratios (0.37) well above those considered adequate for root growth under nonsaline conditions. The increased membrane Na resulted in a leakage of cytosolic K (^{86}Rb) ions. The specific displacement of Ca was determined by adding chlorotetracycline (CTC) and measuring the amount of fluorescence resulting when CTC reacts with bound Ca. The Ca displaced may be from different kinds of binding sites (Cramer and Läuchli, 1986). Using similar techniques, displacement of Ca by other ions, including Na, was also shown with protoplasts isolated from corn root cells (Lynch et al., 1987). Other aspects of mineral nutrition besides preserving the integrity of membranes and physiological functions generally, illustrate the importance of adequate Ca in the ability of plants to cope with salinity stress. Exclusion of Na, a feature of salt-sensitive plants like beans (LaHaye and Epstein, 1971), as well as less sensitive plants like cotton (Cramer et al. , 1987), is an important aspect of the effective functioning of K/Na selective mechanisms. Salinity influences anatomical features of cotton root cells, and these effects are ameliorated by additional Ca (Kurth et al., 1986). The decrease in cell production and effects on cell shape associated with saline conditions showed some similarity to effects of ethylene.

Recent findings indicate the possibility of a linkage between the functions of Ca and intermediary carbohydrate metabolism in plants under salinity stress. The transfer of Ca out of fusogenic carrot protoplasts was accelerated in the presence of added inositol triphosphate (Rincon and Boss, 1987). The effectiveness of this as a regulatory mechanism involved in salinity stress response may be related to changes in inositol metabolism. Both leaves and roots of salt-tolerant tomato plant breeding lines were found to contain much higher concentrations of *myo*-inositol than the salt-sensitive lines (Sacher and Staples, 1985). Other findings about the possible role of inositol phospholipids as a Ca messenger system, and the possible involvement of calmodulin, are reviewed by Poovaiah et al. (1987).

Interspecific and intraspecific differences in phytotoxicities of different kinds of salts indicate other ion specific metabolic effects. Two selected lines of bread wheat differed in their responses to the kinds of salts used for preparing the solutions in which the plants were cultured (Kingsbury and Epstein, 1986). High external Na concentrations were much more toxic to the salt-sensitive line than were high Cl solutions. The lack of adverse effects on growth and photosynthesis of the salt-tolerant wheat was attributed to greater efficiency in Ca uptake. In other studies, less Ca was taken up into the shoots of a more-salt-tolerant barley (cv. 'Arivat') than by the less-salt-tolerant cv. 'Briggs,' when both were grown at higher soil salinity levels (Lynch and Läuchli, 1985).

Ion-specific salinity effects have also been observed in the effects of salinity on N nutrition. The uptake of NO_3^- by barley seedlings was more severely inhibited by Cl^- than by SO_4^{2-} when the comparison was based on osmolality, but on a concentration (micromolar per gram of fresh weight per hour) basis the reverse was noted (Aslam et al., 1984). These effects were attributed primarily to differences in their influences on the NO_3^- transporter rather than on subsequent assimilation. Salinity had much less effect on in situ NO_3^- reductase activity than on NO_3^- uptake. When determined in vitro, activity of nitrate reductase in leaves of salt-treated plants was much lower than in the controls, but its activity measured in situ showed little adverse effect of salt. Possible reasons for the greater effect of Cl^- than of SO_4^{2-} on NO_3^- uptake include differences between the carriers by which they are transported, and in the relatively greater hydration of SO_4^{2-}. Results of subsequent studies showed that the adverse effects on transporter activity were minimized by adequate Ca (Ward et al., 1986).

Uptake of NO_3^- by the barley seedlings was inhibited similarly by K and Na salts. Other studies had shown that K lessened the inhibitory effects of NaCl salinity (Helal et al., 1975), but the basal solution K level used for comparison was lower than in the Aslam et al. (1984) studies, and a different variety of barley was used. Other effects of salinity, including decreases in dry matter and water uptake, need to be considered in interpreting influences of saline conditions on N uptake (Pessarakli and Tucker, 1988).

Principles for managing plant growth in saline soils

A detailed discussion of managing saline soils is beyond the intended subject matter coverage in this book. In general, plant growth impairment resulting from saline soil conditions can be lessened by decreasing the salt concentration in the soil, either by (1) removing some of the salts, or (2) maintaining water content above that needed under nonsaline conditions. Ionic strength is decreased and ψ_s increased (made less negative) in the soil water by salt removal and by adding low-salt water. Where salinity is the result of seepage, as in the northern Great Plains, growing high-water-using crops such as alfalfa in the recharge area will lessen the downslope movement of salts (Brown et al., 1980).

Maintaining very moist soil conditions can have adverse effects on aeration, especially in heavier textured soils. Low O_2 concentrations impair the Na exclusion mechanism that contributes to the salt tolerance of plants (Drew and Läuchli, 1985). Sodium transport from roots to shoots in corn increased when O_2 concentration was reduced from ambient (21 percent volume per unit air volume) to 15 percent, whereas K transport was not inhibited until the O_2 concentration was lowered to <5 percent.

Some mineral nutrient fertilization practices used for nonsaline soils may need modification for use on saline soils, but reports from studies where comparisons are made under the two situations are not consistent (Kafkafi, 1984). Higher rates of N applied as NO_3^- may lessen the possibility of Cl^- damage, but these fertilizer salts dissolve readily and thus can increase soil salinity levels. Ammoniacal N may increase Cl^- uptake because of counter ion effects, but in sodic saline soils ammoniacal N may lower the pH at the soil-plant root interface. Phosphate additions can aggravate the adverse effects of salinity on plant growth by favoring reactions that immobilize Ca, and thus lessen its effectiveness in aiding plants to cope with salinity stress.

Frequently, the best management strategy in dealing with the growth of plants in saline soils is to choose more tolerant species and varieties. The possibilities of this approach have been investigated for a number of species, including barley, wheat, and tomato (Epstein et al., 1980). Field tests with selections made from Composite Cross XXI, a barley synthesized from 6200 lines, showed that some lines were able to produce very respectable seed yields when grown on dune sand irrigated with seawater (approx. 45.8 dS m^{-1}). Results from solution culture studies have shown differences in tolerance of salinity among genotypes of chickpea (Lauter and Munns, 1986) and of soybeans (Läuchli and Wieneke, 1979). A comprehensive review of the attempts to develop salt tolerant crops has been published by Epstein (1985).

Calcareous Soils

Occurrence of carbonates

By definition, calcareous soils are those containing sufficient Ca (also Mg) carbonates to effervesce visibly when treated with cold 0.1 N HCl. The presence of this quantity of carbonate (usually > 1 to 2 percent) confers physical, chemical, and biological characteristics that are important in soil-plant relationships. Carbonate particles influence the nature of the soil solution and provide surfaces on which mineral nutrients can be retained. According to one estimate, calcareous soils cover 30 percent of the earth's terrestrial surface area (Chen and Barak, 1982).

In some soils, $CaCO_3$ originates from parent materials, in others it is formed in situ (pedogenic formation). Differences between these soils, with regard to their serving as media for plant growth, may be less a matter of carbonate source than differences in soil-forming factors and cultural conditions to which they have been, or are currently, exposed. Plant growth factors in areas of semiarid to arid weathering conditions where $CaCO_3$ occurs naturally are quite different from those in which $CaCO_3$ is of pedogenic origin. Some very fertile soils, such as in parts of the northern midwestern United States, were derived from limestone glacial till, but some of these soils are no longer calcareous because of postglacial climatic changes. Some soils in depressional areas (e.g., Drummer silty clay loam in central Illinois) have calcareous surfaces as a result of deposition of diatoms and snails.

In some calcareous soils, $NaCO_3$ also accumulates. Severe sodic conditions completely inhibit the growth of most plants, primarily because of adverse physical conditions. Soluble salts may be present at levels high enough to be phytotoxic. Details of sodic-calcareous soils will not be considered further here.

Plant growth in calcareous soils

Growth limitations. Plant growth limitations associated with calcareous soils vary under different circumstances. With the generally low rainfall in some areas in which such soils occur, insufficient water is the most likely limiting factor under natural conditions. In more humid areas, e.g., in the chalk lands in Britain, insufficient nutrients, especially N and P, may be more important causes of growth limitations (Bradshaw, 1969). Interspecific and intraspecific differences exist between plants with regard to the ability to become established and grow well on calcareous soils. Plants growing better under those conditions have been designated *calcicoles* to distinguish them from those less-well-adapted *calcifuges*. As is discussed later, however, other factors may blur this separation between and within species.

When brought under cultivation, the physical, chemical, and biological features of calcareous soils are changed, particularly when plant growth is enhanced by the addition of irrigation water. Weathering processes and biological activity are accelerated, salts commonly abundant in calcareous soils may be moved out of the root zone, aeration may be impeded, ionic strength of the soil solution may be lowered, levels of CO_2 may be elevated, and soluble Ca, pH, and redox conditions may change. These factors are interrelated in their influences on soil as a medium for plant growth.

Nitrogen is the most common mineral nutrient deficiency in calcareous soils. The arid conditions occurring in some calcareous soil areas are not conducive to accumulation of organic matter, and thus the level of total N is typically low; lack of moisture limits biological activity.

Interrelationships of soluble and exchangeable Ca, pH, and CO_2 in calcareous soils.   Calcium carbonate may precipitate or be dissolved in calcareous soils by reactions with the HCO_3^- or with the H^+ produced when CO_2 dissolves in water. If soluble Ca is present, the precipitation of $CaCO_3$ may occur according to the following reaction:

$$Ca^{2+} + 2HCO_3^- = CaCO_3 + CO_2 \ (gas) + H_2O \qquad (7.7)$$

This reaction can account for the reported occurrence of $CaCO_3$ precipitates around roots of perennial plants (Barber, 1974). Soluble Ca may accumulate at soil-plant root interfaces if the rate of Ca transport to the roots by mass flow exceeds its uptake rate (Barber and Ozanne, 1970). Precipitation of Ca-oxalate has also been suggested (Inskeep and Comfort, 1986).

The dissolution of $CaCO_3$ in the vicinity of plant roots may be aided by the extrusion of H^+:

$$CaCO_3 + 2H^+ = Ca^{2+} + CO_2 \ (gas) + H_2O \qquad (7.8)$$

This expression provides a basis for estimating the activity of Ca in the presence of $CaCO_3$. Parameters needed for the calculation are Henry's constant K_H for the relationship of gaseous to dissolved CO_2, the first K_1 and second K_2 dissociation constants for carbonic acid, and the K_{IAP} (ion activity product) of $CaCO_3$. Expressing these parameters and P_{CO_2} as negative logs, pK_H, pK_1, pK_2, pK_{IAP}, and pP_{CO_2}, respectively, the Ca activities associated with different pHs and partial pressures of CO_2 can be estimated from the following derived expression:

$$pCa - 2\,pH = \Sigma pK - pP_{CO_2} \qquad (7.9)$$

The term ΣpK represents the sum of pK_H, pK_1, pK_2, and pK_{IAP}. The pCa^{2+} and pP_{CO_2} terms represent values for the negative logs of Ca^{2+} activity and partial pressures of CO_2, respectively.

A soluble Ca activity of approximately 0.4 mM is estimated from Eq. 7.9 in a soil in which $P_{CO_2} = 3.3 \times 10^{-4}$ atm, pH = 8.3 (the theoretical value for a calcareous soil in CO_2 equilibrium with ambient atmosphere), and the IAP for $[Ca^{2+}]\,[CO_3^{2-}] = 10^{-8}$. If P_{CO_2} increases 100 times to 3.3×10^{-2} atm, as may occur in soils (Stolzy, 1974), the estimated Ca activities at pH 8.3 and 7.5 (more typical of calcareous soils) are approximately 0.013 and 0.5 mM, respectively. These values are well above the minimum concentrations necessary for plant root growth (Chap. 2).

The results from these calculations help illustrate interrelationships between the P_{CO_2}, pH, and soluble Ca, but substantial adjustments in the parameters may be necessary when using this model for predictive purposes over a wide range of different soils, The estimated Ca activities are probably too low for many soils. A solubility diagram was constructed using an equation similar to Eq. 7.9, published calcite IAP values, and experimental results (Fig. 7.14). The upper broken line, representing a hypothetical $CaCO_3$, was calculated assuming pIAP = 8.0, which was based on an analysis of drainage waters from irrigated lands containing calcite (Suarez, 1977). A soluble Ca concentration exceeding that of calcite was attributed to the presence of Ca-containing aluminosilicates, such as anorthite, a less stable species than pedogenic $CaCO_3$. The values of ΣpK used to calculate the regression lines for calcite and a hypothetical $CaCO_3$ were 9.82 and 10.14, respectively.

Soil solutions in Calciaquolls in western Minnesota are oversaturated fortyfold relative to pure calcite (Inskeep and Bloom, 1986c). The disparity is attributed to effects of substitution of Mg for Ca in carbonates and to the interference in carbonate crystallization by soil organic components (Inskeep and Bloom, 1986b). Dolomites may be present in calcareous soils, but they are not likely to be important contributors to soluble Ca pools, because their solubility is very much lower than calcite (Evangelou et al., 1984). Soil dolomites generally are not of pedogenic origin (Suarez and Wood, 1984).

Time factors may be important in relating interactions of pH, P_{CO_2}, and soluble Ca to soil-plant relationships, but a thermodynamics-based model such as Eq. 7.9 does not provide information about rates of processes. Differences in temperature, high concentrations of soluble salts, and soil buffering capacity affect quantitative relationships. Sizes of carbonate precipitates vary widely (Rostad and Arnaud, 1970) and influence dissolution rates. Bicarbonate ions extruded from plant roots react with soluble Ca and precipitate $CaCO_3$. Vertical distribution of the precipitates in soil profiles depends upon the conditions under which they form (Gile et al., 1965).

Adsorption and precipitation of nutrients on carbonate surfaces. Cations (e.g., Mg^{2+}, Fe^{2+}, Mn^{2+}, Zn^{2+}, and Cu^{2+}), anions (e.g., $H_2PO_4^{2-}$ and SO_4^{2-}), and salts (e.g., $CaSO_4$) can be adsorbed on the surfaces of carbonates. The mechanisms by which these chemical species become bound are not easily discerned, and in some cases precipitation also may be involved. Whether adsorption or precipitation has occurred, these reactions affect the roles of these ions as plant nutrients.

Immobilization of phosphates by $CaCO_3$ adsorption and precipitation is the retention mechanism of most common concern relative to plant nutrition. A higher proportion of P is present as HPO_4^{2-} in calcareous soils than in soils at lower pH. Thus there is a greater possibility for the occurrence of the neutral complex dicalcium phosphate ($CaHPO_4$) and for the exchange of HPO_4^{2-} with CO_3^{2-} ions. Results using $CaCO_3$ mineral species in purified form have provided some insights regarding the mechanisms involved, and the rates at which absorption occurs (Griffin and Jurinak, 1974). Two simultaneous reactions were indicated, one a simple adsorption following second-order kinetics, and a second first-order reaction interpreted as an anion rearrangement on the adsorbing surface. The characterization of adsorption mechanisms in soils is more complicated than on pure min-

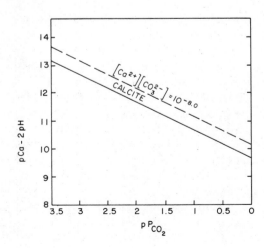

Figure 7.14 Relationships between pP_{CO_2}, Ca activity, and pH in the presence of calcite and a hypothetical $CaCO_3$ with an ion activity product of 10^{-8}. (*Reproduced in modified form from D. L. Suarez and J. D. Rhoades, Soil Science Society of America Journal, volume 46, pages 716–722, 1982, by permission of the Soil Science Society of America, Inc.*)

erals, because surface contaminants change adsorbing properties by influencing both the adsorption capacity and energy of retention. The adsorption of phosphate can, in time, lead to the formation of a surface coating of hydroxyapatite on $CaCO_3$ particles (Talibudeen, 1981).

Fe deficiency in calcareous soils. Insufficient Fe commonly limits plant growth when calcareous soils are brought under cultivation. Plants with insufficient Fe commonly show a pronounced yellowing of new leaves. Because of the conditions under which it occurs and its manifestations, the deficiency has been termed *lime-induced chlorosis.*

In noncalcareous soils, Fe deficiency has been related to soluble soil Fe concentrations, with approximately 10^{-8} M being defined as the critical level for plant growth (Lindsay and Schwab, 1982). The critical level for plants growing in calcareous soils may be different because other soil factors may influence the effectiveness of soil Fe as a nutrient source (reviewed by Loeppert, 1986). Between pH 7.5 and 8.5, the equilibrium concentration of $Fe(OH)_3^0$, the dominant solution phase species in well-aerated soils, is $10^{-10.4}$ M. The quantity, mineralogy, and crystallinity of Fe oxides influenced soil Fe availability for growth of sorghum plants in 24 calcareous soils (Loeppert and Hallmark, 1985). Clay content and organic matter were also positively correlated with Fe availability. Soluble and exchangeable Mg were negatively correlated with chlorosis of the plants.

Plant factors are a more important aspect of Fe nutrition in calcareous than in acidic soils. The suggested reasons for greater plant effects include metabolic reactions in roots that influence the external supply, and reactions that influence Fe utilization in roots and shoots. The extent of infection of roots by vesicular-arbuscular mycorrhizae also may be a contributing factor. Primary physiological reasons for the restricted growth and the chlorotic appearance of plants grown in calcareous soils are not yet clear, however, despite much intensive research on the problem. Plants showing the chlorotic appearance typical of Fe deficiency are not necessarily lower in total Fe concentrations than similar green plants. In some instances, the deficient plants may contain higher concentrations of Fe than green plants. This was noted in grape plants, and also a lower proportion of the total Fe in the chlorotic leaves was soluble in dilute acid (Mengel et al., 1984).

Brown et al. (1959) and Boxma (1972) implicated HCO_3^- as a major factor in lime-induced Fe chlorosis, and other subsequent research findings have supported this view. These later studies include the determination of the direct effects of different levels of HCO_3^- in nutrient solutions (Coulombe et al., 1984), and of plant responses to changes in soil conditions that are expected to elevate soil HCO_3^- concentrations. The data shown in Fig. 7.15 and Table 7.6 are from a greenhouse study involving growing soybeans in calcareous soils at various bulk densities and soil water contents. At higher soil densities and soil water levels, aeration is restricted and soil air equilibrates much more slowly with the atmosphere above the soil. Thus the PCO_2 and concentration of HCO_3^- in the soil air increase and influence the degree of leaf chlorosis. Bicarbonate, when expressed in terms of quantity per unit soil volume (Fig. 7.16), correlated better with leaf chlorophyll than when expressed in terms of concentration (Fig. 7.15a). This greater correlation of the response was interpreted as an indication that the HCO_3^- in contact with roots is more important than the concentration of HCO_3^- in solution. The difference in slope of the regression for the HG soil, compared to the other soils, was attributed to a lower available soil P level (Table 7.6). The involvement of P in Fe stress reponses has been described in various plants, including soybeans and cotton (Chaney and Coulombe, 1982) and grapevines (Kolesch et al., 1987). Results from these studies indicate important varietal differences in the interaction between Fe, P, and HCO_3^-.

Besides the likely greater immobilization of plant Fe by higher tissue HCO_3^- levels, other effects on Fe availability may result from internal pH changes. A greater efficiency in Fe uptake by some plants was attributed to their ability to regulate the pH of the rhizosphere by excretion of H^+ (Römheld and Marschner, 1984). Roots of grapevine cultivars, less susceptible to chlorosis, excreted more H^+ than those that became chlorotic more easily. The beneficial effects of adding NH_4^+ on the regreening of chlorotic corn plants grown in nutrient solutions were attributed to improved Fe utilization because apoplastic pH was lowered (Mengel and Geurtzen, 1986).

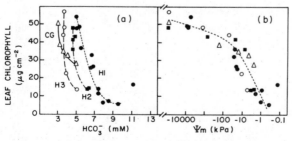

Figure 7.15 Relationships of leaf chlorophyll concentrations in Anoka soybeans to (a) HCO_3^- concentrations in extracted solutions, and (b) moisture matric potentials ψ_m in soils from four sites (see Table 7.6). (*Reproduced from W. P. Inskeep and P. R. Bloom, Soil Science Society of America Journal, volume 50, pages 1431–1437, 1986a, by permission of the Soil Science Society of America, Inc.*)

TABLE 7.6   Properties of the Soils Used to Obtain the Data for Figs. 7.15 and 7.16

Soil series*	Organic carbon, g kg^{-1}	Total CaCO$_3$, g kg^{-1}	DTPA ext. Fe, mg kg^{-1}	HCO$_3^-$ ext. P, mg kg^{-1}
Harps† 1 (H1)	35	135	5.3	53
Harps 2 (H2)	41	136	11	44
Harps 3 (H3)	49	126	11	35
Harps (HG)	24	63	5.1	14
Canisteo‡ (CG)	37	19	15	61

*In field studies, plants were chlorotic at sites H1, H2, and H3.
†Fine-loamy, mesic Typic Calciaquoll.
‡Fine-loamy, mixed (calcareous) mesic Typic Haplaquoll.
SOURCE: Inskeep and Bloom, 1986a.

Zinc nutrition in calcareous soils.   Zinc deficiency is a common occurrence in plants growing on calcareous soils, especially when they are brought under cultivation and irrigated (Kissel et al., 1985). During leveling, topsoil with organic ligands that form soluble Zn complexes are removed, thereby lessening the uptake of Zn by plant roots.

The CaCO$_3$ in calcareous soils affects Zn nutrition by influencing soil pH and by reactions of the carbonates related to size and surface properties (Tiller et al., 1972). As the pH increases, and particularly above pH 8, a higher proportion of the ionic Zn is present as Zn(OH)$^+$ and Zn(OH)$_3^-$ (Lindsay, 1972); these Zn species are less available than Zn^{2+} for plant uptake. Under such conditions, the critical level of $10^{-10.6}$ M soluble Zn (Halvorson and Lindsay, 1977) is difficult to

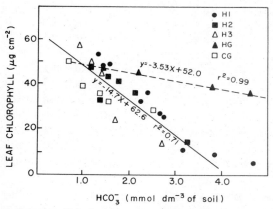

Figure 7.16   Relationships of leaf chlorophyll concentrations in Anoka soybeans and the HCO$_3^-$ concentrations, on a soil volume basis, in soils from five sites (see Table 7.6). (*Reproduced from P. R. Bloom and W. P. Inskeep, Journal of Plant Nutrition, volume 9, pages 215–228, 1986, by permission of Marcel Dekker, Inc.*)

maintain; exchangeable Zn^{2+} becomes hydroxylated and less effective for meeting plant needs. The presence of organic components that can react to form complexes will lessen the likelihood of Zn deficiency. Such complexes may account for over one-half of the Zn present in some soils (Hodgson et al., 1966). As with Fe, better Zn nutrition is achieved if the pH of the rhizosphere is lowered by the excretion of protons by plant roots.

Plants growing on calcareous soils have shown signs of Zn deficiency following applications of P fertilizers. Whether this deficiency occurs because of an external reaction, or is a physiological response, has not been established. Reactions involving P may interfere with the translocation of Zn from roots to shoots (Pauli et al., 1968).

Principles of management of calcareous soils. Management practices that have been used to improve plant growth on calcareous soils include the following: (1) lowering the soil pH; (2) applying nutrients that are relatively more insoluble at higher pH levels; (3) applying water judiciously to minimize HCO_3^- accumulation; (4) avoiding excessive applications of mineral nutrients, e.g., P, that might induce other nutrient deficiencies, e.g., Zn; (5) increasing organic matter that provides metal-binding organic ligands, and helps to minimize adverse effects of particulate $CaCO_3$ on plant availability of essential micronutrients; and (6) removing phytotoxic substances from the root zone. The emphasis that needs to be placed on any one of these four principles differs for different soils and for different crops.

The pH of calcareous soils is frequently lowered in order to grow some fruit crops and ornamentals. Elemental S is the amendment most commonly applied for this purpose. Large rates of application are necessary to change the pH of well-buffered, highly calcareous soils. The pH of a loessial subsoil in which elemental S was mixed at rates of 0.5 and 5 g kg^{-1}, decreased from 8.1 to 7.8 and 7.3, respectively, over a 75-day period (Hassan and Olson, 1966). Yields of corn grown in the soil were not affected by the S treatments, but uptakes of S, Fe, Mn, Mg, Zn, and Cu were increased significantly. Uptakes of Ca and P were not significantly affected. Placing acidifying materials in bands or holes, rather than complete mixing, may be more feasible in some plant culture systems.

Various ways of correcting plant Fe deficiencies commonly occurring on calcareous soils have been tested. Very high rates of inorganic Fe salts, e.g., over 500 kg ha^{-1} of $FeSO_4$ (Mortvedt, 1986), may be needed in some cases. Much lower rates of Fe chelates may be effective, but these materials are much more costly.

If a soil is sodic as well as calcareous, lowering the pH and improving the suitability of the soil as a plant growth medium is more complex. Not only soluble Na, but also Na held on exchange sites must be removed. Such soils do not leach readily because of the effects of Na on their physical condition. Sulfuric acid is the most effective material for solubilizing Ca and removing Na from sodic-calcareous soils (Overstreet et al., 1951). Theoretically, a maximum of 4 mol of adsorbed Na can be replaced by each mole of H_2SO_4:

$$H_2SO_4 + 2CaCO_3 + 4Na(ad) \rightarrow 2Ca(ad) + Na_2SO_4 + 2NaHCO_3 \quad (7.10)$$

Actual efficiencies of replacement are generally somewhat lower, with some CO_2 being lost to the atmosphere.

Various industrial by-products containing H_2SO_4 are also effective for reclaiming sodic soils, but caution must be exercised in use of some because of the possibility of their containing environmental or health hazards, or phytotoxic substances (Stroehlein and Pennington, 1986). Elemental S applied to sodic soils renders Na leachable similarly to H_2SO_4, but reclamation is generally slower because biological activity is required to oxidize S.

Because of its possible acidifying effects, ammoniacal N may be more effective than nitrates for correcting N deficiencies in calcareous soils. A better yield was obtained when ammoniacal N rather than nitrate was used to grow an Fe-inefficient soybean (cv. 'Hawkeye') on a calcareous soil (Wallace and Cha, 1986). Such differences in the effect of N sources in helping to solubilize heavy metal nutrients depends upon soil pH buffering capacity.

The possibility of volatilization losses of NH_3, especially in drier soils, must be considered. The pH of calcareous soils is very conducive to nitrification, so if moisture and temperature conditions are also favorable, ammoniacal N will be readily converted to nitrate. Volatilization losses thus would be minimal. Ample soluble soil Ca levels are effective in minimizing volatilization losses from applications of ammoniacal mineral salts and urea (Fenn et al., 1981).

Anhydrous or aqueous NH_3 applied in irrigation water may result in the precipitation of $CaCO_3$. This may increase SAR and accentuate the adverse effects of Na on plant growth. Sulfuric acid applied with the ammoniated water is effective in lessening this possibility (Miyamoto and Ryan, 1976).

Phosphorus fertilizer sources should be chosen that will not produce further alkalinization to correct P deficiencies in calcareous soils. Saturated solutions of diammonium phosphate are alkaline; those of monocalcium phosphate and monoammonium phosphate are acidic (Kissel et al., 1985). When soluble orthophosphate fertilizers are added to calcareous soils, more insoluble forms, including dicalcium phosphate dihydrate (Sample et al., 1980) and octacalcium phosphate (Bell and Black, 1970), may be produced. The possibility of inducing a

Zn deficiency by applying high rates of P fertilizer also needs to be considered. Raw rock phosphates are ineffective as plant P sources in calcareous soils.

Conservation Tillage

Types of tillage

Conservation tillage is *any* tillage system that reduces the loss of soil or water relative to conventional tillage; it often is a form of noninversion tillage that retains protective amounts of residue mulch on the soil surface. Conventional tillage, on the other hand, is the combined primary and secondary tillage operations performed in preparing a seedbed for a given crop grown in a given area (Soil Conservation Society of America, 1982).

Mannering and Fenster (1983) have discussed a number of conservation tillage systems for row crop and small grain agriculture. Their categories for row crop conservation tillage systems are narrow strip tillage, ridge planting, full-width, no-plow tillage, and full-width, plow tillage. Their subdivisions for small grain agriculture are stubble mulch tillage, ecofallow, and direct drill.

Narrow strip tillage is divided into no-tillage and strip rotary tillage. *No-tillage* is a method of planting that requires no seedbed preparation other than opening a soil slit for seed placement at the desired depth. Coulters, narrow chisels, or angled disks are used to open the slit. *Strip rotary tillage* limits seedbed preparation to a rototilled strip 50 to 200 mm wide and 20 to 100 mm deep in the row area. A conventional planter is then used in the strip.

Ridge planting is a conservation tillage system where one row of crop is planted on each ridge. In *conventional planting on a ridge,* ridges are shaped at the last cultivation or after harvest of the previous crop. Little or no spring seedbed preparation is used. *Till planting* involves scalping the old crop row, leaving crop residue in the unscalped area. Seedbed preparation and planting are completed in one operation.

Full-width, no-plow tillage is accomplished using chisel or disk tillage rather than a moldboard plow. *Full-width, plow tillage* uses strip seedbed preparation on land that has been moldboard plowed, usually a few hours before planting. The two principal forms are wheel-track plant and plow plant.

Stubble mulch tillage is a system of small grain farming where a cover of vegetative residue is maintained on the soil surface at all times. The two types of tillage machines used in stubble mulch tillage are those that stir and mix the soil and those that cut the soil beneath the surface without inverting the tilled layer. Stirring and mixing machines are one-way, offset and tandem disks, field cultivators, chisel plows, and mulch treaders. Subsurface tillers include sweeps, rotary rod weeders, and rod weeders with short chisels.

Ecofallow, sometimes called chemical fallow, is a form of stubble mulch tillage where a persistent herbicide is used to control weeds. Subsurface tillage sometimes is used if the herbicides are not effective in controlling all weeds. The land is left fallow until the next crop, which may be 4 to 16 months, depending on rainfall. The following crop is planted into the residue.

Direct drilling is a system of seeding cereals directly into the residue of the previous crop, which remains on the soil surface. Weed control is accomplished with herbicides.

Effects of residues on soil characteristics

The basic goal of any conservation tillage system is to reduce soil and water loss below that of the conventional tillage system, hoping that the net income from the land will not be reduced. This goal often can best be approached by leaving as much residue as possible on the soil surface, especially during the times that the erosion potential is the greatest. Implements that till below the soil surface leave 75 to 90 percent of the residue on top; moldboard and disk plows that invert the furrow bury almost all of the residue; listers and rotary tillers also bury almost all of the residue; one-way disk plows and chisel plows bury intermediate amounts of the residue (Woodruff et al., 1966).

The effects of a specific quantity of residue left on the soil surface in reducing water and wind erosion depend on rainfall and wind conditions, soil erodibility, topography, crop management, and the presence of conservation structures such as terraces and contour rows.

In a test conducted on a 4 percent slope of Morley clay loam, Mannering and Fenster (1977) showed that no-till soybean land lost only one-third as much soil as plowed soybean land and that no-till corn land lost only one-ninth as much soil as plowed corn land (Table 7.7).

In a Nebraska test, soil loss was 20 t ha^{-1} under conventional tillage, 10 t ha^{-1} under disk-chisel, 4.4 t ha^{-1} under flat strip till, and 1.8 t ha^{-1} under no-till (American Association for Vocational Instructional Material, 1983).

Residues left on the soil surface after tillage increase soil water storage. Under conditions where inadequate water supply during the growing season limits crop yield, an increased amount of mulch results in an increased yield. In an experiment using winter wheat straw on the southern Great Plains, Unger (1978) found that a 3-year

TABLE 7.7   Crop Tillage Effects on Surface Cover and Soil Loss, Morley Clay Loam, 4 Percent Slope

Tillage	Amount of residue cover		Soil loss after	
	Soybean, %	Corn, %	Soybean, t ha^{-1}	Corn, t ha^{-1}
No-till	26	69	13.4	2.4
Chisel up and down slope	12	25	30.3	15.0
Plow (conventional)	1	7	40.0	21.8

SOURCE: Mannering and Fenster, 1977.

average sorghum grain yield progressively increased from 1780 kg ha^{-1} with no mulch to 3990 kg ha^{-1} where 12 metric tons per hectare of mulch was present and that precipitation effectiveness increased from 22.6 percent with no mulch to 46.2 percent with 12 t ha^{-1} of mulch (Table 7.8).

Surface residues alter soil temperature primarily by changing the albedo, or reflection coefficient, thereby altering the net radiation balance at the soil surface. Thus, the fraction of the soil surface actually covered by residue is important. Voorhees et al. (1981) present equations to predict the percentage of ground cover from the dry residue weight for wheat, corn, soybeans, and oats. Van Doren and Allmaras (1978) developed a relationship to predict the soil temperature reduction from the fraction of soil surface covered by residue. A 100 percent ground cover by residue causes 4 to 8° reduction below that with no residue cover.

A 4°C temperature depression caused by a 100 percent mulch cover directly over the planted row can delay emergence by a week or two in the Corn Belt and can delay growth significantly. Many experiments have shown that mulches over the row will result in slower growth than

TABLE 7.8   Effects of Straw-Mulch Rates on 3-Year Average Values for Sorghum Grain and Forage Yields and Precipitation Effectiveness

	Mulch rate, kg ha^{-1}			
	0	2000	8000	12000
Grain yield, kg ha^{-1}	1780c*	2600c	3680ab	3990a
Forage yield, kg ha^{-1}	2680d	3660bc	3530bc	4430a
Precip. effectiveness, grain, kg ha^{-1} cm^{-1}	31.7	45.5	67.2	77.0
Precip. effectiveness, forage, kg ha^{-1} cm^{-1}	47.7	64.1	64.4	85.5

*Row values followed by the same letter are not significantly different at the 5 percent level (Duncan's Multiple Range Test).
SOURCE: Unger, 1978.

will occur when the mulch was buried. On the other hand, a 4°C temperature depression near a lethally high temperature will cause a significant increase in growth and survival, so mulches are effective in increasing stands of grass established in hot arid and semiarid locations.

Tillage systems that leave most of the residue on the soil surface also create other soil physical conditions that differ substantially from those created by tillage systems that bury the residue.

Lindstrom et al. (1984) investigated the effects of a conventional tillage system of fall moldboard plowing and spring disking, a reduced system of fall chisel plowing and spring disking, and a no-till system modified by using a cultivator during the previous crop system to form a ridge. They compared residue effects by harvesting the residue from the same half of the plot areas during the first 2 years of the experiment, and then measuring infiltration rates and other soil physical factors during the third year. They found that the no-till plots had lower infiltration rates than the conventionally tilled plots, with reduced tillage plots being intermediate. Harvesting the crop residues for 2 years had only minimal effects on infiltration rates (Table 7.9). They also found that the surface 150 mm of conventionally tilled soil had a significantly lower bulk density and penetrometer resistance and a significantly greater saturated conductivity and macropore volume than the no-till soil. The reduced tillage soil was intermediate in bulk density, saturated conductivity, and micropore volume (Table 7.10).

The results comparing soil physical properties under no-till with those where profile inversion occurs are site-specific, however. Blevins et al. (1983) found no differences among bluegrass sod, no-till, or conventional plowing in saturated hydraulic conductivity or soil bulk density of a Maury silt loam at Lexington, Kentucky.

TABLE 7.9 Infiltration Rates Measured on Barnes Loam Immediately after Planting in the Third Year of Tillage Management Systems, Dry and Wet Runs, with and without Residue Harvest

Tillage treatments	Infiltration rate			
	Residue not harvested, mm h^{-1}*		Residue harvested, mm h^{-1}*	
	Wet run	Dry run	Wet run	Dry run
Conventional	54	22	54	23
Reduced	54	22	53	19
No-till	36	20	33	13
LSD‡ (0.05)	5	3	5	5

*Water application rate was 56 mm h^{-1}.
†Wet run was for 45 min the day after a 1-h dry infiltration run.
‡Least significant difference.
SOURCE: Lindstrom et al., 1984.

TABLE 7.10 Physical Properties in the Ap (0 to 150 mm) Horizon of Barnes Loam Soil Measured Immediately after Planting in the Third Year of Tillage Management

Tillage treatments	Bulk density, mg M^{-3}	Penetrometer resistance, MPa	Saturated conductivity, mm h^{-1}	Macropore volume,* %
Conventional	1.04	0.05	180	18.3
Reduced	1.17	0.04	99	12.9
No-till	1.34	1.60	3	7.6
LSD (0.05)	0.07	0.22	69	3.6

*Pores drained at −500-mm weight water potential.
SOURCE: Lindstrom et al., 1984.

Because moldboard and disk plowing tend to mix soil to the depth that is plowed, these systems create a set of chemical properties near the soil surface that are substantially different from those that occur in no-till systems. When fertilizers and soil amendments are surface-applied and the soil remains largely undisturbed for several years, certain nutrients and organic matter accumulate at the soil surface. For example, Triplett and Van Doren (1969) found that the P concentration in the surface 60 mm of a no-till profile was more than twice that of a moldboard-plowed soil and that K also was much greater in the no-till soil (Fig. 7.17). Blevins et al. (1983) found that N fertilization rate differentials affected K concentrations in the surface 50 mm of no-till corn (Table 7.11).

Another obvious change under no-till is a rapid drop in the pH of a neutral to acid soil. When equal amounts of N fertilizer were added for 10 years to a Maury silt loam soil, the pH of the surface 0 to 50 mm of conventionally tilled soil ranged from 6.5 with no N added to corn to 5.6 when 336 kg ha^{-1} was added annually. The pH of no-till soil was 5.8 with zero added N and 4.5 with 336 kg ha^{-1} (Fig. 7.18). The pH of the 50- to 150-mm layer also was lower at all N fertilizer levels in the no-till than in the conventionally tilled soil (Blevins et al., 1983).

TABLE 7.11 K Concentration of Maury Silt Loam Soil for No-till (NT) and Conventionally Tilled (CT) Plots at Two Rates of N Fertilization after 10 Years of Continuous Corn Production

Soil depth, mm	No N		168 kg ha^{-1}N	
	NT, meq 100 g^{-1}	CT, meq 100 g^{-1}	NT, meq 100 g^{-1}	CT, meq 100 g^{-1}
0–50	0.68	0.39	0.44	0.39
50–150	0.34	0.43	0.34	0.43
150–300	0.21	0.29	0.20	0.29

SOURCE: Blevins et al., 1983.

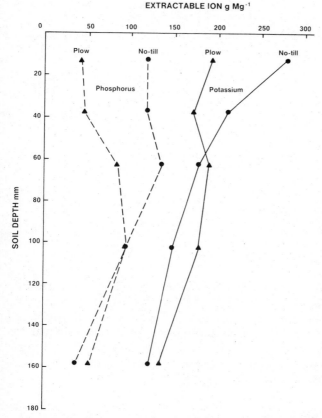

Figure 7.17   P and K concentrations in the row as functions of soil depth and tillage systems. (*Data of Triplett and Van Doren, 1969; used with permission.*)

After 10 years of corn production, Blevins et al. (1983) found that organic matter in the surface 50 mm of soil was about twice as great in the no-till as in the conventionally tilled soil (Fig. 7.19). The accumulation of organic matter at the surface, together with the increased water content there, significantly increased microbial activity there. This increased microbial activity caused a greater immobilization of N during spring in no-till than in the conventional plots. At low N application rates, Blevins et al. (1983) found that corn yields were lower on no-till than on conventionally tilled plots, probably due to the N immobilization of the residue. Howard (1987) has shown that a greater N rate is required to obtain an equal yield of grain sorghum in Tennessee for no-till than for conventional inversion tillage (Fig. 7.20).

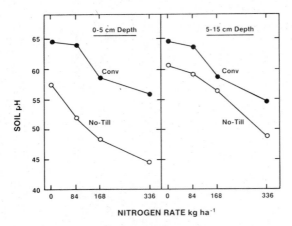

Figure 7.18 Soil pH at two soil depths after 10 years of corn production by no-till and conventional tillage under different levels of fertilization. (*After Blevins et al., 1983; used with permission.*)

In addition to the temperature depression and N immobilization problems associated with some conservation tillage systems, there is some possibility of increased pest problems. There are documented instances where insects, rodents, nematodes, fungi, and other pests have increased when conservation tillage is compared to inversion tillage. Some of these pests have become resistant to chemicals, thereby caus-

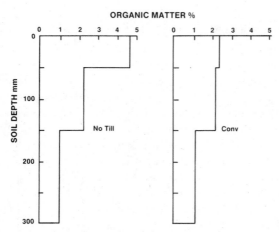

Figure 7.19 Grain sorghum yields as affected by N fertilization rate and tillage for 1982–1984. (*Data of Howard, 1987; used with permission.*)

ing greater quantities or different chemicals to be used in their control (Hinkle, 1983).

Conservation tillage sometimes has contributed to an increase in plant disease epidemics, along with uniform planting susceptible varieties. The disease problems usually are intensified by large quantities of residue left on the soil surface (Hinkle, 1983).

Some weed species and some individuals within species are resistant to a specific herbicide. When that herbicide is used in a conservation tillage program, the resistant weeds can become a serious problem to crop production. Methods to delay development of resistance include herbicide rotation (Hinkle, 1983).

There is one other problem that should be mentioned—the water quality consequences of mulch tillage systems. Many chemicals that are used in crop production under conservation tillage practices are applied to, and remain near, the soil surface. Losses of chemicals from the land where conservation tillage systems are used often may be greater than their losses under conventional tillage, even though soil and water loss is reduced by conservation tillage.

Chemicals can be transported from the land (1) in solution in subsurface drainage, (2) in solution in surface runoff, and (3) in association with sediment suspended in runoff. Chemical losses from the land are determined by the amount of water that leaves the field and con-

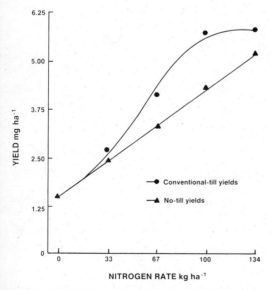

Figure 7.20 Soil organic matter distribution after 10 years of no-till and conventional tillage corn production. (*After Blevins et al., 1983; used with permission.*)

centration of the chemical in that water. Even though the conservation tillage system may reduce the amount of water leaving the field, chemical loss from the land may be greater because its concentration in the water is greater with conservation tillage (Baker and Laflen, 1983).

This section has emphasized that soil conditions differ significantly between inversion tillage systems and conservation tillage systems. These altered soil conditions sometimes cause crop yields to be reduced under conservation tillage.

Cannell et al. (1978) and Cannell (1981) have attempted to rationalize recommendations for simplified cultivation systems in Great Britain, and Cosper (1983) has discussed soil suitability for conservation tillage using *Soil Taxonomy* as a guide.

Cannell et al. (1978) and Cannell (1981) divided the cereal-growing soils of Great Britain into three categories. Category 1 soils are chalk, limestone, and well-drained loam soils. Yields on these soils should be similar to those from conventional tillage for both autumn and spring sown cereals. Category 2 soils are calcareous clays and other clays if drained. With good management, yields of winter cereal are likely to be similar to those from conventional tillage, but yields of spring cereals likely will be lower. Category 3 soils are sandy, silty, and wet alluvial soils. When compared to conventional tillage, yields of cereals probably will be less, especially with spring sown cereals.

Reduced-tillage systems leave greater quantities of residues on the soil surface and usually reduce erosion, but they often require greater management skills than tillage systems that invert the plow layer. Despite this fact, reduced-tillage systems have become the conventional tillage system for areas such as the Great Plains cereal-producing area. Indeed the proper question often is, Why should we till? rather than, Can we do without tillage? Our aim in this section has been to furnish some clues about soil-plant interrelationships as modified by current conservation tillage practices.

Bibliography

Ackello-Ogutu, C., Q. Paris, and W. A. Williams. 1985. Testing a von Liebig crop response function against polynomial specifications. *Am. J. Agric.Econ.* 67:873–880.

Adams, F. 1971. Ionic concentrations and activities in soil solutions. *Soil Sci. Soc. Am. Proc.* 35:420–426.

Adams, F. 1974. Soil solution. In: E. W. Carson (ed.). *The Plant Root and its Environment,* pp. 441–481. University Press of Virginia, Charlottesville, VA.

Adams, F. 1984. Crop response to lime in the southern United States. In: F. Adams (ed.). *Soil Acidity and Liming. Agron.* 12, 2d. ed., pp. 211–265. Am. Soc. Agron., Madison, WI.

Adams, F., and P. J. Hathcock. 1984. Aluminum toxicity and calcium deficiency in acid subsoil horizons of two coastal plains soil series. *Soil Sci. Soc. Am. J.* 48:1305–1309.

Adams, F., and Z. F. Lund. 1966. Effect of chemical activity of soil solution aluminum on cotton root penetration of acid subsoils. *Soil Sci.* 101:193–198.

Adams, F., and B. L. Moore. 1983. Chemical factors affecting root growth in subsoil horizons of coastal plain soils. *Soil Sci. Soc. Am. J.* 47:99–102.

Alley, M. M., D. E. Brann, W. D. Gravelle, and K. D. S. M. Joseph. 1983. Maximum winter wheat yields for humid region growing conditions. 1983 Annual Report, Potash and Phosphate Institute, Atlanta, GA.

Allmaras, R. R., W. W. Nelson, and W. B. Voorhees. 1975. Soybean and corn rooting in southwestern Minnesota. II. Root distribution and related water inflow. *Soil Sci. Soc. Am. Proc.* 39:771–777.

Alva, A. K., D. G. Edwards, C. J. Asher, and F. P. C. Blamey. 1986. Effects of phosphorus/aluminum molar ratio and calcium concentration on plant response to aluminum toxicity. *Soil Sci. Soc. Am. J.* 50:133–137.

Alva, A. K., D. G. Edwards, C. J. Asher, and S. Suthipradit. 1987. Effects of acid soil infertility factors on growth and nodulation of soybean. *Agron. J.* 79:302–306.

American Association of Vocational Instructional Materials. 1983. *Fundamentals of no-till farming.* Athens, GA.

Anderson, J. M., and M. J. Cormier. 1978. Calcium dependent regulator of NAD kinase in higher plants. *Biochem. Biophys. Res. Comm.* 85:595–602.

Anderson, W. B., and W. D. Kemper. 1964. Corn growth as affected by aggregate stability, soil temperature, and soil moisture. *Agron. J.* 56:453–456.

Andersson, B., C. Critchley, I. J. Ryrie, C. Jansson, C. Larsson, and J. M. Anderson. 1984. Modification of the chloride requirement for photosynthetic O_2 evolution. *FEBS* (1290) 168:113–116.

Arkley, R. J. 1963. Relationships between plant growth and transpiration. *Hilgardia* 34:559–584.

Arkley, T. H. 1961. Sulfur compounds of soil systems. Ph.D. dissertation. University of California, Berkeley.

Armstrong, W., and T. J. Gaynard. 1976. The critical oxygen pressures for respiration in intact plants. *Physiol. Plant.* 37:200–206.

Ashton, F. M., and A. S. Crafts. 1973. *Mode of action of herbicides.* Wiley, New York.

Aslam, M., R. C. Huffaker, and D. W. Rains. 1984. Early effects of salinity on nitrate assimilation in barley seedlings. *Plant Physiol.* 76:321–325.

Ayers, R. S., and D. W. Westcot. 1985. Water quality for agriculture. *FAO Irrigation and Drainage Paper 29*. Food and Agriculture Organization of the United Nations, Rome.

Bailey, L. D., and E. G. Beauchamp. 1971. Nitrate reduction and redox potentials measured with permanently and temporarily placed platinum electrodes in saturated soils. *Can. J. Soil Sci.* 51:51–58.

Baker, J. L., and J. M. Laflen. 1983. Water quality consequences of conservation tillage. *J. Soil and Water Cons.* 38:186–193.

Baker, J. M., and C. HJ. M. Van BBavel. 1986. Resistance of plant roots to water loss. *Agron. J.* 78:641–644.

Baker. J. M., and C. H. M. Van Bavel. 1988. Water transfer through cotton plants connecting soil regions of differing water potential. *Agron. J.* 80:993–997.

Balba, M. A., and R. H. Bray. 1956. The application of the Mitscherlich equation for the calculation of plant composition due to fertilizer increments. *Soil Sci. Soc. Am. Proc.* 20:515–518.

Barber, S. A. 1962. A diffusion and mass-flow concept of soil nutrient availability. *Soil Sci.* 93:39–49.

Barber, S. A. 1974. Nutrients in the soil and their flow to plant roots. In: J. K. Marshall (ed.). *The Below Ground Ecosystem: A Synthesis of Plant-Associated Processes. Range Sci. Series* 26, pp. 161–168. Colorado State University, Boulder, CO.

Barber, S. A. 1984. *Soil Nutrient Bioavailability.* Wiley, New York.

Barber, S. A., and P. G. Ozanne. 1970. Autoradiographic evidence for the differential effect of four plant species in altering the Ca content of the rhizosphere soil. *Soil Sci. Soc. Am. Proc.* 34:635–637.

Barber, S. A., J. M. Walker, and E. H. Vasey. 1962. Principles of ion movement through the soil to the plant root. *Proc. Intern. Soil Conf., New Zealand*, pp. 121–124.

Barrow, N. J. 1985. Reaction of anions and cations with variable-charge soils. *Adv. Agron.* 38:183–232.

Barrs, H. D., and P. E. Weatherley. 1962. A reexamination of the relative turgidity technique for estimating water deficits in leaves. *Aust. J. Biol. Sci.* 15:413–428.

Bar-Yosef, B., and U. Kafkafi. 1972. Rates of growth and nutrient uptake of irrigated corn as affected by N and P fertilization. *Soil Sci. Soc. Am. Proc.* 36:931–936.

Bar-Yosef, B., and J. R. Lambert. 1981. Corn and cotton root growth in response to soil impedance and water potential. *Soil Sci. Soc. Am. J.* 45:930–935.

Bassett, D. M., W. D. Anderson, and C. H. E. Werkhoven. 1970. Dry matter production and nutrient uptake in irrigated cotton (*Gossypium hirsutum*). *Agron. J.* 62:299–303.

Baule, B., 1918. Zum Mitscherlich Gesetz der Physiologischen beziehungen. *Lanwirtschaftl. Jahrb.* 51:363–385.

Baver, L. D., and R. B. Farnsworth. 1940. Soil structure effects in the growth of sugar beets. *Soil Sci. Soc. Am. Proc.* 5:45–48.

Beaton, J. D., R. C. Speer, and G. Brown. 1965. Effect of soil temperature and length of reaction period on water solubility of phosphorus and soil fertilizer reaction zones. *Soil Sci. Soc. Am. J.*29:194–198.

Beauchamp, E. G., L. W. Kannenberg, and R. B. Hunter. 1976. Nitrogen accumulation and translocation in corn genotypes following silking. *Agron. J.* 68:418–422.

Beauchamp, E. G., W. D. Reynolds, D.Brasche-Villeneuve, and K.Kirby. 1986. Nitrogen mineralization kinetics with different soil pretreatments and cropping histories. *Soil Sci. Soc. Am. J.* 50:1478–1483.

Beaufils, E. R. 1973. Diagnosis and Recommendation Integrated System (DRIS). A general scheme for experimentation and calibration based on principles developed from research in plant nutrition. *Soil Sci. Bull. No. 1, Univ. of Natal,* So. Africa. 1–34.

Beaufils, E. R., and M. E. Sumner. 1977. Effect of time of sampling on the diagnosis of the N, P, K, Ca, and Mg requirements of sugarcane by the DRIS approach. *Proc. So. African Sugar Technologists' Association* 51:62–67.

Beckett, P. H. T. 1964. Studies on soil potassium. II. The "immediate" Q/I relations of labile potassium in the soil. *J. Soil Sci.* 15:9–23.

Bell, L. C., and C. A. Black. 1970. Crystalline phosphates produced by interaction of orthophosphate fertilizers with slightly acid and alkaline soils. *Soil Sci. Soc. Am. Proc.* 34:735–740.

Beringer, H., and F. Nothdurft. 1985. Effects of potassium on plant and cellular structures. In: R. Munson (ed.). *Potassium in Agriculture.* Am. Soc. Agron., Crop Sci. Soc. Am., Soil Sci. Soc. Am., Madison, WI.

Bernstein, L. 1961. Osmotic adjustment of plants to saline media. I. Steady state. *Am. J. Bot.* 48:909–918.

Bernstein, L. 1975. Effects of salinity and sodicity on plant growth. *Annu. Rev. Phytopathol.* 13:295–312.

Bettany, J. R., S. Saggar, and J. W. B. Stewart. 1980. Comparison of the amounts and forms of sulfur in soil organic matter fractions after 65 years of cultivation. *Soil Sci. Soc. of Am. J.* 44:70–75.

Bhowmik, P. C., and J. D. Doll. 1979. Evaluation of allelopathic effects of selected weed species on corn and soybeans. *Proc. North Cent. Weed Control Conf.* 34:43–45. As quoted by Rice (1984).

Bieleski, R. L. 1973. Phosphate pools, phosphate transport, and phosphate availability. *Annu. Rev. Plant Physiol.* 24:225–252.

Bieleski, R. L. 1976. Passage of phosphate from soil to plant. In: G. J. Blair (ed.) *Prospects for improving efficiency of phosphorus utilization. Reviews in Rural Science* III. pp. 125–129. University of New England, Armidale, Australia.

Bieleski, R. L., and I. B. Ferguson. 1983. Physiology and metabolism of phosphate and its compounds. In: A. Läuchli and R. L. Bieleski (eds.). *Encyclopedia of Plant Physiology,* new series, vol. 15A, pp. 422–448.

Bierhuizen, J. F., and R. O. Slatyer. 1965. Effect of atmospheric concentration of water vapor and CO_2 in determining transpiration-photosynthesis relationships of cotton leaves. *Agric. Meteorol.* 2:259–270.

Black, A. L., P. L. Brown, A. D. Halvorson, and F. H. Siddoway. 1981. Dryland cropping strategies for efficient water-use to control saline seeps in the Northern Great Plains, USA. *Agric. Water Mgmt.* 4:295–311.

Blamey, F. P. C., D. G. Edwards, C. J. Asher, and M. K. Kim. 1982. Response of sunflower to low pH. In: A. Scaife (ed.). *Proc. Ninth Int. Plant Nutrition Colloq.* vol. 1, pp. 66–71. Commonwealth Agric. Bureaux, Farnham House, Farnham Royal, U. K.

Blamey, F. P. C., and K. Nathanson. 1977. Relationships between aluminum toxicity and sunflower yields on an Avalon medium sandy loam. *Agrochemophysica* 9:59–66.

Blanchar, R. W., and D. S. Lipton. 1986. The pe and pH in alfalfa seedling rhizospheres. *Agron. J.* 78:216–218.

Blanchar, R. W., and C. E. Marshall. 1981. Eh and pH measurement in Menfro and Mexico soils. In: R. H. Dowdy et al. (eds.) *Chemistry in the Soil Environment.* ASA Spec. Publ. 40. Am. Soc. Agron. and Soil Sci. Soc. Am., Madison, WI.

Blanchar, R. W., and G. K. Stearman. 1984. Ion products and solid-phase activity to describe phosphate sorption by soils. *Soil Sci. Soc. Am. J.* 48:1253–1258.

Blevins, D. G. 1985. Role of potassium in protein metabolism in plants. In: R. D. Munson (ed.). *Potassium in Agriculture.* Am. Soc. Agron., Crop Sci. Soc. Am., Soil Sci. Soc. Am., Madison, WI, pp. 413–424.

Blevins, R. L., M. S. Smith, G. W. Thomas, and W. W. Frye. 1983. Influence of conservation tillage on soil properties. *J. Soil Water Conserv.* 38:301–304.

Bloom, A. J. 1985. Wild and cultivated barleys show similar affinities for mineral nitrogen. *Oecologia (Berlin)* 65:555–557.

Bloom, P. R. 1981. Metal-organic matter interactions in soil. In: R. H. Dowdy et al. (ed. Comm.). *Chemistry in the Soil Environment,* pp. 129–150. ASA Special Publ. No. 40. Am. Soc. Agron., Madison, WI.

Bloom, P. R., and W. P. Inskeep. 1986. Factors affecting bicarbonate chemistry and iron chlorosis in soils. *J. Plant Nutr.* 9:215–228.

Bloom P. R., and M. B. McBride. 1979. Metal ion binding and exchange with hydrogen ions in acid-washed peat. *Soil Sci. Soc. Am. J.* 43:687–692.

Blue, W. G., and C. L. Dantzman. 1977. Soil chemistry and root development in acid soils. *Proc. Soil and Crop Sci. Soc. of Florida.* 36:9–15.

Boardman, N. K. 1975. Trace elements in photosynthesis. In: D. J. D. Nicholas and A.

R. Egan (eds.). *Trace Elements in Soil-Plant-Animal Systems,* pp. 199–212. Academic Press, New York.

Bock, B. R. 1984. Efficient use of nitrogen in cropping systems. In: R. D. Hauck (ed.). *Nitrogen in Crop Production.* Am. Soc. Agron., pp. 273—294. Crop Sci. Soc. Am., Soil Sci. Soc. Am., Madison, WI.

Bodman, G. B., and E. A. Colman. 1943. Moisture and energy conditions during downward entry of water into soils. *Soil Sci. Soc. Am. Proc.* 8:116–122.

Böhm, W. 1979. *Methods of Studying Root Systems.* Springer-Verlag, Berlin.

Bohn, H. L. 1983. Ion activity products in soil solutions. In: D. W. Nelson (ed., comm. chair). *Chemical Mobility and Reactivity in Soil Systems.* SSSA Special Publ. No. 11. pp. 1–10. Soil Sci. Soc. Am., Madison, WI.

Bohn, H. L., N. J. Barrow, S. S. S. Rajan, and R. L. Parfitt. 1986. Reaction of inorganic sulfur in soils. In: M. A. Tabatabai (ed.). *Sulfur in Agriculture,* Agronomy No. 27, pp. 233–246. Am. Soc. Agron., Madison, WI.

Bohn, H. L., B. L. McNeal, and G. A. O'Connor. 1985. *Soil Chemistry,* 2d. ed., Wiley-Interscience, New York.

Bollard, E. G. 1983. Involvement of unusual elements in plant growth and nutrition. In: A. Läuchli and R. L. Bieleski (eds.). *Encyclopedia of Plant Physiol.,* vol. 15B, pp. 695–744. Springer-Verlag, Berlin.

Borg, H., and D. W. Grimes. 1986. Depth development of roots with time: an empirical description. *Trans. Am. Soc. Agric. Engnr.* 29:194–197.

Bouldin, D. R. 1961. Mathematical description of diffusion processes in the soil-plant system. *Soil Sci. Soc. Am. Proc.* 25:476–480.

Boxma, R. 1972. Bicarbonate as the most important soil factor in lime-induced chlorosis in the Netherlands. *Plant Soil* 37:233–243.

Boyer, J. S. 1968. Relationship of water potential to growth of leaves. *Plant. Physiol.* 43:1056–1062.

Boyer, J. S. 1974. Water transport in plants: Mechanism of apparent changes in resistance during absorption. *Planta* 117:187–207.

Bradshaw, A. D. 1969. An ecologist's viewpoint. In: I. H. Rorison (ed.). *Ecological aspects of the mineral nutrition of plants,* pp. 415–427. Blackwell Scientific Publ., Oxford and Edinburgh.

Bray, R. H. 1944. Soil-plant relations: I. The quantitative relation of exchangeable potassium to crop yields, and to crop response to potash additions. *Soil Sci.* 58:305–324.

Briggs, L. J., and H. L. Shantz. 1913. The water requirement of plants. II. A review of the literature. USDA Bureau Plant Industry Bull. 285.

Briggs, L. J., and H. L. Shantz. 1917. The water requirement of plants as influenced by environment. *Proc. 2nd Pan-Am. Sci. Cong.* 3:95–107. Washington, D.C.

Briskin, D. P. 1986. Plasma membrane H^+-transporting ATPase: Role in potassium ion transport. *Physiol. Plant.* 68:159–163.

Broadbent, F. E. 1984. Plant use of soil nitrogen. In: R. D. Hauck (ed.). *Nitrogen in Crop Production,* pp. 171–182. Am. Soc. Agron., Madison, WI.

Broadbent, F. E. 1986. Empirical modeling of soil nitrogen mineralization. *Soil Sci.* 141:208–213.

Broadbent, F. E., S. K. De Datta, and E. V. Laureles. 1987. Measurement of nitrogen utilization efficiency in rice genotypes. *Agron. J.* 79:786–791.

Brouwer, R., and C. T. deWit. 1969. A simulation model of plant growth with special attention to root growth and its consequences. In: W. J. Whittington (ed.). *Root Growth,* pp. 224–244. Buttersworth, London.

Brouwer, R., and A. Hoogland. 1964. Responses of bean plants to root temperatures. II. Anatomical responses. *Jaarb. I. B. S. 1964.* pp. 23–31.

Brown, J. C., O. R. Lunt, R. S. Holmes, and L. O. Tiffin. 1959. The bicarbonate ion as an indirect cause of iron chlorosis. *Soil Sci.* 88:260–266.

Brown, P. H., R. M. Welch, and E. E. Cary. 1987. Nickel: A micronutrient essential for higher plants. *Plant Physiol.* 85:801–803.

Brown, P. L., A. D. Halvorson, F. H. Siddoway, H. F. Mayland, and M. R. Miller. 1982. Saline-seep diagnosis, control, and reclamation. *U.S. Dept. Agric. Cons. Res. Report,* no. 30.

Buchanan, B. B. 1984. The ferredoxin/thioredoxin system: A key element in the regulatory function of light in photosynthesis. *BioScience* 34:378–383.

Bunce, J. A. 1978. Effects of shoot environment on apparent root resistance to water flow in whole soybean and cotton plants. *J. Exp. Bot.* 29:595–601.

Bunting, A. H. and B. Anderson,. 1960. Growth and nutrient uptake of natal common groundnuts in Tanzanyika. *J. Agric. Sci.* (Cambridge) 55:35–46.

Burstrom, H. 1952. Studies on growth and metabolism of roots. VIII. Calcium as a growth factor. *Physiol. Plant* 5:391–401.

Cailloux, M. 1972. Metabolism and the absorption of water by root hairs. *Can. J. Bot.* 557–573.

Caldwell, C. R., and C. E. Whitman. 1987. Temperature-induced protein conformational changes in barley root plasma membrane-enriched microsomes. I. Effect of temperature on membrane protein and lipid mobility. *Plant Physiol.* 84:918–923.

Cannell, R. Q. 1981. Potentials and problems of simplified cultivation and conservation tillage. *Outlook on Agric.* 10:379–384.

Cannell, R. Q., D. B. Davies, D. Mackney, and J. D. Pidgeon. 1978. The suitability of soils for sequential direct drilling of combine-harvested crops in Britain: A provisional classification. *Outlook on Agric.* 9:306–316.

Cannell, R. Q., and M. B. Jackson. 1981. Alleviating aeration stresses. In: G. F. Arkin and H. M. Taylor (eds.). *Modifying the Root Environment to Reduce Crop Stresses*, pp. 141–192. Am. Soc. Agric. Engr., St. Joseph, MI.

Canny, M. J. 1987. Processes of uptake of water and nutrients by plant roots. (abs.) *3rd. Int. Symp. Structure and Function of Roots*, p. 32, Aug., 1987. Nitra, Czechoslovakia.

Caradus, J. R. 1980. Distinguishing between grass and legume species for efficiency of phosphorus use. *New Zealand J. Agric. Res.* 23:75–81.

Carski, T. H., and D. L. Sparks. 1987. Differentiation of soil nitrogen fractions using a kinetic approach. *Soil Sci. Soc. Am. J.* 51:314–317.

Cassel, D. K., D. R. Nielsen, and J. W. Biggar. 1969. Soil water movement in response to imposed temperature gradients. *Soil Sci. Soc. Am. Proc.* 33:493–500.

Cassman, K. G., and D. N. Munns. 1980. Nitrogen mineralization as affected by soil moisture, temperature and depth. *Soil Sci. Soc. Am. J.* 44:1233–1237.

Chaney, R. L., and B. A. Coulombe. 1982. Effect of phosphate on regulation of Fe-stress response in soybean and peanut. *J. Plant Nutr.* 5:469–487.

Chapin, F. S. III. 1980. The mineral nutrition of wild plants. *Annu. Rev. Ecol. Systems* 11:233–260.

Chapin, F. S. III, and R. Bieleski.1982. Mild phosphorus stress in barley and a low-phosphorus-adapted barley grass: Phosphorus fractions and phosphorus absorption in relation to growth. *Physiol. Plant.* 54:309–317.

Chemical Rubber Co. 1983. *CRC Handbook of Chemistry and Physics*, 64th edition. R. C. Weast (ed.). CRC Press Inc. Boca Raton, FL.

Chen, Y., and P. Barak. 1982. Iron nutrition in calcareous soils. *Adv. Agron.* 35:217–240.

Chen, Y., and S. J. Roux. 1986. Characterization of nucleoside triphosphatase activity in isolated pea nuclei and its photoreversible regulation by light. *Plant Physiol.* 81:609–613.

Cheniae, G. M., and I. F. Martin. 1969. Photoactivation of the manganese catalyst in photosynthetic oxygen evolution. *Plant Physiol.* 44:351–360.

Ching, P. C., and S. A. Barber. 1979. Evaluation of temperature effects on potassium uptake by corn. *Agron. J.* 71:1040–1044.

Cholick, F. A., J. R. Welsh, and C. V. Cole. 1977. Rooting patterns of semi-dwarf and tall winter wheat cultivars under dryland field conditions. *Crop Sci.* 17:637–639.

Christensen, N. W., R. L. Powelson, and M. Brett. 1987. Epidemiology of wheat take-all as influenced by soil pH and temporal changes in inorganic soil N. *Plant Soil* 98:221–230.

Christensen, N. W., R. G. Taylor, T. L. Jackson, and B. L. Mitchell. 1981. Chloride effects on water potentials and yield of winter wheat infected with take-all root rot. *Agron. J.* 73:1053–1058.

Claassen, N., and S. A. Barber. 1976. Simulation model for nutrient uptake from soil by a growing plant root system. *Agron. J.* 68:961–964.

Clarkson, D. T. 1976. The influence of temperature on the exudation of the xylem sap from detached root systems of rye (*Secale cereale*) and barley (*Hordeum vulgare*). *Planta* 132:297–304.

Clarkson, D. T. 1981. Nutrient interception and transport by root systems. In: C. B. Johnson (ed.). *Physiological Processes Limiting Plant Productivity*, pp. 307–330. Buttersworth, London.

Clarkson, D. T. 1985. Factors affecting mineral nutrient acquisition by plants. *Ann. Rev. Plant Physiol.* 36:77–115.

Clarkson, D. T., and J. B. Hanson. 1980. The mineral nutrition of higher plants. *Annu. Rev. Plant Physiol.* 31:239–298.

Clarkson, D. T., and J. Sanderson. 1978. Sites of absorption and translocation of iron in barley roots. *Plant Physiol.* 61:731–736.

Clarkson, D. T., and A. J. Warner. 1979. Relationship between root temperature and the transport of ammonium and nitrate ions by Italian and perennial ryegrass (*Lolium multiflorum* and *Lolium perenne*). *Plant Physiol.* 64:557–561.

Cole, P. J., and A. M. Alston. 1974. Effect of transient dehydration on absorption of chloride by wheat roots. *Plant Soil* 40:243–247.

Cooper, H. D., D. T. Clarkson, H. E. Ponting, and B. C. Loughman. 1986. Nitrogen assimilation in field-grown winter wheat: Direct measurements of nitrate reduction in roots using ^{15}N. *Plant Soil* 91:397–400.

Cornish, P. S. 1981. Resistance to water flow in the intracoleoptile internode of wheat. *Plant Soil* 59:119–125.

Cosgrove, D. 1986. Biophysical control of plant growth. *Annu. Rev. Plant Physiol.* 37:377–405.

Cosper, H. R. 1983. Soil suitability for conservation tillage. *J. Soil and Water Conser.* 38:152–155.

Coughenour, M. B., S. J. McNaughton, and L. L. Wallace. 1984. Modelling primary production of perennial graminoids—uniting physiological processes and morphometric traits. *Ecological Modelling* 23:101–134.

Coughlan, S. J., and R. G. Wyn-Jones. 1980. Some responses of *Spinacea oleracea* to salt stress. *J. Exp. Bot.* 31:883–893.

Coulombe, B. A., R. L. Chaney, and W. J. Wiebold. 1984. Use of bicarbonate in screening soybeans for resistance to iron chlorosis. *J. Plant Nutr.* 7:411–425.

Cowan, I. R. 1965. Transport of water in the soil-plant-atmosphere system. *J. Appl. Ecol.* 2:221–239.

Cowan, I. R., and F. L. Milthorpe. 1968. Plant factors influencing the water status of plant tissues. In: T. T. Kozlowski (ed.). *Water Deficits and Plant Growth*, pp. 137–193. Academic Press, NY.

Cox, F. R., F. Adams, and B. B. Tucker. 1982. Liming, fertilization, and mineral nutrition. In: H. E. Pattee and C. T. Young (eds.). *Peanut science and technology*, pp. 139–163. North Carolina State University, Raleigh, NC.

Cox, G., K. J. Moran, F. Sanders, C. Nockolds, and P. B. Tinker. 1980. Translocation and transfer of nutrients in vesicular-arbuscular mycorrhizas III. Polyphosphate granules and phosphorus translocation. *New Phytol.* 84:649–659.

Cox, M. C., C. O. Qualset, and D. W. Rains. 1985. Genetic variation for nitrogen assimilation and translocation in wheat. I. Dry matter and nitrogen accumulation. *Crop Sci.* 25:430–435.

Cramer, G. R., and A. Läuchli. 1986. Ion activities in solution in relation to Na$^+$–Ca^{2+} interactions at the plasmalemma. *J. Exp. Bot.* 37:330–331.

Cramer, G. R., A. Läuchli, and E. Epstein. 1986. Effects of NaCl and CaCl$_2$ on ion activities in complex nutrient solutions and root growth of cotton. *Plant Physiol.* 81:792–797.

Cramer, G. R., A. Läuchli, and V. S. Polito. 1985. Displacement of Ca^{2+} by Na$^+$ from the plasmalemma of root cells. *Plant Physiol.* 79:207–211.

Cramer, G. R., J. Lynch, A. Läuchli, and E. Epstein. 1987. Influx of Na$^+$, K$^+$, and Ca^{2+} into roots of salt-stressed cotton seedlings. *Plant Physiol.* 83:510–516.

Crawford, T. W., Jr., V. V. Rendig, and F. E. Broadbent. 1982. Sources, fluxes, and sinks of nitrogen during early reproductive growth of maize (*Zea mays* L.). *Plant Physiol.* 70:1654–1660.

Crossett, R. N., and D. J. Campbell. 1975. The effects of ethylene in the root environment upon the development of barley. *Plant Soil* 42:453–464.

Currie, J. A. 1970. Movement of gases in soil respiration. In: *Soc. Chem. Indus. Monogr.* 37:152 (quoted from Russell, 1977).

Cushman, J. H. 1979. An analytical solution to solute transport near root surfaces for low initial concentration. *Soil Sci. Soc. Am. J.* 43:1087–1095.

Dart, P. J. 1974. The infection process. In: A. Quispel (ed.). *Biological Nitrogen Fixation,* pp. 381–429. North Holland, Amsterdam.

David, M. B., S. C. Schindler, M. J. Mitchell, and J. E. Strick. 1983. Importance of organic and inorganic sulfur in mineralization processes in a forest soil. *Soil Biol. Biochem.* 15:671–677.

Davidson, R. L. 1969. Effect of root-leaf temperature differentials on root/shoot ratios in some pasture grasses and clover. *Ann. Bot.* 33:561–569.

Day, J. L., and M. B. Parker. 1985. Fertilizer effects on crop removal of P and K in "Coastal" bermudagrass forage. *Agron. J.* 77:110–114.

Deans, J. R., J. A. E. Molina, and C. E. Clapp. 1986. Models for predicting potentially mineralizable nitrogen and decomposition rate constants. *Soil Sci. Soc. Am. J.* 50:323–326.

DeDatta, S. K. and D. S. Mikkelsen. 1985. Potassium nutrition of rice. In: R. Munson (ed.). *Potassium in Agriculture,* pp. 665–685. Am. Soc. Agron. Crop Sci. Soc. Am., Soil Sci. Soc. Am., Madison, WI.

Delhaize, E., M. J. Dilworth, and J. Webb. 1986. The effects of copper nutrition and developmental state on the biosynthesis of diamine oxidase in clover leaves. *Plant Physiol.* 82:1126–1131.

Dendooven, L., K. Vlassak, and L. M. M. Verstraeten. 1986. A kinetic approach to determine mineralisable soil nitrogen. In: H. Lambers, J. J. Neeteson, and I. Stulen (eds.). *Fundamental, Ecological and Agricultural Aspects of Nitrogen Metabolism in Higher Plants,* pp. 443–446. Martinus Nijhoff, Dordrecht, the Netherlands.

Deverall, B. J. 1981. *Fungal parasitism,* 2d ed., Studies in Biology No. 17. Edward Arnold, London.

de Vos, C. R. 1986. Rhizosphere acidification as a response to iron deficiency in bean plants. *Plant Physiol.* 81:842–846.

de Wit, C. T. 1958. *Transpiration and crop yields. Versl. Landbouwk. Onderz.* 64.6. Inst. Biol. and Chem. Res. on Field Crops and Herbage. Wageningen, the Netherlands.

Dexter, A. R., and J. S. Hewett. 1978. The deflection of plant roots. *J. Agric. Engng. Res.* 23:17–22.

Dhindsa, R. S., C. A. Beasley, and L. W. Ting. 1975. Osmoregulation in cotton fiber. *Plant Physiol.* 56:393–398.

Dieter, P. 1984. Calmodulin and calmodulin-mediated processes in plants. *Plant, Cell and Environment* 7:371–380.

Diggle, A. J. 1988. ROOTMAP—a model in three-dimensional coordinates of the growth and structure of fibrous root systems. *Plant and Soil* 105:169–178.

Dittmer, H. J. 1949. Root hair variations in plant species. *Am. J. Bot.* 36:152–155.

Dobereiner, J., and F. O. Pedrosa. 1987. *Nitrogen-fixing Bacteria in Nonleguminous Crop Plants.* Sci. Tech. Publishers, Madison, WI.

Dracup, M. N. H., E. G. Barrett-Lennard, H. Greenway, and A. D. Robson. 1984. Effect of phosphorus deficiency on phosphatase activity of cell walls from roots of subterranean clover. *J. Exp. Bot.* 35:466–480.

Drew, M. C. 1987. Function of root tissues in nutrient and water transport. In: P. J. Gregory, J. V. Lake, and D. A. Rose (eds.). *Root Development and Function,* pp. 71–101. Cambridge University Press, Cambridge.

Drew, M. C., A. Chamel, J. P. Garrec, and A. Fourcy. 1980. Cortical air spaces (aerenchyma) in roots of corn subjected to oxygen stress: Structure and influence on uptake and translocation of ^{86}rubidium ions. *Plant Physiol.* 65:506–511.

Drew, M. C., and A. Läuchli, 1985. Oxygen-dependent exclusion of sodium ions from shoots by roots of Zea mays (cv. Pioneer 3906) in relation to salinity damage. *Plant Physiol.* 79:171–176.

Drew, M. C., P. H. Nye, and L. V. Vaidyanathan, 1969. The supply of nutrient ions by diffusion to plant roots in soil. I. Absorption of potassium by cylindrical roots of onions and leek. *Plant Soil* 30:252–270.

Dudal, R. 1976. Inventory of the major soils of the world with special reference to mineral stress hazards. In: M. J. Wright (ed.). *Plant Adaptation to Mineral Stress in*

Problem Soils. Cornell Univ. Agric. Exp. Sta. Spec. Publ., pp. 3–13. Cornell University, Ithaca, NY.

Dugger, W. M. 1983. Boron in plant metabolism. In: A. Läuchli and R. L. Bieleski (eds.). *Encyclopedia of Plant Physiology*, new series, vol. 15B, pp. 626–650. Springer-Verlag, Berlin and New York.

Duke, S. H., and H. M. Reisenauer. 1986. Roles and requirements of sulfur in plant nutrition. In: M. A. Tabatabai (ed.). *Sulfur in Agriculture*, Agron. no. 27, pp. 123–168. Am. Soc. Agron., Crop Sci. Soc. Am., Soil Sci. Soc. Am., Madison, WI.

Duncan, R. R., R. B. Clark, and P. R. Furlani. 1983. Laboratory and field evaluations of sorghum for response to aluminum and acid soil. *Agron. J.* 75:1023–1026.

DuPont, F. M., and R. T. Leonard. 1977. The use of lanthanum to study the functional development of the Casparian strip in corn roots. *Protoplasma* 91:315–323.

Eavis, B. W., L. F. Ratliff, and H. M. Taylor. 1969. Use of a dead-load technique to determine axial root pressure. *Agron. J.* 61:640–643.

Eavis, B. W., and H. M. Taylor. 1979. Transpiration of soybeans as related to leaf area, root length and soil water content. *Agron. J.* 71:441–445.

Eavis, B. W., H. M. Taylor, and M. G. Huck. 1971. Radicle elongation of pea seedlings as affected by oxygen concentrations and gradients between shoot and root. *Agron. J.* 63:770–772.

Ehlers, W., B. K. Khosla, U. Köpke, R. Stulpnagel, W. Böhm, and K. Baeumer. 1980. Tillage effects on root development, water uptake and growth of oats. *Soil Tillage Res.* 1:19–34.

Ekdahl, I. 1977. The growth of root hairs and roots in nutrient media and distilled water and the effects of oxylate. *Landbrukshoegsk Ann.* 23:497–518.

Elliott, G. C., J. Lynch, and A. Läuchli. 1984. Influx and efflux of P in roots of intact maize plants. *Plant Physiol.* 76:336–341.

Emerson, W. W. 1954. Water conduction by severed grass roots. *J. Agric. Sci.* 45:241–245.

Emerson, W. W. 1984. Soil structure in saline and sodic soils. In: I. Shainberg and J. Shalhevet (eds.). *Soil Salinity Under Irrigation: Processes and Management, Ecol. Studies*, vol. 51, pp. 65–76. Springer-Verlag, Berlin.

Epstein, E. 1972. *Mineral Nutrition of Plants: Principles and Perspectives*. Wiley, New York.

Epstein, E. 1983. Crops tolerant of salinity and other mineral stresses. In: *Better Crops for Food, Ciba Foundation Symp. 97*, pp. 61–82. Pitman, London.

Epstein, E. 1985. Salt-tolerant crops: origins, development, and prospects for the concept. *Plant Soil* 89:187–198.

Epstein, E., and C. E. Hagen. 1952. A kinetic study of the absorption of alkali cations by barley roots. *Plant Physiol.* 27:457–474.

Epstein, E., J. D. Norlyn, D. W. Rush, R. W. Kingsbury, D. B. Kelley, G. A. Cunningham, and A. F. Wrona. 1980. Saline culture of crops: A genetic approach. *Science* 210:399–404.

Evangelou, V. P., A. D. Karathanasis, and R. L. Blevins. 1986. Effect of soil organic matter accumulation on potassium and ammonium quantity-intensity relationships. *Soil Sci. Soc. Am. J.* 50:378–382.

Evangelou, V. P., L. D. Whittig, and K. K. Tanji. 1984. An automated manometric method for quantitative determination of calcite and dolomite. *Soil Sci. Soc. Am. J.* 48:1236–1239.

Faiz, S. M. A., and P. E. Weatherley. 1977. The location of the resistance to water movement in the soil supplying the roots of transpiring plants. *New Phytol.* 78:337–347.

Faiz, S. M. A., and P. E. Weatherley. 1978. Further investigations into the location and magnitude of the hydraulic resistances in the soil:plant system. *New Phytol.* 81:19–28.

Fellner, S. 1963. Zinc-free plant carbonic anhydrase: lack of inhibition by sulphonamides. *Biochim. Biophys. Acta* 77:155–156.

Fenn, L. B., J. E. Matocha, and E. Wu. 1981. Ammonia losses from surface-applied urea and ammonium fertilizers as influenced by rate of soluble calcium. *Soil Sci. Soc. Am. J.* 45:883–886.

Fischer, R. A. 1968. Stomatal opening: Role of potassium uptake by guard cells. *Science* 160:784–785.

Fischer, R. A., and N. C. Turner. 1978. Plant productivity in the arid and semi-arid zones. *Annu. Rev. Plant Physiol.* 29:277–317.

Fishman, S., H. Talpaz, M. Dinar, M. Levy, Y. Arazi, Y. Rozman, and S. Yarshowsky. 1984. A phenomenological model of dry matter partitioning among plant organs for simulation of potato growth. *Agric. Systems* 14:159–169.

Fleming, J. F., and L. T. Alexander. 1961. Sulfur acidity in South Carolina tidal marsh soils. *Soil Sci. Sco. Am. Pro.* 25:94–95.

Follett, R. F., and S. A. Barber. 1967. Properties of the available and the soluble molybdenum fractions in a Raub silt loam. *Soil Sci. Soc. Am. Proc.* 31:191–192.

Follett, R. F., J. F. Power, D. L. Grunes, and C. A. Klein. 1977. Effect of N, K, and P fertilization, N source, and clipping on potential tetany hazard of bromegrass. *Plant Soil* 48:485–508.

Food and Agricultural Organization of the United Nations (FAO). 1974. *FAO-UNESCO soil map of the world,* vol. 1, Legend. UNESCO, Paris.

Foy, C. D. 1974. Effects of aluminum on plant growth. In: E. W. Carson (ed.). *The Plant Root and its Environment,* pp. 601–642. University Press of Virginia, Charlottesville, VA.

Foy, C. D. 1984. Physiological effects of hydrogen, aluminum, and manganese toxicities in acid soil. In: F. Adams (ed.). *Soil Acidity and Liming,* Agron. 12 (2d ed.), pp. 57–97. Am. Soc. Agron., Madison, WI.

Foy, C. D., and A. L. Fleming. 1982. Aluminum tolerances of two wheat genotypes related to nitrate reductase activities. *J. Plant Nutr.* 5:1313–1333.

Foy, C. D., R. L. Chaney, and M. C. White. 1978. The physiology of metal toxicity in plants. *Annu. Rev. Plant Physiol.* 29:511–566.

Franz, K. B., H. Rüddel, G. L. Todd, T. A. Dorheim, J. C. Buell, and R. S. Eliot. 1985. Physiologic changes during a marathon, with special reference to magnesium. *J. Am. Coll. Nutr.* 4:187–194.

Freney, J. R. 1986. Forms and reactions of organic sulfur compounds in soils. In: M. A. Tabatabai (ed.). *Sulfur in Agriculture,* Agronomy no. 27, pp. 207–232. Amer. Soc. Agron., Madison, WI.

Freney, J. R., G. E. Melville, and C. H. Williams. 1975. Soil organic matter fractions as sources of plant-available sulphur. *Soil Biol. Biochem.* 7:217–221.

Friedrich, J. W., and Schrader, L. E. 1978. Sulfur deprivation and nitrogen metabolism in maize seedlings. *Plant Physiol.* 61:900–903.

Frietag, D. R. 1971. Methods of measuring soil compaction. In: K. K. Barnes, W. M. Carleton, H. M. Taylor, R. I. Throckmorton, and G. E. Vanden Berg (eds.). *Compaction of Agricultural Soils,* pp. 47–103. Am. Soc. Agric. Engr., St. Joseph, MI.

Gandar, P. W. 1983. Growth in root apices: The kinematic description of growth. *Bot. Gaz.* 144:1–10.

Gardner, F. P., R. B. Pearce, and R. L. Mitchell. 1985. *Physiology of Crop Plants,* Iowa State University Press, Ames, Iowa.

Gardner, W. K., D. A. Barber, and D. G. Parbery. 1983. The acquisition of phosphorus by Lupinus albus L. III. The probable mechanism by which phosphorus movement in the soil/root interface is enhanced. *Plant Soil* 70:107–124.

Gardner, W. R. 1960. Dynamic aspects of water availability to plants. *Soil Sci.* 89:63–73.

Gardner, W. R. 1964. Relation of root distribution to water uptake and availability. *Agron. J.* 56:41–45.

Gardner, W. R. 1965. Dynamic aspects of soil-water availability to plants. *Annu. Rev. Plant Physiol.* 16:323–342.

Gardner, W. R. 1983. Soil properties and efficient water use: An overview. In: H. M. Taylor, W. R. Jordan, and T. R. Sinclair (eds.). *Limitations to Efficient Water Use in Crop Production,* pp. 45–64. Am. Soc. Agron., Madison, WI.

Gardner, W. R., and C. F. Ehlig. 1962. Some observations on the movement of water to the plant. *Agron. J.* 54:453–456.

Gardner, W. R., and C. F. Ehlig. 1963. The influence of soil water on transpiration by plants. *J. Geophysical Res.* 681:5719–5724.

Gardner, W. R., and R. H. Nieman. 1966. Lower limit of water availability to plants. *Science* 143:1460–1462.

Gerwitz, A., and E. R. Page. 1974. An empirical mathematical model to describe plant root systems. *J. App. Ecol.* 11:773–782.

Gile, L. H., F. F. Peterson, and R. B. Grossman. 1965. The K horizon: A master soil horizon of carbonate accumulation. *Soil Sci.* 99:74–82.

Gilmour, J. T., and J. A. Kittrick. 1979. Solubility and equilibria of zinc in a flooded soil. *Soil Sci. Soc. Am. J.* 43:890–892.

Glass, A. D. M., and J. E. Perley. 1980. Varietal differences in potassium uptake by barley. *Plant Physiol.* 65:160–164.

Glinski. J., and W. Stepniewski. 1985. *Soil Aeration and Its Role for Plants.* CRC Press, Inc., Boca Raton, FL.

Glover, D. V., and E. T. Mertz. 1987. Corn. In: R. A. Olson and K. J. Frey (eds.). *Nutritional Quality of Cereal Grains: Genetic and Agronomic Improvement. Agronomy No. 28.*, pp. 183–336. American Society of Agronomy, Inc., Crop Science Society, Inc., and Soil Science Society, Inc., Madison, WI.

Goldberg, S., and R. A. Glaubig. 1986. Boron adsorption on California soils. *Soil Sci. Soc. Am. J.* 50:1173–1176.

Goldberg, S., and G. Sposito. 1984. A chemical model of phosphate adsorption by soils: I. Reference oxide minerals. *Soil Sci. Soc. Am. J.* 48:772–778.

Gonzalez-Erico, E., E. J. Kamprath, G. C. Naderman, and W. V. Soares. 1979. Effect of depth of lime incorporation on the growth of corn on an Oxisol of central Brazil. *Soil Sci. Soc. Am. J.* 43:1155–1158.

Gosewinkel, U., and F. E. Broadbent. 1986. Decomplexation of phosphatase from extracted soil humic substances with electron donatingreagents. *Soil Sci.* 141:261–267.

Grabau, L. J., D. G. Blevins, and H. C. Minor. 1986. P nutrition during seed development. *Plant Physiol.* 82:1008–1012.

Grable, A. R., and E. G. Siemer. 1968. Effects of bulk density, aggregate size and soil water suction on oxygen diffusion, redox potentials and elongation of corn roots. *Soil Sci. Soc. Am. Proc.* 32:180–186.

Greacen, E. L., and C. T. Hignett. 1976. A water balance model and supply index for wheat in South Australia. *CSIRO Aust. Div. Soils Tech. Paper* no. 27.

Greacen, E. L., and J. S. Oh. 1972. Physics of root growth. *Nature* 235:24–25.

Green, V. E., Jr. 1957. The culture of rice on organic soils—A world survey. *Agron. J.* 49:468–471.

Greenland, D. J. 1979. The physics and chemistry of the soil-root interface: Some comments. In: J. L. Harley and R. S. Russell (eds.). *The Soil-Root Interface,* pp. 83–98. Academic Press, London.

Greenwood, D. J., and D. Goodman.1971. Studies on the supply of oxygen to the roots of mustard seedlings. *New Phytol.* 70:85–96.

Gregory, P. J., M. McGowan, P. V. Briscoe, and B. Hunter. 1978. Water relations of winter wheat. I. Growth of the root system. *J. Agric. Sci. (Cambridge)* 91:91–102.

Griedanus, T., L. A. Peterson, L. E. Schrader, and M. N. Dana. 1972. Essentiality of ammonium for cranberry nutrition. *J. Am. Soc. Hort. Sci.* 97:272–277.

Griffin, R. A., and R. G. Burau. 1974. Kinetic and equilibrium studies of boron desorption from soil. *Soil Sci. Soc. Am. Proc.* 38:892–897.

Griffin, R. A., and J. J. Jurinak. 1973. Estimation of activity coefficients from electrical conductance of natural aquatic systems and soil extracts. *Soil Sci.* 116:26–30.

Griffin, R. A., and J. J. Jurinak, 1974. Kinetics of the phosphate interaction with calcite. *Soil Sci. Soc. Am. Proc.* 38:75–79.

Gross, J., and D. Marmé. 1978. ATP-dependent Ca^{2+} uptake into plant membrane vesicles. *Proc. Natl. Acad. Sci. USA* 75:1232–1236.

Grunes, D. L., P. R. Stout, and J. R. Brownell. 1970. Grass tetany of ruminants. *Adv. Agron.* 22:331–374.

Gurr, C. G., T. J. Marshall, and J. T. Hutton. 1952. Movement of water in soil due to a temperature gradient. *Soil Sci.* 74:335–342.

Gustafson, S. W., D. A. Raynes, and R. G. Jensen. 1987. Photosynthesis and activity of ribulose bisphosphate carboxylase of wheat and maize seedlings during and following exposure to O_2-low, CO_2-free N_2. *Plant Physiol.* 83:170–176.

Hallmark, W. B., C. J. deMooy, H. F. Morris, J. Pesek, K. P. Shao, and J. D.Fontenot.

1988. Soybean phosphorus and potassium deficiency detection as influenced by plant growth stage. *Agron. J.* 80:586–591.

Halvorson, A. D., and W. L. Lindsay. 1977. The critical Zn^{2+} concentration for corn and the nonabsorption of chelated zinc. *Soil Sci. Soc. Am. J.* 41:531–534.

Ham, G. E. 1980. Inoculation of legumes with *Rhizobium* in competition with naturalized strains, pp. 131–138. In: W. E. Newton and W. H. Orme-Johnson (eds.), *Nitrogen Fixation*, vol. 2. Symbiotic associations and cyanobacteria. University Park Press, Baltimore, MD.

Hamblin, A. P. 1985. The influence of soil structure on water movement, crop root growth, and water uptake. *Adv. Agron.* 38:95–158.

Hanks, R. J. 1974. Model for predicting plant yield as influenced by water use. *Agron. J.* 66:660–665.

Hanks, R. J. 1983. Yield and water-use relationships: An overview. In: H. M. Taylor, W. R. Jordan, and T. R. Sinclair (eds.). *Limitations to Efficient Water Use in Crop Production*, pp. 393–411. Am. Soc. Agron. Madison, WI.

Hannaway, D. B., J. E. Leggett, L. P. Bush, and P. E. Shuler. 1984. Magnesium (Mg) and rubidium (Rb) absorption by tall fescue. *J. Plant Nutrition* 7:1127–1147.

Hanway, J. J., and R. A. Olson. 1980. Phosphate nutrition of corn, sorghum, soybeans, and small grains. In: F. E. Khasawneh, E. C. Sample, and E. J. Kamprath (eds.). *The Role of Phosphorus in Agriculture*, pp. 681–695. Am. Soc. Agron., Crop Sci. Soc. Am., Soil Sci. Soc. Am., Madison, WI.

Harter, R. D. 1983. Effect of soil pH on adsorption of lead, copper, zinc, and nickel. *Soil Sci. Soc. Am. J.* 47:47–51.

Hassan, N., and R. A. Olson. 1966. Influence of applied sulfur on availability of soil nutrients for corn (*Zea mays* L.) nutrition. *Soil Sci. Soc. Am. Proc.* 30:284–286.

Hatch, M. D., and T. Kagawa. 1974. NAD malic enzyme in leaves with C4-pathway photosynthesis and its role in C4 acid decarboxylation. *Arch. Biochem. Biophys.* 160:346–349.

Haug, A. 1983. Molecular aspects of Al toxicity. In: *CRC Critical Reviews in Plant Sciences*, vol. 1, pp. 345–373. Chemical Rubber Co., Boca Raton, FL.

Haynes, J. L. and W. Robbins. 1948. Calcium and boron as essential factors in the root environment. *Agron. J.* 40:795–803.

Haynes, R. J. 1986. The decomposition process: Mineralization, immobilization, humus formation, and degradation. In: R. J. Haynes (ed.). *Mineral Nitrogen in the Plant-Soil System*, pp. 52–112. Academic Press, NY.

Heady, E. O., J. T. Pesek, and W. G. Brown. 1955. Crop response surfaces and economic optima in fertilizer use. *Iowa Agric. Res. Bull.* 424:292–332.

Helal, M., K. Koch, and K. Mengel. 1975. Effect of salinity and potassium on the uptake of nitrogen and on nitrogen metabolism in young barley plants. *Physiol. Plant.* 35:310–313.

Helal, H. M., and K. Mengel. 1979. Nitrogen metabolism of young barley plants as affected by NaCl-salinity and potassium. *Plant Soil* 51:457–462.

Helal, H. M., and K. Mengel. 1981. Interaction between light intensity and NaCl salinity and their effects on growth, CO_2 assimilation, and photosynthate conversion in young broad beans. *Plant Physiol.* 67:999–1002.

Heldt, H. W., C. J. Chon, and G. H. Lorimer. 1978. Phosphate requirement for the light activation of ribulose-1,5-biphosphate carboxylase in intact spinach chloroplasts. *FEBS Lett.* 92:234–240.

Herrick, J. B. 1980. A professional look at animal health. *Ani. Nutr. Health* 35 (7): 36.

Higinbotham, N. 1964. Electropotentials and ion transport in cells of seed plants. *Abs. Xth Intern. Bot. Congress*, pp. 169–170, Edinburgh, UK.

Hill, J. 1980. The remobilization of nutrients from leaves. *J. Plant Nutr.* 2:407–444.

Hillel, D. 1980. *Fundamentals of Soil Physics*. Academic Press, NY.

Hinkle, M. K. 1983. Problems with conservation tillage. *J. Soil and Water Cons.* 38:201–206.

Hirsch, A., W. L. Pengelly, and J. G. Torrey. 1982. Endogenous IAA levels in boron-deficient and control root tips of sunflower. *Bot. Gaz.* 143:15–19.

Hodges, S. C. 1987. Aluminum speciation:A comparison of five methods. *Soil Sci. Soc. Am. J.* 51:57–64.

Hodgson, J. F., W. L. Lindsay, and J. T. Trierweiler, 1966. Micronutrient cation complexing in soil solution. II. Complexing of zinc and copper in displaced solution from calcareous soil. *Soil Sci. Soc. Am. Proc.* 30:723–726.

Hoffman, G. J., and C. J. Phene. 1971. Effect of constant salinity levels on water-use efficiency of bean and cotton. *Trans. Am. Soc. Agric. Eng.* 14:1103–1106.

Hoffman, G. J., S. L. Rawlins, M. J. Garber, and E. M. Cullen. 1971. Water relations and growth of cotton as influenced by salinity and relative humidity. *Agron. J.* 63:822–826.

House, G. J., and R. W. Parmelee. 1985. Comparison of soil arthropods and earthworms from conventional and no-tillage agroecosystems. *Soil and Tillage Res.* 5:351–360.

Howard, D. D. 1987. Nitrogen fertilization effects on grain sorghum in conventional and no-till systems. *Tennessee Farm and Home Sci.* Winter Issue: 3–4.

Howard, D. D., and F. Adams. 1965. Calcium requirement for penetration of subsoils by primary cotton roots. *Soil Sci. Soc. Am. Proc.* 29:558–562.

Hsiao, T. C., and K. J. Bradford. 1983. Physiological consequences of cellular water deficits. In: H. M. Taylor, W. R. Jordan, and T. R. Sinclair (eds.). *Limitations to Efficient Water Use in Crop Production,* pp. 227–265. Am. Soc. Agron. Madison, WI.

Hsiao, T. C., and A. Läuchli. 1986. Role of potassium in plant-water relations. In: B. Tinker and A. Läuchli (eds.). *Adv. Plant Nutrition,* vol. 2, pp. 281–312. Praeger Scientific, NY.

Hubbell, D. H., and M. H. Haskins. 1984. Associative N_2 fixation with *Azospirillum.* In: M. Alexander (ed.). *Biological Nitrogen Fixation,* Plenum Press, NY.

Huber, S. C. 1985. Role of potassium in photosynthesis and respiration. In: R. D. Munson (ed.). *Potassium in Agriculture,* pp. 369–396. Am. Soc. Agron., Crop Sci. Soc. Am., Soil Sci. Soc. Am., Madison, WI.

Huffaker, R. C., and D. W. Rains. 1978. Factors influencing nitrate acquisition by plants: Assimilation and fate of reduced nitrogen. In: D. R. Nielsen and J. G. MacDonald (eds.). *Nitrogen in the Environment,* vol. 2, pp. 1–44. Academic Press, NY.

Hunter, A. S., and O. J. Kelley. 1946a. A new technique for studying the absorption of moisture and nutrients from soil by plant roots. *Soil Sci.* 162:447–450.

Hunter, A. S., and O. J. Kelley. 1946b. The extension of plant roots into dry soils. *Plant Physiol.* 21:445–457.

Inskeep, W. P., and P. R. Bloom 1986a. Effects of soil moisture on soil pCO_2, soil solution bicarbonate, and iron chlorosis in soybeans. *Soil Sci. Soc. Am. J.* 50:946–952.

Inskeep, W. P., and P. R. Bloom. 1986b. Kinetics of calcite precipitation in the presence of water-soluble organic ligands. *Soil Sci. Soc.Am. J.* 50:1167–1172.

Inskeep, W. P., and P. R. Bloom. 1986c. Calcium carbonate supersaturation in soil solution of Calciaquolls. *Soil Sci. Soc. Am. J.* 50:1431–1437.

Inskeep, W. P., and S. D. Comfort 1986. Thermodynamic predictions for the effects of root exudates on metal speciation in the rhizosphere. *J. Plant Nutr.* 9:567–586.

International Society Soil Science. 1975. Soil Physics Terminology. *ISSS Commission I (Soil Physics). Bull.* 48:16–122.

Islam, A. K. M. S., D. G. Edwards, and C. J., Asher. 1980. pH optima for crop growth. Results of a flowing solution culture experiment with six species. *Plant Soil* 54:339–357.

Itoh, S., and S. A. Barber. 1983. Phosphorus uptake by six plant species as related to root hairs. *Agron. J.* 75:457–461.

Iyengar, S. S., D. C. Martens, and W. P. Miller. 1981. Distribution and plant availability of soil zinc fractions. *Soil Sci. Soc. Am. J.* 45:735–739.

Jackson, M. B. 1979. Rapid injury to peas by soil waterlogging. *J. Sci. Food Agric.* 30:143–152.

Jackson, M. B., T. M. Fenning, and W. Jenkins. 1985. Aerenchyma (gas space) formation in adventitious roots of rice (*Oryza sativa* L.) is not controlled by ethylene or small partial pressures of oxygen. *J. Exp. Bot.* 36:1566–1572.

Jackson, P. C. 1982. Differences between effects of undissociated and anionic 2,4-dinitrophenol on permeability of barley roots. *Plant Physiol.* 70:1373–1379.

Jackson, T. L., and H. M. Reisenauer. 1984. Crop response to lime in the western United States. In: F. Adams (ed.). *Soil Acidity and Liming.* Agron. no. 12 (2d ed.), pp. 333–347. Am. Soc. Agron., Madison, WI.

Jansson, S. L., and J. Persson. 1982. Mineralization and immobilization of soil nitrogen. In: F. J. Stevenson (ed.). *Nitrogen in Agricultural Soils,* Agron. no. 22, pp. 229–252. Am. Soc. Agron., Madison, WI.

Jarvis, S. C., and A. D. Robson. 1983. The effects of nitrogen nutrition of plants on the development of acidity in Western Australian soils. *Aust. J. Agric. Res.* 34:341–365.

Jauregui, M. A., and H. M. Reisenauer. 1982. Dissolution of oxides of manganese and iron by root exudate components. *Soil Sci. Soc. Am. J.* 46:314–317.

Jenkins, M. B., and P. J. Bottomley. 1984. Seasonal response of uninoculated alfalfa to N fertilizer: Soil N, nodule turnover, and symbiotic effectiveness of *Rhizobium meliloti. Agron. J.* 76:959–963.

Jensen, R. K., S. A. Taylor, and H. H. Wiebe. 1961. Negative transport and resistance to water flow through plants, *Plant Physiol.* 36:633–638.

Jin, J., D. C. Martens, and L. W. Zelazny. 1987. Distribution and plant availability of soil boron fractions. *Soil Sci. Soc. Am. J.* 51:1228–1231.

Johnson, C. M., and H. Nishita. 1952. Microestimation of sulfur in plant materials, soils, and irrigation water. *Anal. Chem.* 24:736–742.

Johnson, I. R. 1983. A model of the partitioning of growth between shoots and roots of vegetative plants. *Ann. Bot.* 55:421–431.

Johnson, I. R., and J. H. M. Thornley. 1985. Dynamic model of the response of a vegetative grass crop to light, temperature, and nitrogen. *Plant Cell Environ.* 8:485–499.

Jones, C. A. 1981. Proposed modifications of the Diagnosis and Recommendation Integrated System (DRIS) for interpreting plant analyses. *Commun. Soil Sci. Plant Anal.* 12:785–794.

Jones, C. A. 1984. Estimation of percent aluminum saturation from soil chemical data. *Commun. Soil Sci. Plant Anal.* 15:327–335.

Jones, C. A., W. L. Bland, J. T. Ritchie, and J. R. Williams. 1989. Simulation of root growth. In: J. T. Ritchie and R. J. Hanks (ed.). *Simulation of Agricultural Processes.*

Jones, C. A., A. D. Tomas, R. A. Leigh, and R. G. Wyn-Jones. 1983. Water-relations parameters of epidermal and cortical cells in the primary root of *Triticum aestivum* L. *Planta* 158:230–236.

Jones, M. B., D. M. Center, C. E. Vaughn, and F. L. Bell. 1986. Using DRIS to assay nutrients in subclover. *Calif. Agric.* Sept.–Oct., 19–21.

Juma, N. G., E. A. Paul, and B. Mary. 1984. Kinetic analysis of net nitrogen mineralization in soil. *Soil Sci. Soc. Am. J.* 48:753–757.

Jurinak, J. J. 1984. Salt-affected soils: Thermodynamic aspects of the soil solution. In: I. Shainberg and J. Shalhevet (eds.). *Soil Salinity under Irrigation, Ecol. Studies,* vol. 51, pp. 15–31. Springer-Verlag, Berlin.

Kafkafi, U. 1984. Plant nutrition under saline conditions. In: I. Shainberg and J. Shalhevet (eds.). *Soil Salinity Under Irrigation, Ecol. Studies,* vol. 51, pp. 319–331.

Kamprath, E. J. 1984. Crop response to lime on soils in the tropics. In: F. Adams (ed.). *Soil Acidity and Liming.* Agron. no. 12, pp. 349–368. Am. Soc. Agron., Madison, WI.

Kamprath, E. J., and C. D. Foy. 1985. Lime-fertilizer-plant interactions in acid soils. In: O. P. Engelstad (ed.). *Fertilizer Technology and Use,* 3d ed., pp. 91–151. Soil Sci. Soc. Am., Madison, WI.

Kamprath, E. J., W. L. Nelson, and J. W. Fitts. 1957. Sulfur removed from soils by field crops. *Agron. J.* 49:289–293.

Karlen, D. L., R. L. Flannery, and E. J. Sadler. 1988. Aerial accumulation and partitioning of nutrients by corn. *Agron. J.* 80:232–242.

Karlen, D. L., P. G. Hunt, and T. A. Matheny. 1982a. Accumulation and distribution of K, Ca, and Mg by selected soybean cultivars grown with and without irrigation. *Agron. J.* 74:347–354.

Karlen, D. L., P. G. Hunt, and T. A. Matheny. 1982b. Accumulation and distribution of P, Fe, Mn, and Zn by selected determinate soybean cultivars grown with and without irrigation. *Agron. J.* 74:297–303.

Kaspar, T. C. 1982. Evaluation of the taproot elongation rates of soybean cultivars. Ph.D. Dissertation. Iowa State (Ames) University Library. University Microfilms (82-24332), Ann Arbor, MI.

Kaspar, T. C. 1985. Growth and development of soybean root systems. In: R. M. Shibles (ed.). *Proc. World Soybean Res. Conf. III,* pp. 841–847. Westview Press, Boulder, CO.

Kaspar, T. C., Woolley, D. G., and Taylor, H. M. 1981. Temperature effect on the inclination of lateral roots of soybeans. *Agron. J.* 73:383–385.

Kawase, M. 1978. Aerenchyma formation: How plants adapt to waterlogging. *Ohio Agric. Res. Develop. Ctr. Rpt.*, Jan.–Feb., 1978., pp. 14–15.

Kelley, W. P., B. M. Laurance, and H. D. Chapman, 1949. Soil salinity in relation to irrigation. *Hilgardia* 18:635–665.

Kemp, A. and M. L.'t Hart. 1957. Grass tetany in grazing milking cows. *Neth. J. Agric. Sci.* 5:4–17.

Keren, R., and F. Bingham. 1985. Boron in water, soils and plants. *Adv. Agron.* 1:229–276.

Keyser, H. H., and D. N. Munns. 1979. Effects of calcium, manganese, and aluminum on growth of rhizobia in acid media. *Soil Sci. Soc. Am. J.* 43:500–503.

Keyser, H. H., D. N. Munns, and J. S. Hohenberg. 1979. Acid tolerance of rhizobia in culture and in symbiosis with cowpea. *Soil Sci. Soc. Am. J.* 43:719–722.

Kingsbury, R. W., and E. Epstein. 1986. Salt sensitivity of wheat. A case for specific ion toxicity. *Plant Physiol.* 80:651–654.

Kinraide, T. B., and D. R. Parker. 1987. Cation amelioration of aluminum toxicity in wheat. *Plant Physiol.* 83:546–551.

Kirkby, E. A., and K. Mengel. 1967. Ionic balance in different tissues of the tomato plant in relation to nitrate, urea, or ammonium nutrition. *Plant Physiol.* 42:6–14.

Kirlew, P. W., and D. R. Bouldin. 1987. Chemical properties of the rhizosphere in an acid subsoil. *Soil Sci. Soc. Am. J.* 51:128–132.

Kissel, D. E., E. P. Gentzsch, and G. W. Thomas. 1971. Hydrolysis of nonexchangeable acidity in soils during salt extractions of exchange acidity. *Soil Sci.* 111:293–297.

Kissel, D. E., D. H. Sander, and R. Ellis, Jr. 1985. Fertilizer-plant interactions in alkaline soils. In: Engelstad, O. P. (ed.). *Fertilizer Technology and Use*, 3d ed., pp. 153–196. Soil Sci. Soc. Am., Madison, WI.

Klepper, B., H. M. Taylor, and E. L. Fiscus. 1973. Water relations and growth of cotton in drying soil. *Agron. J.* 65:307–310.

Kliewer, W. M., and J. A. Cook. 1971. Arginine and total free amino acids as indicators of the nitrogen status of grapevines. *J. Am. Soc. Hort. Sci.* 96:581–587.

Klute, A. 1973. Soil water flow theory and its application in field situations. In: R. R. Bruce, K. W. Flach, and H. M. Taylor (eds.). *Field Soil Water Regime, SSSA Spec. publ.* 5, pp. 9–35. Am. Soc. Agron., Madison, WI.

Ko, W. H. 1971. Biological control of seedlings root rot of papaya caused by *Phytophtera palmivora*. *Phytophathology* 61:780–782.

Kochian, L. V., and W. J. Lucas. 1982. Potassium transport in corn roots. I. Resolution of kinetics into a saturable and linear component. *Plant Physiol.* 70:1712–1731.

Kolesch, H., W. Höfner, and K. Schaller. 1987. Effect of bicarbonate and phosphate on iron-chlorosis of grape-vines with special regard to the susceptibility of the rootstocks. I. Field experiments. *J. Plant Nutr.* 10:207–230.

Köpke, U., W. Böhm, and Th. Jachmann. 1982. Rooting patterns of three wheat cultivars in a field and greenhouse experiment. *Z. Acker-U.Pflanzenbau.* 151:42–48.

Kozinka, V., and M. Luxova. 1971. Specific conductivity of conducting and non-conducting tissues of *Zea mays* root. *Biol. Plant.* 13:257–266.

Krueger, R. W., C. J. Lovatt, and L. S. Albert. 1987. Metabolic requirement of *Cucurbita pepo* for boron. *Plant Physiol.* 83:254–258.

Ku, M. S. B., M. R. Schmitt, and G. E. Edwards. 1979. Quantitative determination of RuBPCarboxylase-oxygenase protein in leaves of several C3 and C4 plants. *J. Exp. Bot.* 30:89–98.

Kurth, E., G. R. Cramer, A. Läuchli, and E. Epstein. 1986. Effects of NaCl and CaCl$_2$ on cell enlargement and cell production in cotton roots. *Plant Physiol.* 82:1102–1106.

Kust, C. A., and B. E. Struckmeyer. 1971. Effects of trifluralin on growth, nodulation and anatomy of soybeans. *Weed Sci.* 19:147–152.

Kutschera, L. 1960. *Wurzelatlas mitteleuropaischer Ackerunkrauter und Kulturpflanzen.* Frankfurt/M.:DLG-Verlag.

Ladd, J. N., and R. B. Jackson. 1982. Biochemistry of ammonification. In: F. J. Stevenson (ed.). *Nitrogen in Agricultural Soils*, Agron. no. 22, pp. 173–228. Am. Soc. Agron., Madison, WI.

LaHaye, P. A., and E. Epstein. 1969. Salt toleration by plants: enhancement with calcium. *Science* 166:395–396.

Läuchli. A. 1976*a*. Apoplastic transport in tissues. In: U. Lüttge and M. G. Pitman (eds.). *Encyclopedia of Plant Physiol.,* vol. 2B, pp. 3–34. Springer-Verlag.

Läuchli, A. 1976*b*. Symplasmic transport and ion release to the xylem. In: I. F. Wardlaw and J. B. Passioura (eds.). *Transport and transfer processes in plants,* pp. 101–112. Academic Press, NY.

Läuchli, A., and R. Pfluger. 1979. Potassium transport through plant cell membranes and metabolic role of potassium in plants. In: P. A. Gething and A. von Peter (eds.). *Potassium research—review and trends,* pp. 111–163. Potash Inst., Bern, Switzerland.

Läuchli, A., A. R. Spurr, and E. Epstein. 1971. Lateral transport of ions into xylem of corn roots. I. Kinetics of a stelar pump. *Plant Physiol.* 48:118–124.

Läuchli, A., and J. Wieneke. 1979. Studies on growth and distribution of Na^+, K^+ and C^- in soybean varieties differing in salt tolerance. *Z. Pflanzenernaehr. Bodenkd.* 154:3–13.

Lauer, D. A. 1985. Nitrogen uptake patterns of potatoes with high-frequency sprinkler-applied N fertilizer. *Agron. J.* 77:193–197.

Lauter, D. J., and D. N. Munns. 1986. Salt resistance of chickpea genotypes in solutions salinized with NaCl or Na_2SO_4. *Plant Soil* 95:271–279.

Lee, J., and M. W. Pritchard. 1984. Aluminium toxicity expression on nutrient uptake, growth and root morphology of Trifolium repens L. cv. 'Grasslands Huia.' *Plant Soil* 82:101–116.

Lee, S. G., and S. Aronoff. 1967. Boron in plants: A biochemical role. *Science* 158:798–799.

Leggett, J. E., and E. Epstein. 1956. Kinetics of sulfate absorption by barley roots. *Plant Physiol.* 31:222–226.

Lehman, R. G., and R. D. Harter. 1984. Assessment of copper-soil bond strength by desorption kinetics. *Soil Sci. Soc. Am. J.* 48:769–772.

Leigh, R. A.,, and R. G. Wyn-Jones. 1984. A hypothesis relating critical potassium concentrations for growth to the distribution and functions of this ion in the plant cell. *N. Phytol.* 97:1–13.

Lemon, E. R., and C. L. Wiegand. 1962. Soil aeration and plant root relation II. Root respiration. *Agron. J.* 54:171–175.

Leo, M. W. M. 1964. Plant-water-salt relationships: as studied with a split-root technique. *Irish J. Agric. Res.* 3:129–131.

Leonard, R. T. 1984. Membrane-associated ATPases and nutrient absorption by roots. In: P. B. Tinker and A. Läuchli (eds.). *Advances in Plant Nutrition,* vol. 1. Praeger, New York, pp. 71–86.

Leshem, Y., S. Sridhara, and J. E. Thompson. 1984. Involvement of calcium and calmodulin in membrance deterioration during senescence of pea foliage. *Plant Physiol.* 75:329–335.

Letey, J., C. Roberts, M. Penberth, and C. Vasek. 1986. *An agricultural dilemma: Drainage water and toxics disposal in the San Joaquin Valley.* University of California Publ. 3319, Kearney Foundation of Soil Science, UC.

Levitt, J. 1972. *Responses of Plants to Environmental Stress.* Academic Press. NY.

Lewis, D. H. 1973. Concepts in fungal nutrition and the origin of biotrophy. *Biol. Rev.* 48:261–278.

Liebig, J. von 1840. *Organic Chemistry in its Application to Agriculture and Physiology.* Playfair, London.

Lindsay, W. L. 1972. Zinc in soils and plant nutrition. *Adv. Agron.* 24:147–186.

Lindsay, W. L. 1979. *Chemical Equilibria in Soils.* Wiley, NY.

Lindsay, W. L., and A. P. Schwab. 1982. The chemistry of iron in soils and its availability to plants. *J. Plant Nutr.* 5:821–840.

Lindstrom, M. J., W. B. Voorhees, and G. A. Onstad. 1984. Tillage system and residue corn effects on infiltration in northwestern corn belt soils. *J. Soil Water Conserv.* 39:64–68.

Lockhart, J. A. 1965. Cell extension. In: J. Bonner and J. E. Varner (eds.). *Plant Biochemistry,* pp. 826–829. Academic Press, NY.

Loeppert, R. H. 1986. Reactions of iron and carbonates in calcareous soils. *J. Plant Nutr.* 9:195–214.

Loeppert, R. H., and C. T. Hallmark. 1985. Indigenous soil properties influencing the availability of iron in calcareous soils. *Soil Sci. Soc. Am. J.* 49:597–603.

Loneragan, J. F. 1979. The interface in relation to root function and growth. In: J. L. Harley and R. S. Russell (eds.). *The Soil-Root Interface,* pp. 351–367. Academic Press, London.

Loneragan, J. F. 1975. The availability and absorption of trace elements in soil-plant systems and their relation to movement and concentrations of trace elements in plants. In: D. J. D. Nicholas and A. R. Egan (eds.). *Trace Elements in Soil-Plant-Animal Systems,* pp. 109–134. Academic Press, NY.

Loneragan, J. F., E. Delhaize, and J. Webb. 1982. Enzymic diagnosis of copper deficiency in subterranean clover. I. Relationship of ascorbate oxidase activity in leaves to plant copper status. *Aust. J. Agric. Res.* 33:967–979.

Loneragan, J. F., D. L. Grunes, R. M. Welch, E. A. Aduayi, A. Tengah, V. A. Lazar, and E. E. Cary. 1982. Phosphorus accumulation and toxicity in leaves in relation to zinc supply. *Soil Sci. Soc. Am. J.* 46:345–352.

Longstreth, D. J., and P. S. Nobel. 1979. Salinity effects on leaf anatomy. *Plant Physiol.* 63:700–703.

Lorenz, O. A., and M. T. Vittum. 1980. Phosphorus nutrition of vegetable crops and sugar beets. In: F. E. Khasawneh, E. C. Sample, and E. J. Kamprath (eds.). *The Role of Phosphorus in Agriculture,* pp. 737–762. Am. Soc. Agron., Crop Sci. Soc. Am., Soil Sci. Soc. Am. Madison, WI.

Lund, Z. F. 1970. The effect of calcium and its relation to some other cations on soybean root growth. *Soil Sci. Soc. Am. Proc.* 34:456–459.

Lüttge, U. 1983. Import and export of mineral nutrients in plant roots. In: A. Läuchli and R. Bieleski (eds.). *Encyclopedia of Plant Physiology,* new series, vol. 15A, pp. 181–211. Springer-Verlag, NY.

Lüttge, U., and N. Higinbotham. 1979. *Transport in Plants.* Springer-Verlag, NY.

Lynch, J., G. R. Cramer, and A. Läuchli. 1987. Salinity reduces membrane-associated calcium in corn root protoplasts. *Plant Physiol.* 83:390–394.

Lynch, J., E. Epstein, and A. Läuchli. 1982. Na$^+$-K$^+$ relationships in salt-stressed barley. In: A. Scaife (ed.). *Plant Nutrition. Proc. IXth Int. Plant Nutr. Colloq.,* vol. 2, pp. 347–352. Commonwealth Agric. Bureaux, Slough, UK.

Lynch, J., and A. Läuchli. 1985. Salt stress disturbs the calcium nutrition of barley (*Hordeum vulgare* L.). *New Phytol.* 99:345–354.

Lynch, J. M. 1983. *Soil Biotechnology.* Blackwell Scientific, Oxford, England.

Maas, E. V. 1986. Salt tolerance of plants. *Appl. Agric. Res.* 1:12–25.

Maas, E. V., G. J. Hoffman, G. D. Chaba, J. A. Poss, and M. C. Shannon. 1983. Salt sensitivity of corn at various growth stages. *Irrig. Sci.* 4:45–57.

Machlis, L. 1944. The respiratory gradient in barley roots. *Am. J. Bot.* 31:281–282.

Mack, A. R., and S. A. Barber. 1960. Influence of temperature and moisture on soil phosphorus. I. Effect on soil phosphorus fractions. *Soil Sci. Soc. Am. Proc.* 24:381–385.

MacKey, J. 1980. *Plant Roots: A Compilation of Ten Seminars.* Dept. of Agronomy, Iowa State University, Ames, IA.

MacKown, C. T., R. J. Volk, and W. A. Jackson. 1981. Nitrate accumulation, assimilation, and transport by decapitated corn roots. *Plant Physiol.* 68:133–138.

Macnicol, R. D., and P. H. T. Beckett. 1985. Critical concentrations of potentially toxic elements. *Plant Soil* 85:107–129.

Macy, P. 1936. The quantitative mineral nutrient requirements of plants. *Plant Physiol.* 11:749–764.

Maier-Maercker, U. 1983. A critical assessment of the role of potassium and osmolarity in stomatal opening. *J. Exp. Bot.* 34:811–824.

Mannering, J. V., and C. R. Fenster. 1977. Vegetative water erosion control for agricultural areas. In: *National Symp. Soil Erosion Sedimentation,* ASAE Publ. 4-77, pp. 91–106. Am. Soc. Agric. Eng., St. Joseph, MI.

Mannering, J. V., and C. R. Fenster. 1983. What is conservation tillage? *J. Soil Water Cons.* 38:141–143.

Marschner, H. 1986. *Mineral Nutrition in Higher Plants.* Academic Press, London.

Marschner, H., R. Handley, and R. Overstreet 1966. Potassium loss and changes in fine structure of corn root tips induced by H+ ions. *Plant Physiol.* 41:1725–1735.

Marsh, K. B., R. W. Tillman, and J. K. Syers. 1987. Charge relationships of sulfate sorption by soils. *Soil Sci. Soc. Am. J.* 51:318–323.

Marx, C., J. Dexheimer, V. Gianinazzi-Pearson, and S. Gianinazzi. 1982. Enzymatic studies on the metabolism of vesicular-arbuscular mycorrhizas. IV. Ultracyto-enzymological evidence (ATPase) for active transfer processes in the host-arbuscule interface. *N. Phytol.* 90:37–43.

Mason, W. K., A. T. P.Bennie, H. R. Rowse, T. C. Kaspar, and H. M. Taylor. 1982. Responses of soybeans to two row spacings and two soil water levels. II. Water use, root growth, and plant water status. *Field Crops Res.* 5:15–29.

Mayland, H. F., and D. L. Grunes. 1979. Soil-climate-plant relationships in the etiology of grass tetany. In: V. V. Rendig and D. L. Grunes (eds.). *Grass Tetany, ASA Special Publication,* no. 35, pp. 123–179. Am. Soc. Agron., Crop Sci. Soc., Soil Sci. Soc., Madison, WI.

McBride, M. B. 1979. Chemisorption and precipitation of Mn^{2+} at $CaCO_3$ surfaces. *Soil Sci. Soc. Am. J.* 43:693–698.

McBride, M. B., and J. J. Blasiak. 1979. Zinc and copper solubility as a function of pH in an acid soil. *Soil Sci. Soc. Am. J.* 43:866–870.

McClendon, J. H. 1976. Elemental abundance as a factor on the origins of mineral element requirements. *J. Mol. Evol.* 81:175–195.

McClure, P. R., T. E. Omholt, G. M. Pace,, and P. Y. Bouthyette. 1987. Nitrate-induced changes in protein synthesis and translation of RNA in maize roots. *Plant Physiol.* 84:52–57.

McCully, M. E. 1987a. Selected aspects of the structure and development of field-grown roots with special reference to maize. In: P. J. Gregory, J. V. Lake, and D. A. Rose (eds.). *Root Development and Function,* pp. 53–70. Cambridge University Press, Cambridge.

McCully, M. E. 1987b. Pathways and connections in maize roots (abs.). *Third Int. Symp. Structure and Function of Roots,* p. 91. August 1987, Nitra, Czechoslovakia.

McGill, W. B., and C. V. Cole, 1981. Comparative aspects of cycling of organic C, N, S, and P through soil organic matter. *Geoderma* 26:267–286.

McGraw, R. L., M. P. Russelle, and J. Grava. 1986. Accumulation and distribution of dry mass and nutrients in birdsfoot trefoil. *Agron. J.* 78:124–131.

McWillliams, J. R. 1982. Temperature-induced water stress in chilling sensitive plants. *Aust. J. Plant Physiol.* 9:343–352.

McWilliams, J. R., and P. J. Kramer. 1968. The nature of the perennial response in Mediterranean grasses. *Aust. J. Agric. Res.* 19:381–395.

Mengel, K. 1985. Potassium movement within plants and its importance in assimilate transport. In: R. D. Munson (ed.). *Potassium in Agriculture.* pp. 397–412. Am. Soc. Agron., Crop Sci. Soc. Am., Soil. Sci. Soc. Am., Madison WI.

Mengel, K., and W. W. Arneke. 1982. Effect of potassium on the water potential, the pressure potential, the osmotic potential and cell elongation in leaves of *Phaseolus vulgaris. Physiol. Plant.* 54:402–408.

Mengel, K., W. Bubl,, and H. W. Scherer. 1984. Iron distribution in vine leaves with HCO_3^- induced chlorosis. *J. Plant Nutr.* 7:715–724.

Mengel, K., and G. Geurtzen. 1986. Iron chlorosis on calcareous soils. Alkaline nutritional condition as the cause for the chlorosis. *J. Plant Nutr.* 9:161–173.

Mengel, K., and E. A. Kirkby. 1982. *Principles of Plant Nutrition,* 3d ed. Int. Potash Inst., Worblaufen-Bern, Switzerland.

Merckx, R., J. H. van Ginkel, J. Sinnaeve, and A. Cremers. 1986. Plant-induced changes in the rhizosphere of maize and wheat. *Plant Soil* 96:95–107.

Mertz, E. T., L. S. Bates, and O. E. Nelson. 1964. Mutant gene that changes protein composition and increases lysine content of maize endosperm. *Science* 145:279–280.

Meyer, R. D., and W. E. Martin. 1983. Plant analysis as a guide for fertilization of alfalfa. In: H. M. Reisenauer (ed.). *Soil and Plant Tissue Testing in California, Bull. 1879,* pp. 32–33. Div. Agric. Sci., University of California, Berkeley.

Mikkelsen, D. S., and D. C. Finfrock. 1957. Availability of ammoniacal nitrogen to low-land rice as influenced by fertilizer placement. *Agron. J.* 49:296–300.

Minnich, M. M., M. B. McBride,, and R. L. Chaney. 1987. Copper activity in soil solution: II. Relation to copper accumulation in young snapbeans. *Soil Sci. Soc. Am. J.* 51:573–578.

Mitchell, R. L., and W. J. Russell. 1971. Root development and rooting patterns of soybean [*Glycine max* (L.) Merr.] evaluated under field conditions. *Agron. J.* 63:313–316.

Mitscherlich, E. A. 1909. Das Gesetz des Minimus und das Gesetz des abnehemenden Bodenertrages. *Landwirtschaftl. Jahrb.* 38:537–552.

Mitscherlich, E. A. 1947. Das Ergebnis von über 27,000 Feldüngungs-versuchen. *Z. Pflanzenernähr. Düng. Bodenk.* 38:22–35.

Miyamoto, S., and J. Ryan. 1976. Sulfuric acid for the treatment of ammoniated irrigation water: II. Reducing calcium precipitation and sodium hazard. *Soil Sci. Soc. Am. J.* 40:305–309.

Moll, R. H., E. J. Kamprath, and W. A. Jackson. 1982. Analysis and interpretation of factors which contribute to efficiency of nitrogen utilization. *Agron. J.* 74:562–564.

Mombiela, F., J. J. Nicholaides, III, and L. A. Nelson. 1981. A method to determine the appropriate mathematical form for incorporating soil test levels in fertilizer response models for recommendation purposes. *Soil Sci. Soc. Am. J.* 73:937–941.

Mooney, H. A., S. L. Gulmon, P. W. Rundel, and J. Ehleringer. 1980. Further observations on the water relations of *Prosopis tamarugo* of the Northern Atacama Desert. *Oecologia*, 44:177–180.

Moorby, H., and P. H. Nye. 1984. The effect of temperature variation over the root system on root extension and phosphate uptake by rape. *Plant and Soil* 78:283–293.

Moraghan, J. T. 1987. Nitrogen fertilizer effects on uptake and partitioning of chloride in sugarbeet plants. *Agron. J.* 79:1054–1057.

Morgan, K. J., G. L. Stampley, M. E. Zabik, and D. R. Fischer. 1985. Magnesium and calcium dietary intakes of the U.S. population. *J. Am.Coll. Nutr.* 4:195–206.

Morgan, M. A., W. A. Jackson, W. L. Pan, and R. J. Volk. 1986. Partitioning of reduced nitrogen derived from exogenous nitrate in maize roots: Initial priority for protein synthesis. *Plant Soil* 91:343–347.

Mortvedt, J. J. 1986. Iron sources and management practices for correcting iron chlorosis problems. *J. Plant Nutr.* 9:961–974.

Muchovej, R. M. C., V. G. Allen, D. C. Martens, L. W. Zelazny, and D. R. Notter. 1986. Aluminum, citric acid, nitrilotriacetic acid, and soil moisture effects on aluminum and iron concentrations in ryegrass. *Agron. J.* 78:138–145.

Munns, D. N. 1986. Acid soil tolerance in legumes and rhizobia. In: P. B. Tinker and A. Läuchli (eds.). *Advances in Plant Nutrition*, pp. 63–91. Praeger Publishers, NY.

Munns, R., H. Greenway, R. Delane, and J. Gibbs. 1982. Ion concentration and carbohydrate status of the elongating leaf tissue of Hordeum vulgare growing at high external NaCl. *J. Exp. Bot.* 33:574–583.

Munns, R., and A. Termaat. 1986. Whole-plant responses to salinity. *Aust. J. Plant Physiol.* 13:143–160.

Munson, R. 1985. *Potassium in Agriculture.* Am. Soc. of Agron., Crop Sci. Soc., Soil Sci. Soc. Madison, WI.

Murrmann, R. P., and F. R. Koutz. 1972. Role of soil chemical processes in reclamation of wastewater applied to land. In: S. Reed (coordinator). *Waste-water management by disposal on land.* Spec. Rep. 171. U.S. Army Cold Regions Res. and Engr. Lab., Hanover, NH.

Naidoo, G., J. McD. Steward, and R. J. Lewis. 1978. Accumulation sites of Al in snapbean and cotton roots. *Agron. J.* 70:489–492.

Neales, T. F. 1960. Some effects of boron on root growth. *Aust. J. Biol. Sci.* 13:232–248.

Neales, T. F. 1964. A comparison of the boron requirements of intact tomato plants and excised tomato roots grown in sterile culture. *J. Exp. Bot.* 15:647–653.

Nelson, D. W. 1984. Effect of nitrogen excess on quality of food and fiber. In: R. D. Hauck (ed.). *Nitrogen in Crop Production.* Am. Soc. Agron., Crop Sci. Soc. Am., Soil Sci. Soc. Am. Madison, WI.

Nelson, L. A., R. D. Voss, and J. Pesek. 1985. Agronomic and statistical evaluation of fertilizer response. In: O. P. Englestad (ed.). *Fertilizer Technology and Use,* 3d ed. Soil Sci. Soc. Am.. Madison, WI.

Neumann, P. M., and Stein, Z. 1986. Ion supply capacity of roots in relation to rejuvenation of primary leaves in vivo. *Physiol. Plant.* 67:97–101.

Newman, E. I. 1969*a.* Resistance to water flow in soil and plant. I. Soil resistance in relation to amounts of root: Theoretical estimates. *J. Appl.Ecol.* 6:1–12.

Newman, E. I. 1969*b.* Resistance to water flow in soil and plant. II. A review of experimental evidence on the rhizosphere resistance. *J. Appl. Ecol.* 6:261–272.

Newman, E. I. 1976. Water movement through root systems. *Phil. Trans. Royal Soc. London B.* 273:463–478.

Newman, P. R., and L. E. Moser. 1988. Seedling root development and morphology of cool-season and warm-season forage grasses. *Crop Sci.* 28:148–151.

Nielsen, D. R., R. D. Jackson, J. W. Cary, and D. D. Evans. 1972. *Soil Water.* Am. Soc. Agron., Soil Sci. Soc. Am., Madison, WI.

Nimah, M. N., and R. J. Hanks. 1973. Models for estimating soil water, plant and atmospheric interrelations. I. Description and sensitivity. *Soil Soc. Am. Proc.* 37:522–527.

Nishio, J. N., S. E. Taylor, and N. Terry. 1985. Changes in thylakoid galactolipids and proteins during iron nutrition-mediated chloroplast development. *Plant Physiol.* 77:705–711.

Norvell, W. A. 1972. Equilibria of metal chelates in soil solution. In: J. J. Mortvedt, P. M. Giordano, and W. L. Lindsay (eds.). *Micronutrients in Agriculture,* pp. 115–138. Soil Sci. Soc. Am., Madison, WI.

Nosenko, P. P., and I. S. Zonn. 1976. Land drainage in the world. Int. Comm. Irrig. and Drainage. I.C.I.D. Bull. January 1976: 65–70.

Nuttall, W. F. 1985. Effect of N, P, and S fertilizers on alfalfa grown on three soil types in northeastern Saskatchewan. II. Nitrogen, P, and S uptake and concentration in herbage. *Agron. J.* 77:224–228.

Nye, P. H. 1966. The effect of the nutrient intensity and buffering power of a soil, and the absorbing power, size and root hairs of a root, on nutrient absorption by diffusion. *Plant Soil* 25:81–105.

Nye, P. 1981. Changes of pH across the rhizosphere induced by roots. *Plant Soil* 61:7–26.

Nye, P. H. 1984. pH changes and phosphate solubilization near roots—An example of coupled diffusion processes. In: S. A. Barber and D. R. Bouldin (eds.). *Roots, Nutrient and Water Influx, and Plant Growth.* ASA Spec. Publ. 40. Soil Sci. Soc. Am., Crop Sci. Soc. Am., Am. Soc. Agron., Madison, WI.

Nye, P. H., and F. H. C. Marriott. 1969. A theoretical study of the distribution of substances around roots resulting from simultaneous diffusion and mass flow. *Plant Soil* 30:459–472.

Nye, P. H., and P. B. H. Tinker. 1969. The concept of a root demand coefficient. *J. Appl. Ecol.* 6:293–300.

Nye, P. H., and P. B. Tinker. 1977. *Solute Movement in the Soil-Root System.* University of California Press, Berkeley.

Oaks, A., and B. Hirel. Nitrogen metabolism in roots. *Annu. Rev. Plant Physiol.* 36:345–365.

Oates, K., and Barber, S. A. 1987. Nutrient uptake: A microcomputer program to predict nutrient absorption from soil by roots. *J. Agron. Educ.* 16:65–68.

Ochiai, E-L. 1977. *Bioinorganic Chemistry.* Allyn and Bacon, Boston.

Okon, Y., and Y. Kapulnik. 1986. Development and function of *Azospirillum*-inoculated roots. *Plant Soil* 90:3–16.

Olsen, R. A., and J. C. Brown. 1980. Factors related to iron uptake by dicotyledonous and monocotyledonous plants. I. pH and reductant. *J. Plant Nutr.* 2:629–645.

Olson, R. A., and L. T. Kurtz. 1982. Crop nitrogen requirements, utilization, and fertilization. In: F. J. Stevenson (ed.). *Nitrogen in Agricultural Soils, Agronomy no. 22,* pp. 567–604. Am. Soc. Agron., Crop Sci. Soc. Am., Soil Sci. Soc. Am., Madison, WI.

Onderdonk, J. J., and J. W. Ketcheson. 1973. Effect of soil temperature on direction of corn root growth. *Plant and Soil* 39:177–186.

Ono, T-A., H. Kajikawa, and U. Inoue. 1986. Changes in protein composition and Mn abundance in photosystem II particles on photoactivation of the latent O_2-evolving system in flash-grown wheat leaves. *Plant Physiol.* 80:85–90.

Oosterhuis, D. M. 1985. Osmotic adjustment in water-stressed cotton leaves and roots. *Arkansas Farm Res.*, November–December, 1985, pp. 5–6.

Oputa, C. O. 1971. Amide nitrogen and soluble sugar interrelationships in *Zea mays* L. as influenced by sulfur nutrition. Ph.D. Dissertation, University of California, Davis.

Orme-Johnson, W. H. 1973. Iron-sulfur proteins: structure and functions. *Annu. Rev. Biochem.* 42:159–204.

Overstreet, R., J. C. Martin, and H. M. King. 1951. Gypsum, sulfur and sulfuric acid for reclaiming an alkali soil of the Fresno series. *Hilgardia* 21:113–127.

Ozanne, P. G. 1980. Phosphate nutrition of plants—A general treatise. In: F. E. Khasawneh, E. C. Sample, and E. J. Kamprath (eds.). *The Role of Phosphorus in Agriculture.* pp. 559–589. Am. Soc. Agron., Madison, WI.

Pan, W. L., J. J. Camberato, W. A. Jackson, and R. H. Moll. 1986. Utilization of previously accumulated and concurrently absorbed nitrogen during reproductive growth in maize. *Plant Physiol.* 82:247–253.

Papadopoulos, I., and V. V. Rendig. 1983. Interactive effects of salinity and nitrogen on growth and yield of tomato plants. *Plant Soil* 73:47–57.

Papadopoulos, I., V. V. Rendig, and F. E. Broadbent. 1985. Growth, nutrition, and water uptake of tomato plants with divided roots growing in differentially salinized soil. *Agron. J.* 77:21–26.

Papp, J. C., M. C. Ball, and N. Terry. 1983. A comparative study of the effects of NaCl salinity on respiration, photosynthesis, and leaf extension growth in *Beta vulgaris* L. (sugar beet). *Plant, Cell Environ.* 6:675–677.

Parlange, J. Y. 1973. Movement of salt and water in relatively dry soils. *Soil Sci.* 116:249–255.

Passioura, J. B. 1974. The effect of root geometry on the water relations of temperate cereals (wheat, barley, oats). In: J. Kolek (ed.). *Structure and Function of Primary Root Tissue*, pp. 357–363. Veda, Bratislava, Czechoslovakia.

Passioura, J. B., and R. Munns. 1984. Hydraulic resistance of plants. II. Effects of rooting medium, and time of day, in barley and lupin. *Aust. J. Plant Physiol.* 11:341–350.

Pate, J. S. 1973. Uptake, assimilation and transport of nitrogen compounds by plants. *Soil Biol. Biochem.* 5:109–119.

Patrick, W. H., Jr., D. S. Mikkelsen, and B. R. Wells. 1985. Plant nutrient behavior in flooded soil. In: O. P. Englestad (ed.). *Fertilizer Technology and Use*, 3d ed., pp. 197–228. Am. Soc. Agron., Madison, WI.

Patrick, W. H., Jr., W. S. Quirk, III, F. F. Peterson, and M. D. Faulkner. 1967a. Effect of continuous submergence versus alternate flooding and drying on growth, yield and nitrogen uptake of rice. *Agron. J.* 59:418–419.

Patrick, W. H., Jr., F. J. Peterson, J. E. Seaholm, M. D. Faulkner, and R. J. Miears. 1967b. Placement of nitrogen fertilizers for rice. *Louisiana Agric. Exp. Sta. Bull.* 619:19.

Pauli, A. W., R. Ellis, Jr., and H. C. Moser. 1968. Zinc uptake and translocation as influenced by phosphorus and calcium carbonate. *Agron. J.* 60:394–396.

Pavan, M. A., F. T. Bingham, and P. F. Pratt. 1982. Toxicity of aluminum to coffee in Ultisols and Oxisols amended with $CaCO_3$, $MgCO_3$, and $CaSO_4 \cdot 2H_2O$. *Soil Sci. Soc. Am. J.* 46:1201–1207.

Penman, H. L. 1948. Natural evaporation from open water, bare soil and grass. *Proc. Roy. Soc. London*, Ser. A 193:120–146.

Peoples, T. R., and D. W. Koch. 1979. Role of potassium in carbon dioxide assimilation in *Medicago sativa* L. *Plant Physiol.* 63:878–881.

Pessarakli, M., and T. C. Tucker. 1988. Dry matter yield and nitrogen-15 uptake by tomatoes under sodium chloride stress. *Soil Sci. Soc. Am. J.* 52:698–700.

Pfeffer, W. 1893. Druck und arbeitsleistung durch wachsends pflanzen. *Abhandlungen der Koniglich Sachsischen Gesellschaft der Wissenschaften* 33:235–474. (trans. by W. R. Gill).

Philip, J. R. 1957. The physical principles of soil water movement during the irrigation cycle. *3rd Int. Comm. on Irrig. and Drainage* 8:125–154.

Philip, J. R., and D. A. DeVries. 1975. Moisture movement in porous materials under temperature gradients. *Trans. Am. Geophys.Union* 38:222–232.

Phillips, W. S. Depth of roots in soil. *Ecology* 44:424.

Pierre, W. H. 1928. Nitrogenous fertilizers and soil acidity. I. Effect of various nitrogenous fertilizers on soil reaction. *J. Am. Soc. Agron.* 20:254–269.

Pierre, W. H., J. Meisinger, and J. R. Birchett. 1970. Cation-anion balance in crops as a factor in determining the effect of nitrogen fertilizers on soil acidity. *Agron. J.* 62:106–112.

Pierre, W. H., J. R. Webb, and W. D. Shrader. 1971. Quantitative effects of nitrogen fertilizer on the development and downward movement of soil acidity in relation to level of fertilization and crop removal in a continuous corn cropping system. *Agron. J.* 63:291–297.

Pitman, M. G. 1972. Uptake and transport of ions in barley seedlings. III. Correlation between transport to the shoot and relative growth rate. *Aust. J. Biol Sci.* 25:243–257.

Pitman, M. G. 1982. Transport across plant roots. *Q. Rev. Biophys.* 15:481–554.

Pitman, M. G., A. Läuchli, and R. Stelzer. 1981. Ion distribution in roots of barley seedlings measured by electron probe X-ray microanalysis. *Plant Physiol.* 68:673–679.

Plaut, Z., M. L. Mayoral, and L. Reinhold. 1987. Effect of altered sink:source ratio on photosynthetic metabolism of source leaves. *Plant Physiol.* 85:786–791.

Ponnamperuma, F. N. 1981. Some aspects of the physical chemistry of paddy soils. In: Institute of Soil Science, Academia Sinica (ed.). *Proc. Symp. on Paddy Soil,* pp. 59–93. Sci. Press, Beijing, Springer-Verlag, Berlin.

Poovaiah, B. W., A. S. N. Reddy, and J. J. McFadden. 1987. Calcium messenger system: Role of protein phosphorylation and inositol bisphospholipids. *Physiol. Plant.* 69:569–573.

Portas, C. A. M., and H. M. Taylor. 1976. Growth and survival of young plant roots in dry soil. *Soil Sci.* 121:170–175.

Porter, J. R., B. Klepper, and R. K. Belford. 1986. A model (WHTROOT) which synchronizes root growth and development with shoot development for winter wheat. *Plant Soil* 92:133–145.

Power, J. F., D. L. Grunes, G. A. Reichman, and W. O. Willis. 1964. Soil temperature effects on phosphorus availability. *Agron. J.* 56:545–548.

Proffitt, A. P. B., P. R. Berliner, and D. M. Oosterhuis. 1985. A comparative study of root distribution and water extraction efficiency by wheat under high and low-frequency irrigation. *Agron. J.* 77:655–662.

Pumphrey, F. V., and D. P. Moore. 1965. Sulfur and nitrogen content of alfalfa herbage during growth. *Agron. J.* 57:237–239.

Radin, J. W., and M. P. Eidenbock. 1984. Hydraulic conductance as a factor limiting leaf expansion of phosphorus-deficient cotton plants. *Plant Physiol.* 75:372–377.

Radin, J. W., and M. P. Eidenbock. 1986. Vascular patterns in roots of phosphorus and nitrogen-deficient cotton seedlings. *Proc. Beltwide Cotton Prod. Res. Conf.,* pp. 85–88.

Rains, D. W., W. E. Schmid, and E. Epstein. 1964. Absorption of cations by roots. Effects of hydrogen ions and essential role of calcium. *Plant Physiol.* 39:274–278.

Raju, P. S., R. B. Clark, J. R. Ellis, and J. W. Maranville. 1987. Effects of mycorrhizae species on growth and mineral uptake of sorghum grown at varied temperatures (abs.). *Agron. Abs.* no. 98. Am. Soc. Agron. Madison, WI.

Raloff, J. 1984. Salt of the earth. *Sci. News* 126:298–301.

Reddy, N. R., S. K. Sathe, and D. K. Salunkhe. 1982. Phytates in legumes and cereals. *Adv. Food Res.* 28:1–77.

Reisenauer, H. M. 1964. Mineral nutrients in soil solution. In: P. L. Altman and D. S. Dittmer (eds.). *Environmental Biology,* pp. 507–508. Fed. Am. Soc. Exp. Biol., Bethesda, MD.

Reisenauer, H. M. 1983. Soil and plant tissue testing in California. *Agric. Exp. Sta. Bull.*1879, University of California, Berkeley, CA.

Reisenauer, H. M., C. R. Clement, and L. H. P. Jones. 1982. Comparative efficacy of ammonium and nitrate for grasses. *Plant Nutrition. 9th Int. Plant Nutr. Colloquium,* pp. 539–544.

Reisenauer, H. M., A. A. Tabikh, and P. R. Stout. 1962. Molybdenum reactions with soils and the hydrous oxides of iron, aluminum, and titanium. *Soil Sci. Soc. Am. Proc.* 26:23–27.

Reith, J. W. W., R. H. E. Inkson, W. Holmes, D. S. Maclusky, D. Reid, R. G. Heddle, and G. J. F. Copeman. 1964. The effects of fertilizers on herbage production. *J. Agric. Sci.* 63:209–219.

Rendig, V. V. 1956. Sulfur and nitrogen composition of fertilized and unfertilized alfalfa grown on a sulfur-deficient soil. *Soil Sci. Soc. Amer. Proc.* 20:237–240.

Rendig, V. V., and T. W. Crawford, Jr. 1985. Partitioning into maize grain N fractions of N absorbed through the roots before and after pollination. *J. Sci. Food Agric.* 36:645–650.

Rendig, V. V., C. Oputa, and E. A. McComb. 1976. Effects of sulfur deficiency on nonprotein nitrogen, soluble sugars, and N/S ratios in young corn (*Zea mays* L.) plants. *Plant Soil* 44:423–437.

Reynolds, J. F., and J. H. Thornley. 1982. A shoot-root partitioning model. *Ann. Bot.* 49:585–597.

Rhoads, F. M., and R. L. Stanley, Jr. 1984. Yield and nutrient utilization efficiency of irrigated corn. *Agron. J.* 76:219–223.

Rice, E. L. 1984. *Allelopathy*, 2d ed. Academic Press, Orlando, FL.

Richards, J. H., and M. M. Caldwell. 1987. Hydraulic lift: Substantial nocturnal water transport between soil layers by *Artemesia tridentata*. *Oecologia* 73:486–489.

Richards, L. A. 1931. Capillary conduction of liquid through porous media. *Physics* 1:318–333.

Richards, L. A. 1965. Physical condition of water in soil. *Agron.* 9:128–152. Am. Soc. Agron., Madison, WI.

Riley, D., and S. A. Barber. 1969. Bicarbonate accumulation and pH changes at the soybean (*Glycine max* (L.) Merr.) root-soil interface. *Soil Sci. Soc. Am. Proc.* 33:906–908.

Rincon, M., and W. F. Boss. 1987. *myo*-Inositol trisphosphate mobilizes calcium from fusogenic carrot (*Daucus carota* L.) protoplasts. *Plant Physiol.* 83:395–398.

Robinson, D. 1986. Limits to nutrient inflow rates in roots and root systems. *Physiol. Plant.* 68:551–559.

Robson, A. D., R. D. Hartley, and S. C. Jarvis. 1981. Effect of copper deficiency on phenolic and other constituents of wheat cell walls. *N. Phytol.* 89:361–371.

Rodgers, R. D., and J. B. Wooley. 1983. Conservation tillage impacts on wildlife. *J. Soil Water Conserv.* 38:212–213.

Rollwagen, B. A., and R. J. Zasoski. 1988. Nitrogen source effects on rhizosphere pH and nutrient accumulation by Pacific Northwest conifers. *Plant Soil* 105:79–86.

Römheld, V., and H. Marschner. 1984. Plant induced pH changes in the rhizosphere of "Fe-efficient" and "Fe-inefficient" soybean and corn cultivars. *J. Plant Nutr.* 7:623–630.

Römheld, V., and H. Marschner. 1986. Evidence for a specific uptake system for iron phytosiderophores in roots of grasses. *Plant Physiol.* 80:175–180.

Römheld, V., C. Müller, and H. Marschner. 1984. Localization and capacity of proton pumps in roots of intact sunflower plants. *Plant Physiol.* 76:603–606.

Rominger, R. S., D. Smith, and L. A. Peterson. 1976. Yield and chemical composition of alfalfa as influenced by high rates of K topdressed as KCl and K_2SO_4. *Agron. J.* 68:573–577.

Rorison, I. H. 1968. The response to phosphorus of some ecologically distinct plant species. I. Growth rates and phosphorus absorption. *New Phytol.* 67: 913–922.

Rose, D. A. 1983. The description of the growth of root systems. *Plant Soil* 75:405–415.

Rosene, H. F. 1943. Quantitative measurement of the velocity of water absorption in individual root hairs by a microtechnique. *Plant Physiol.* 18:588–606.

Ross, D. J., T. W. Speir, J. C. Cowling, and K. N. Whale. 1984. Temporal fluctuations in biochemical properties of soil under pasture. II. Nitrogen mineralization and enzyme activities. *Aust. J. Soil Res.* 2:319–330.

Rossignol, M., A. Lamant, L. Salsac, and R. Heller. 1976. Calcium fixation by the roots of calcicole and calcifuge plants: The importance of membrane systems and their lipid composition. In: M. Theiler et al. (eds.). *Transmembrance Ion Exchanges*, pp. 483–490. CNRS, Paris.

Rossiter, R. C. 1964. The effect of phosphate supply on the growth and botanical composition of annual type pasture. *Aust. J. Agric. Res.* 15:61–76.

Rostad, H. P. W., and R. J. St. Arnaud. 1970. Nature of carbonate minerals in two Saskatchewan soils. *J. Soil Sci.* 50:65–70.

Roux, S. J., R. O. Wayne, and N. Datta, 1986. Role of calcium ions in phytochrome responses: An uptake. *Physiol. Plant.* 66:344–348.

Rovira, A. D. 1979. Biology of the soil-root interface. In: J. L. Harley and R.S. Russell (eds.). *The Soil-Root Interface*, pp. 145–160. Academic Press, London.

Rowell, D. L., and A. Wild. 1985. Causes of soil acidification: A summary. *Soil Use Management.* 1:32–33.

Rowse, H. R., and D. Goodman. 1981. Axial resistance to water movement in broadbean (*Vicia faba*) roots. *J. Exp. Bot.* 32:591–598.

Russell, E. W. 1973. *Soil Conditions and Plant Growth*, 10th ed. Longman Group, London.

Russell, R. S. 1977. *Plant Root Systems: Their Function and Interaction with the Soil.* McGraw-Hill (UK), London.

Russell, R. S., and M. J. Goss. 1974. Physical aspects of soil fertility—The response of roots to mechanical impedance. *Neth. J. Agric. Sci.* 22:305–318.

Russelle, M. P., R. D. Hauck, and R. A. Olson. 1983. Nitrogen accumulation rates of irrigated maize. *Agron. J.* 75:593–598.

Ryan, P. J., S. P. Gessel, and R. J. Zasoski. 1986. Acid tolerance of Pacific Northwest conifers in solution culture. I. Effect of high aluminum concentration and solution acidity. *Plant Soil* 96:239–257.

Sacher, R. F., and R. C. Staples, 1985. Inositol and sugars in adaptation of tomato to salt. *Plant Physiol.* 77:206–210.

Sadusky, M. C., D. L. Sparks, M. R. Noll, and G. J. Hendricks. 1987. Kinetics and mechanisms of potassium release from sandy Middle Atlantic Coastal Plain soils. *Soil Sci. Soc. Am. J.* 51:1460–1465.

Sah, R. N., and D. S. Mikkelsen. 1986. Transformations of inorganic phosphorus during the flooding and drainage cycles of soils. *Soil Sci. Soc. Am. J.* 50:62–67.

Salami, A. U., and D. G. Kenefick. 1970. Stimulation of growth in zinc-deficient corn seedlings by the addition of tryptophan. *Crop Sci.* 10:291–294.

Sample, E. C., R. J. Soper, and G. J. Racz. 1980. Reaction of phosphate fertilizers in soils. In: F. E. Khasawneh, E. C. Sample, and E. J. Kamprath (eds.). *The Role of Phosphorus in Agriculture*, pp. 263–310. Am. Soc. Agron., Madison, WI.

Sanchez, P. A., and J. G. Salinas. 1981. Low-input technology for managing Oxisols and Ultisols in tropical America. *Adv. Agron.* 34:279–406.

Sanderson, J. 1983. Water uptake by different regions of the barley root. Pathways of radial flow in relation to development of the endodermis. *J. Exp. Bot.* 34:240–253.

Sandmann, G., and P. Böger. 1983. The enzymatological function of heavy metals and their role in electron transfer processes in plants. In: A. Läuchli and R. L. Bieleski (eds.). *Encyclopedia of Plant Physiology*, new series, vol. 15A, pp. 563–596. Springer-Verlag, NY.

Schenk, M. K., and S. A. Barber. 1979. Phosphate uptake by corn as affected by soil characteristics and root morphology. *Soil Sci. Soc. Am. J.* 43:880–883.

Schenk, M. K., and S. A. Barber. 1980. Potassium and phosphorus uptake by corn genotypes grown in the field as influenced by root characteristics. *Plant Soil* 54:65–76.

Schofield, R. K. 1935. The pF of the water in soil. *Trans. 3rd Intern. Congr. Soil Sci.* 2:37–48.

Schofield, R. K. 1947. A ratio law governing the equilibrium of cations in the soil solution. *Proc. Int. Congr. Pure Appl. Chem.* 3:257–261.

Schwartz, S. M., R. M. Welch, D. L. Grunes, E. E. Cary, W. A. Norvell, M. D. Gilbert, M. P. Meredith, and C. A. Sanchirico. 1987. Effect of zinc, phosphorus, and root-zone temperature on nutrient uptake by barley. *Soil Sci. Soc. Am. J.* 51:371–375.

Scott, G. D. 1969. *Plant Symbiosis. Studies in Biology*, no.16. Edward Arnold, London.

Seeman, J. R., J. A. Berry, S. M. Freas, and M. A. Krump. 1985. Regulation of ribulose bisphosphate carboxylase activity in vivo by a light-modulated inhibitor of catalysis. *Proc. Natl. Acad. Sci. USA* 82:8024–8028.

Shalhevet, J., and T. C. Hsiao. 1986. Salinity and drought. A comparison of their effects on osmotic adjustment, assimilation, transpiration and growth. *Irrig. Sci.* 7:249–264.

Shalhevet, J., and B. Yaron. 1973. Effect of soil and water salinity on tomato growth. *Plant Soil* 39:285–292.

Shantz, H. L., and L. N. Piemeisel. 1927. The water requirement of plants at Akron, Colo. *J. Agric. Res.* 34:1093–1190.

Shaviv, A., M. Mohsin, P. F. Pratt, and S. V. Mattigod. 1985. Potassium fixation characteristics of five southern California soils. *Soil Sci. Soc. Am. J.* 49:1105–1109.

Siddiqi, M. Y., and A. K. M. Glass. 1982. Simultaneous consideration of tissue and substrate potassium concentration in K^+ uptake kinetics: A model. *Plant Physiol.* 69:283–285.

Silberbrush, M., and S. A. Barber. 1983a. Prediction of phosphorus and potassium uptake by soybeans with a mechanistic-mathematical model. *Soil Sci. Soc. Am. J.* 47:262–265.

Silberbrush, M., and S. A. Barber. 1983b. Sensitivity analysis of parameters used in simulating K uptake with a mechanistic-mathematical model. *Agron. J.* 75:851–854.

Silberbrush, M., and S. A. Barber. 1983c. Sensitivity of simulated phosphorus uptake to parameters used by a mechanistic-mathematical model. *Plant Soil* 74:93–100.

Silberbrush, M., and S. A. Barber, 1984. Phosphorus and potassium uptake of field-grown soybean cultivars predicted by a simulation model. *Soil Sci. Soc. Am. J.* 48:592–596.

Simard, R. R., L. J. Evans, and T. E. Bates. 1986. Effects of $CaCO_3$ and P additions on soil solution P and P availability to corn (*Zea mays* L.) in a podzolic soil (abs.). *XIII Congr. Int. Soc. Soil Sci., Comm. IV,* vol. III, pp. 966–967. Hamburg, West Germany.

Sims, J. T. 1986. Soil pH effects on the distribution and plant availability of manganese, copper, and zinc. *Soil Sci. Soc. Am. J.* 50:367–373.

Sinclair, T. R., and M. M. Ludlow. 1985. Who taught plants thermodynamics? The unfilled potential of plant water potential. *Aust. J. Plant Physiol.* 12:213–217.

Skiles, J. W., J. D. Hanson, and W. J. Parton. 1982. Simulation of above- and below-ground carbon and nitrogen dynamics of *Bouteloua gracilis* and *Agropyron smithii*. In: W. K. Lavenroth, G. V. Skogerboe, and M. Flug (eds.). *Analysis of Ecological Systems: State of the Art in Ecological Modelling*. Elsevier, Amsterdam.

Slatyer, R. O., and S. A. Taylor. 1960. Terminology in plant and soil-water relations. *Nature* 187:922–924.

Sleper, D. A., K. P. Vogel, K. H. Asay, and H. F. Mayland. 1989. Using plant breeding and genetics to overcome the incidence of grass tetany. *J. Ani. Sci.* (In press.)

Smiley, R. W. 1974. Rhizosphere pH as influenced by plants, soils, and nitrogen fertilizers. *Soil Sci. Soc. Am. Proc.* 318:795–799.

Smith, J. L., R. R. Schnabel, B. L. McNeal, and G. S. Campbell. 1980. Potential errors in the first-order model for estimating soil nitrogen mineralization potentials. *Soil Sci. Soc. Am. J.* 44:996–1000.

Smith, K. A., and R. S. Russell. 1969. Occurrence of ethylene, and its significance in anaerobic soil. *Nature* 222:769–771.

Smith, S. J., L. B. Young, and G. E. Miller. 1977. Evaluation of soil nitrogen mineralization potentials under modified field conditions. *Soil Sci. Soc. Am. J.* 41:74–76.

Smucker, A. J. M., and A. E. Erickson. 1976. An aseptic mist chamber system: A method for measuring root processes of peas. *Agron. J.* 68:59–62.

Soil Conservation Society of America. 1982. *Resource Conservation Glossary*. Ankeny, IA.

Soil Survey Staff, USDA. 1975. *Soil taxonomy: A basic system of soil classification for making and interpreting soil surveys*. USDA-SCS Handbook 436, U. S. Government Printing Office, Washington, D.C.

Song, S. K., and P. M. Huang. 1988. Dynamics of potassium release from potassium-bearing minerals as influenced by oxalic and citric acids. *Soil Sci. Soc. Am. J.* 52:383–390.

Sparks, D. L. 1987. Potassium dynamics in soils. *Adv. Soil Sci.* 6:2–63.

Sparks, D. L., and W. C. Liebhardt. 1981. Effect of long-term lime and potassium applications on quantity-intensity (Q/I) relationships in sandy soil. *Soil Sci. Soc. Am. J.* 45:786–790.

Spoelstra, S. F. 1985. Nitrate in silage. *Grass Forage Sci.* 40:1–11.

Sposito, G. 1981. *The Thermodynamics of Soil Solutions*. Clarendon Press, Oxford.

Sposito, G., and P. Fletcher. 1985. Sodium-calcium-magnesium exchange reactions on a montmorillonitic soil. III. Calcium-magnesium exchange selectivity. *Soil Sci. Soc. Am. J.* 49:1160–1163.

Sposito, G., N. Senesi, and K. M. Holtzclaw. 1988. Fluorescence quenching and copper complexation by a chestnut leaf litter extract: Spectroscopic evidence. *Soil Sci. Soc. Am. J.* 52:632–636.

Stanford, G., and E. Epstein. 1974. Nitrogen mineralization-water relations in soils. *Soil Sci. Soc. Am. Proc.* 38:103–107.

Stanford, G., and S. J. Smith. 1972. Nitrogen mineralization potentials of soils. *Soil Sci. Soc. Am. Proc.* 36:465–472.

Staple, W. J. 1965. Moisture tension, diffusivity and conductivity of a loam soil during wetting and drying. *Can. J. Soil Sci.* 45:75–86.

Stevenson, F. J. 1982a. *Humus Chemistry—Genesis, Composition, Reactions.* Wiley, NY.

Stevenson, F. J. 1982b. Organic forms of soil nitrogen. In: F. J. Stevenson (ed.). *Nitrogen in Agricultural Soils,* Agronomy no. 22, pp. 67–122. Am. Soc. Agron., Crop Sci Soc. Am., Soil Sci. Soc. Am., Madison, WI.

Stevenson, F. J. 1986. Cycles of soil carbon, nitrogen, phosphorus, sulfur, micronutrients. Wiley, NY.

Stevenson, F. J., and M. S. Ardakani. 1972. Organic matter reactions involving micronutrients in soils. In: J. J. Mortvedt et al. (eds.). *Micronutrients in Agriculture,* pp. 79–114. Soil Sci. Soc. Am., Madison, WI.

Stewart, J. I. 1972. Prediction of water production functions and associated irrigation programs to minimize crop yield and profit losses due to limited water. Ph.D. Thesis, University of California, Davis, Microfilm No. 73-16934.

Stolzy, L. H. 1974. Soil atmosphere. In: E. W. Carson (ed.). *The Plant Root and its Environment,* pp. 335–362. University Press of Virginia, Charlottesville, VA.

Stolzy, L. H., and K. P. Barley, 1968. Mechanical resistance encountered by roots entering compact soil. *Soil Sci.* 105:297–301.

Stone, J. A., T. C. Kaspar, and H. M. Taylor 1983. Predicting soybean rooting depth as a function of soil temperature. *Agron. J.* 75:1050–1054.

Stone, J. A., and H. M. Taylor. 1982. A water bath system to observe temperature effects on taproot and lateral root development of plants. *Soil Sci. Soc. Am. J.* 46:1343–1345.

Stone, J. A., and H. M. Taylor. 1983. Temperature and the development of the taproot and lateral roots of four indeterminate soybean cultivars. *Agron. J.* 75:613–618.

Strebel, O., H. Grimme, M. Renger, and H. Fleige. 1980. A field study with Nitrogen-15 of soil and fertilizer nitrate uptake and of water withdrawal by spring wheat. *Soil Sci.* 130:205–210.

Stroehlein, J. L., and D. A. Pennington, 1986. Use of sulfur compounds for soil and irrigation water treatments. In: M. A. Tabatabai (ed.). *Sulfur in Agriculture,* pp. 435–454. Am. Soc. Agron., Crop Sci. Soc. Am., Soil Sci. Soc. Am., Madison, WI.

Stumm, W., R. Kummert, and L. Sigg. 1980. A ligand exchange model for the adsorption of inorganic and organic ligands at hydrous oxide interfaces. *Croat. Chem. Acta.* 53:291–312 (cited from Goldberg and Sposito, 1984).

Suarez, D. L. 1977. Ion activity products of calcium carbonate in waters below the root zone. *Soil Sci. Soc. Am. J.* 41:310–315.

Suarez, D. L., and J. D. Rhoades. 1982. The apparent solubility of calcium carbonate in soils. *Soil Sci. Soc. Am. J.* 46:716–722.

Suarez, D. L., and J. D. Wood, 1984. Simultaneous determination of calcite surface area and content in soils. *Soil Sci. Soc. Am. J.* 48:1232–1235.

Suelter, C. H. 1985. Role of potassium in enzyme catalysis. In: R. D. Munson (ed.). *Potassium in Agriculture,* pp. 337–350. Am. Soc. Agron., Crop Sci. Soc. Am., Soil Sci. Soc. Am., Madison, WI.

Sumner, M. E. 1977a. Preliminary N, P, and K foliar diagnosis norms for soybeans. *Agron. J.* 69:226–230.

Sumner, M. E. 1977b. Preliminary NPK foliar diagnostic norms for wheat. *Commun. Soil Sci. Plant Anal.* 8:149–167.

Sumner, M. E. 1981. Diagnosing the sulfur requirement of corn and wheat using foliar analysis. *Soil Sci. Soc. Am. J.* 45:87–90.

Swank, J. C., F. E. Below, R. J. Lambert, and R. H. Hageman. 1982. Interaction of carbon and nitrogen metabolism in the productivity of maize. *Plant Physiol.* 70:1185–1190.

Syltie, P. W., W. C. Dahnke, and R. L. Harrold. 1982. Nutritional value of hard red spring wheat grain protein as influenced by fertilization and cultiva. *Agron. J.* 74: 366–371.

Tabatabai, M. A., and A. A. Al-Khafaji. 1980. Comparison of nitrogen and sulfur mineralization in soils. *Soil Sci. Soc. Am. J.* 44:1000–1006.

Tabatabai, M. A., and J. M. Bremner. 1972. Forms of sulfur, and carbon, nitrogen and sulfur relationships in Iowa soils. *Soil Sci.* 114:380–386.

Tackett, J. L. and R. W. Pearson 1964a. Oxygen requirements for cotton seedling root penetration of compacted soil cores. *Soil Sci. Soc. Am. Proc.* 28:600–605.

Tackett, J. L., and R. W. Pearson. 1964b. Effect of carbon dioxide on cotton seedling root penetration of compacted soil cores. *Soil Sci. Soc. Am. Proc.* 28:741–743.

Takagi, S., K. Nomoto, and T. Takemoto. 1984. Physiological aspect of mugineic acid, a possible phytosiderophore of graminaceous plants. *J. Plant Nutr.* 7:469–477.

Takai, Y., and T. Kamura. 1966. The mechanism of reduction in waterlogged paddy soil. *Folia Microbiol.* 11:304 (quoted in Glinski and Stepniewski, 1985).

Takaki, H. and M. Kushizaki. 1970. Accumulation of free tryptophan and tryptamine in zinc-deficient maize seedlings. *Plant Cell Physiol.* 11:793–804.

Talibudeen, O. 1981. Precipitation. In: D. J. Greenland and M. H. B. Hayes (eds.). *The Chemistry of Soil Processes*, pp. 81–113. Wiley, NY.

Talpaz, H., P. Fine, and B. Bar-Yosef. 1981. On the estimation of N-mineralization parameters from incubation experiments. *Soil Sci. Soc. Am. J.* 45:993–996.

Tanner, C. B., and T. R. Sinclair. 1983. Efficient water use in crop production: Research or research. In: H. M. Taylor, W. R. Jordan, and T. R. Sinclair (eds.). *Limitations to Efficient Water Use in Crop Production*, pp. 1–27. Am. Soc. Agron., Madison, WI.

Taylor, H. M. 1969. The rhizotron at Auburn, Alabama—a plant root observation laboratory. *Auburn Univ. Agric. Exp. Stn. Circ.* 171.

Taylor, H. M. 1972. Effect of drying on water retention of a puddled soil. *Soil Sci. Soc. Am. Proc.* 36:922–973.

Taylor, H. M. 1980. Soybean growth and yield as affected by row spacing and by seasonal water supply. *Agron. J.* 72:543–547.

Taylor, H. M. 1983. Managing root systems for efficient water use: An overview. In: H. M. Taylor, W. R. Jordan, and T. R. Sinclair (eds.). *Limitations to Efficient Water Use in Crop Production*, pp. 87–111. Am. Soc. Agron., Madison, WI.

Taylor, H. M., M. G. Huck, and B. Klepper. 1972. Root development in relation to soil physical conditions. In: D. Hillel (ed.). *Optimizing the Soil Physical Environment toward Greater Crop Yields*, pp. 57–77. Academic Press, NY.

Taylor, H. M., and B. Klepper. 1973. Rooting density and water extraction patterns for corn (*Zea mays* L.). *Agron. J.* 65:965–968.

Taylor, H. M., and B. Klepper. 1975. Water uptake by cotton root systems: An examination of assumptions in the single root model. *Soil Sci.* 120:57–67.

Taylor, H. M., and L. F. Ratliff. 1969a. Root growth pressure of cotton, peas and peanuts. *Agron. J.* 61:398–402.

Taylor, H. M., and L. F. Ratliff 1969b. Root elongation rates of cotton and peanuts as a function of soil strength and soil water content. *Soil Sci.* 108:113–119.

Taylor, H. M., G. M. Roberson, and J. J. Parker, Jr. 1966. Soil strength-root penetration relations for medium-to-coarse textured soil materials. *Soil Sci.* 102:18–22.

Taylor, H. M., and E. E. Terrell. 1982. Rooting pattern and plant productivity. In: M. Rechcigl (ed.). *Handbook of Agricultural Productivity*, vol. 1, pp. 185–200. CRC Press, Boca Raton, FL.

Taylor, H. M., and S. T. Willatt. 1983. Shrinkage of soybean roots. *Agron. J.* 75: 818–820.

Taylor, R. M., L. B. Fenn, and G. L. Horst. 1985. The influence of calcium on growth of selected vegetable species in the presence of ammonium nitrogen. *J. Plant. Nutr.* 8:1013–1023.

Taylor, R. M., R. M. McKenzie, and K. Norrish, 1964. The mineralogy and chemistry of manganese in some Australian soils. *Aust. J. Soil Res.* 2:235–248.

Taylor, S. A., and G. L. Ashcroft. 1972. *Physical Edaphology.* Freeman, San Francisco, CA.

Termaat, A., J. B. Passioura, and R. Munns. 1985. Shoot turgor does not limit shoot growth of NaCl-affected wheat and barley. *Plant Physiol.* 77:869–872.

Terry, N. 1980. Limiting factors in photosynthesis. *Plant Physiol.* 65:114–125.

Terry, N. 1977. Photosynthesis, growth, and the role of chloride. *Plant Physiol.* 60:69–75.

Terry, N., and A. Ulrich. 1973. Effects of potassium deficiency on the photosynthesis and respiration of leaves of sugar beet. *Plant Physiol.* 51:783–786.

Thomas, G. W., and W. L. Hargrove. 1984. The chemistry of soil acidity. In: F. Adams (ed.). *Soil Acidity and Liming.* Agron. no. 12, 2d ed., pp. 3–56. Am. Soc. Agron., Madison, WI.

Thompson, J. F., I. K. Smith, and J. T. Madison. 1986. Sulfur metabolism in plants. In: M. A. Tabatabai (ed.). *Sulfur in Agriculture,* pp. 57–122. Am. Soc. Agron., Crop Sci. Soc. Am., Soil Sci. Soc. Am., Madison, WI.

Thornton, F. C., and C. B. Davey. 1983. Response of the clover-*Rhizobium* symbiosis to soil acidity and *Rhizobium* strain. *Agron. J.* 557–560.

Thorup, R. M. 1969. Root development and phosphorus uptake by tomato plants under controlled soil moisture conditions. *Agron. J.* 61:808–811.

Tiller, K. G., J. L. Honeysett, and M. P. C. de Vries. 1972. Soil zinc and its uptake by plants. II. Soil chemistry in relation to prediction of availability. *Aust. J. Soil Res.* 10:165–182.

Tillotson, W. R., and R. J. Wagenet 1982. Simulation of fertilizer nitrogen under cropped situations. *Soil Sci.* 133–143.

Tinker, P. B. 1976. Transport of water to plant roots in soil. *Phil. Trans. Roy. Soc. London B.* 273:445–461.

Tisdale, S. L., W. L. Nelson, and J. D. Beaton. 1985. *Soil Fertility and Fertilizers.* 4th ed. Macmillan, NY.

Tolley-Henry, L., and C. D. Raper, Jr. 1986. Utilization of ammonium as a nitrogen source. Effects of ambient acidity on growth and nitrogen accumulation by soybean. *Plant Physiol.* 82:54–60.

Townsend, L. R. 1966. Effect of nitrate and ammonium nitrogen on the growth of low bush blueberry. *Can. J. Plant Sci.* 46:209–210.

Traina, S. J., G. Sposito, D. Hesterberg, and U. Kafkafi. 1986. Effects of ionic strength, calcium and citrate on orthophosphate solubility in an acidic, montmorillonitic soil. *Soil Sci. Soc. Am. J.* 50:623–627.

Triplett, G. B., Jr., and D. M. Van Doren, Jr. 1969. Nitrogen, phosphorus and potassium fertilization of no-till maize. *Agron. J.* 61:637–639.

Tsai, C. Y., D. M. Huber, and H. L. Warren. 1980. A proposed role of zein and glutelin as N sinks in maize. *Plant Physiol.* 66:330–333.

Tucker, J. M., D. R. Cordy, L. J. Berry, W. A. Harvey, and T. C. Fuller. 1961. Nitrate poisoning in livestock. *Calif. Agric. Exp. Sta. Circular 506,* University of California, Berkeley, CA.

Ulrich, A., and F. J. Hills. 1967. Principles and practices of plant analysis. 1967. In: *Soil Testing and Plant Analysis,* Part II, pp. 11–24. SSSA Spec. Publ. Series, no. 2. Soil Sci. Soc. Am., Madison, WI.

Ulrich, B., R. Mayer, and P. K. Khanna. 1980. Chemical changes due to acid precipitation in a loess derived soil in Central Europe. *Soil Sci.* 130:193–199.

Unger, P. W. 1978. Straw-mulch rate effect on soil water storage and sorghum yield. *Soil Sci. Soc. Am. J.* 42:486–491.

United States Salinity Laboratory Staff. 1954. *Diagnosis and Improvement of Saline and Alkali Soils.* U. S. Dept. Agric. Handbook 60. U.S. Government Printing Office, Washington, D.C.

Upchurch, D. R., and J. T. Ritchie. 1984. Battery operated color video camera for root observations in mini-rhizotrons. *Agron. J.* 76:1015–1017.

Uribe, E., and F. R. Cox. 1988. Soil properties affecting the availability of potassium in highly weathered soils. *Soil Sci. Soc. Am. J.* 52:148–152.

Van Bavel, C. H. M., R. J. Lascano, and L. Strosnijder. 1984. Test and analysis of a model of water use by sorghum. *Soil Sci.* 137:443–456.

Vancura, V., Y. Abd-el-Malek, and M. N. Zayed. 1965. *Azotobacter* and *Beijerinckia* in the soils and rhizosphere of plants in Egypt. *Fol. Microbiol.* 10:224–229.

Van Doren, D. M., Jr., and R. R. Allmaras. 1978. Effect of residue management practices on the soil physical environment, microclimate and plant growth. In: W. R. Oschwald (ed.). *Crop Residue Management Systems.* Am. Soc. Agron. Spec. Publ. 31, pp. 49–83. Am. Soc. Agron., Madison, WI.

VanWambeke, A. 1976. Formation, distribution and consequences of acid soils in agricultural development. In: M. J. Wright (ed.). *Plant Adaptation to Mineral Stress in Problem Soils,* pp. 15–24. Cornell Univ. Agric. Exp. Sta. Ithaca, NY.

Veihmeyer, F. J., and A. H. Hendrickson. 1931. The moisture equivalent as a measure of field capacity of soils. *Soil Sci.* 32:181–193.

Veluthambi, K., and B. W. Poovaiah. 1986. *In vitro* and *in vivo* protein phosphorylation in *Avena sativa* L. coleoptiles. *Plant Physiol.* 81:836–841.

Viets, F. G., Jr. 1977. A perspective on two centuries of progress in soil fertility and plant nutrition. *Soil Sci. Soc. Am. J.* 41:242–249.

Voorhees, W. B., R. R. Allmaras, and C. E. Johnson. 1981. Alleviating temperature stress. In: G. F. Arkin and H. M. Taylor (eds.). *Modifying the Root Environment to Reduce Crop Stress,* pp. 215–266. Am. Soc. Agric. Engr., St. Joseph, MI.

Waggoner, P. E., and W. A. Norvell, 1979. Fitting the Law of Minimum to fertilizer applications and crop yields. *Agron. J.* 71:352–354.

Wallace, A., and J. W. Cha. 1986. Effects of bicarbonate, phosphorus, iron EDDHA, and nitrogen sources on soybeans grown in calcareous soil. *J. Plant Nutr.* 9:251–256.

Walsh, L. M., and J. D. Beaton (eds.). 1973. *Soil Testing and Plant Analysis.* Soil Sci. Soc. Am., Madison, WI.

Walworth, J. L., and M. E. Sumner. 1987. The diagnosis and recommendation integrated system (DRIS). *Adv. Plant Nutr.* 111:149–188.

Walworth, J. L., M. E. Sumner, R. A. Isaac, and C. O. Plank. 1986. Preliminary DRIS norms for alfalfa in the southeastern United States and a comparison with midwestern norms. *Agron. J.* 78:1046–1052.

Ward, M. R., M. Aslam, and R. C. Huffaker. 1986. Enhancement of nitrate uptake and growth of barley seedlings by calcium under saline conditions. *Plant Physiol.* 80:520–524.

Warncke, D. D., and S. A. Barber. 1973. Ammonium and nitrate uptake by corn (*Zea mays* L.) as influenced by nitrogen concentration and NH_4^+/NO_3^- ratio. *Agron. J.* 65:950–953.

Weatherley, P. E. 1982. Water uptake and flow in roots. In: O. L. Lange, P. S. Nobel, C. B. Osmond, and H. Ziegler (eds.). *Encyclopedia of Plant Physiol.,* vol. 12B, pp. 79–109. Springer-Verlag, Berlin.

Weaver, J. E., and W. E. Bruner. 1927. *Root Development of Vegetable Crops.* McGraw-Hill, NY.

Webb, M. J., and J. F. Loneragan. 1985. Importance of environmental pH during root development on phosphate absorption. *Plant Physiol.* 79:143–148.

Welbank, P. J., M. J. Gibb, P. J. Taylor, and G. D. Williams. 1974. Root growth of cereal crops. *Rothamsted Exp. Stn. Annu. Rep. 1973,* part II: pp. 26–66.

Welch, R. M., M. J. Webb, and J. F. Loneragan. 1982. Zinc in membrane function and its role in phosphorus toxicity. In: A. Scaife (ed.). *Plant Nutrition. Proc. 9th Int. Plant Nutr. Coll.* Warwich, England, August 1982, pp. 710–715. Commonwealth Agric. Bureaux, England.

Westerman, D. T., and C. W. Robbins. 1974. Effect of SO_4-S fertilization on Se concentration of alfalfa (*Medicago sativa* L.). *Agron. J.* 66:207–208.

Whisler, F. D., A. Klute, and R. J. Millington. 1968. Analysis of steady-state evapotranspiration from a soil column. *Soil Sci. Soc. Am. Proc.* 32:167–174.

White, M. C., A. M. Decker, and R. L. Chaney. 1981. Metal complexation in xylem fluid. *Plant Physiol.* 67:292–300.

White, R. E. 1976. Studies on mineral ion absorption by plants. III. The interaction of aluminium, phosphate and pH on the growth of *Medicago sativa*. *Plant Soil* 46:195–208.

Widders, I. E., and O. A. Lorenz. 1982. Potassium nutrition during tomato plant development. *J. Am. Soc. Hort. Sci.* 107:960–964.

Wiese, A. F., and P. W. Unger. 1983. Irrigation + dryland farming + limited tillage: A profitable combination. *J. Soil Water Conserv.* 38:233–236.

Wild, A., V. Skarlou, C. R. Clement, and R. W. Snaydon. 1974. Comparison of potassium uptake by four plant species grown in sand and in flowing solution culture. *J. Appl. Ecol.* 11:801–812.

Wild, A., P. J. Woodhouse, and M. J. Hopper. 1979. A comparison between the uptake of potassium by plants from solutions of constant potassium concentration and during depletion. *J. Exp. Bot.* 30:697–704.

Willatt, S. T., and K. A. Olsson. 1982. Root distribution and water uptake by irrigated soybeans on a duplex soil. *Aust. J. Soil Res.* 20:139–146.

Willatt, S. T., and H. M. Taylor. 1978. Water uptake of soybean roots as affected by their depth and by soil water content. *J. Agric. Sci.* 90:205–213.

Willett, I. R. 1978. CSIRO Report 31. (Quoted in Glinski and Stepniewski, 1985).

Willey, C. R., and C. B. Tanner. 1963. Membrane-covered electrode for measurement of oxygen concentration in soil. *Soil Sci. Soc. Am. Proc.* 27:511–515.

Williams, C. H. 1980. Soil acidification under clover pasture. *Aust. J. Exp. Agric. Anim. Husbandry* 20:561–567.

Williams. C. H. 1975. The chemical nature of sulphur in soils. In: K. D. McLachlan (ed.). *Sulphur in Australasian Agriculture,* pp. 21–30. Sydney University Press.

Williams, R. F. 1948. The effects of phosphorus supply on the rates in intake of phosphorus and nitrogen and upon certain aspects of phosphorus metabolism in graminaceous plants. *Aust. J. Sci. Res. Ser. B* 1:333–361.

Wood, M., J. E. Cooper, and A. J. Holding. 1984. Soil acidity factors and nodulations of *Trifolium repens. Plant Soil* 78:367–379.

Woodruff, N. P., C. R. Fenster, W. W. Harris, and M. Lundquist. 1966. Stubble-mulch tillage and planting in crop residues in the Great Plains. *Trans. Am. Soc. Agric. Eng.* 9:849–853.

Wright, M. J., and K. L. Davidson. 1964. Nitrate accumulation in crops and nitrate poisoning in animals. *Adv. Agron.* 16:197–247.

Index

About the Authors

VICTOR V. RENDIG is Professor Emeritus of Soils and Plant Nutrition at the University of California, Davis, where he has served as chairman of the department.

HOWARD M. TAYLOR is Rockwell Professor of Soil Science at Texas Tech University. He has also held positions for the United States Department of Agriculture and is an Elected Fellow of AAAS, Agronomy Society of America, Soil Science Society of America, and Crop Science Society of America.